GERMAN WARPLANES
OF
WORLD WAR II

GERMAN WARPLANES
OF
WORLD
WAR II

CHRIS CHANT

BARNES
&NOBLE
BOOKS
NEW YORK

This edition published by Barnes & Noble, Inc.,
by arrangement with Amber Books Ltd
2001 Barnes & Noble Books

M 10 9 8 7 6 5 4 3 2 1

ISBN 0-7607-2023-1

Editorial and design by
Amber Books Ltd
Bradley's Close
74-77 White Lion Street
London N1 9PF

Printed in The Slovak Republic

Picture credits
Hugh Cowin: 33, 44-45, 101, 121, 128,
Robert Hunt Library: 10, 19, 21, 32, 67, 70, 75, 95, 100, 118
Salamander Picture Library: 60, 62, 64, 126, 131
TRH Pictures: 2-3, 6, 9, 13, 14, 16-17, 22, 25, 26,
30, 31, 36, 38, 40, 42, 46, 48, 51, 53, 55, 56, 59, 68, 71, 74,
76, 78, 80-81, 82-83, 86, 88, 90, 91, 92, 94, 97, 98-99, 204, 106,
108, 110-111, 112, 113, 116-117, 119, 122, 132, 134, 135, 136,
138-139, 140, 141, back cover

Artwork credits
Aerospace Publishing: 8, 12, 18, 24, 28-29, 34, 37, 42-43, 48-49,
52, 58, 63, 66, 72-73, 78-79, 85, 93, 102-103, 109, 114-115, 123, 124-125,
128-129, 143, 144, 145, 146, 147, 148, 149, 150, 151, 152, 153, 154, 155, 156, 157
TRH Pictures: 96-97, 136-137

Previous pages: Focke-Wulf Fw 190A-0s run their engines, summer 1941.

CONTENTS

CHAPTER I

ARADO AR 234 BLITZ

The Ar 234 Blitz (Lightning) was used only in small numbers in the latter stages of World War II, but was a truly remarkable type and also the first jet-powered bomber to enter service anywhere in the world. Operating mainly in the high-altitude reconnaissance bomber role, the Ar 234 was largely uninterceptable by Allied fighters.

The Arado Ar 234 Blitz (Lightning) was the only turbojet-powered bomber to achieve operational status in World War II, and as such it was an important milestone in the development of military aviation. The origins of the type can be traced to a 1940 requirement for a turbojet-powered fast reconnaissance aeroplane. Early in 1941 the Arado design team led by Professor Walter Blume and Dipl.-Ing. Hans Rebeski started work on its definitive E.370 project that was then ordered in prototype form as the Ar 234.

The Ar 234 was a cantilever shoulder-wing monoplane of stressed-skin light alloy construction. Work on the first of an eventual 30 prototypes began early in 1941. The first 18

LEFT *The Ar 234 V13 was a twin-engined Ar 234B prototype then revised with paired BMW 003A-1 turbojets. The glazed forward fuselage provides aerodynamic cleanliness and good fields of vision. Note also the B2A periscopic dive-bombing sight above the cockpit.*

prototypes were completed to a number of differing standards: the first eight, for instance, were designed to take-off from a tricycle take-off dolly that was released after take-off, and landing, to land on skids that extended from the lower fuselage and underside of the engine nacelles, whereas the last 10 had retractable tricycle landing gear. The aircraft were completed with a number of different two- and four-engined powerplant arrangements, with or without cabin pressurisation, and with an ejection seat or conventional seat. There later followed another 12 prototypes for the planned Ar 234C four-engined reconnaissance and multi-role version.

There were major development problems with the chosen Junkers Jumo 109-004 turbojet, and Ar 234 V1 first prototype made its maiden flight only on 15 June 1943. By this time the planned Ar 234A model with the dolly/skid take-off/landing arrangement had been cancelled as operationally impractical. Further development was centred on the Ar 234B series with the conventional landing gear pioneered in the Ar 234 V9 that first flew in March 1944 and evaluated in 20 Ar 234B-0 pre-production aircraft delivered from June of the same year. Such was the pressure for the type to enter service that the Ar 234 V5 and Ar 234 V7 prototypes, despite their original type of dolly/skid take-off/landing gear, were used for operational evaluation during July 1944, and in the course of their sorties the two aircraft easily evaded interception by Allied fighters. The Ar 234B-0 aircraft were also used operationally pending the arrival of the first production models, which were the Ar

234B-1 optimised for the reconnaissance role with provision for drop tanks, and the Ar 234B-2 with a dual-role capability in the reconnaissance and bombing/pathfinding tasks. Production of these two variants totalled 210 aircraft, and they entered service in September 1944 with the Sonderkommando *Götz*, a specialised strategic reconnaissance unit, and then in November of the same year with two other reconnaissance units, namely the Sonderkommando *Hecht* and Sonderkommando *Sperling*.

In the same month the Ar 234B-2 entered service with Kampfgeschwader 76, the first bomber group to receive the

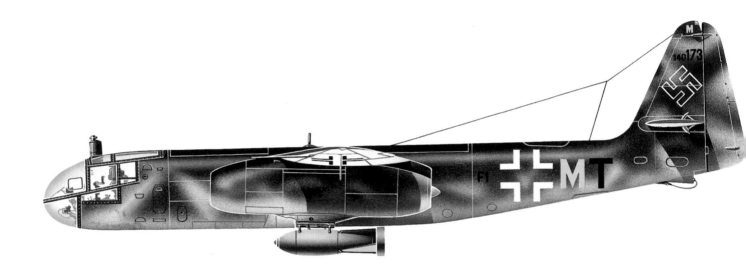

SPECIFICATIONS: Arado Ar 234B-2 Blitz

GENERAL
Type: reconnaissance bomber
Accommodation: pilot in an enclosed cockpit
Equipment: standard communication and navigation equipment, plus a Lofte 7K level-bombing sight, B2A periscopic dive-bombing sight including a rear-view mirror sight for the rearward-firing cannon, and provision for two Rb 50/30 or Rb 75/30 reconnaissance cameras or one Rb 75/30 and one Rb 20/30 cameras
Weights: empty 5200kg (11,464lb); normal take-off 8410kg (18,541lb); maximum take-off 9850kg (21,715lb)

MOTIVE POWER
Powerplant: two Junkers Jumo 109-004B-1/2/3 Orkan turbojets each rated at 8.825kN (1984lb st), and provision for two Walter HWK 109-500 (R 1-202b) RATO units each rated at 4.90kN (1102lb st) for 30 seconds
Fuel capacity: internal fuel 3800 litres

(835.9Imp gal; 1003.85US gal); external fuel up to 600 litres (132Imp gal; 158.5 US gal) in two drop tanks

PERFORMANCE
Maximum speed: 742km/h (461mph) at 6000m (19,685ft) declining to 705km/h (438mph) at sea level
Cruising speed: economical 540km/h (335.5mph) at 4000 m (13,125ft)
Climb: to 6000 m (19,685ft) in 12 minutes 48 seconds with a 500 kg (1102lb) weapons load
Service ceiling: 10,000 m (32,810ft);
Maximum range: 1630km (1013 miles) with drop tanks; typical range 1555km (967 miles) with standard fuel and a 500kg (1102lb) weapons load; endurance 2 hours 30 minutes

DIMENSIONS
Wing span: 14.11m (46ft 3.5 in)
Wing area: 26.40 sq m (284.17sq ft)
Length: 12.64m (41ft 5.64in)

Height: 4.30m (14ft 1.29in)

ARMAMENT
Fixed armament: two 20mm MG151/20 fixed rearward-firing cannon with 200 rounds per gun in the underside of the rear fuselage
Disposable armament: up to 1500kg (3307lb) of disposable stores carried on three hardpoints (one under the fuselage rated at 1400kg (3086lb) and one under each engine nacelle with each unit rated at 250kg (551lb), and generally comprising one 1400kg (3086lb) PC-1400 bomb, or one 1000kg (2205lb) SC-1000 or SD-1000 bomb and two 260kg (551lb) SC-250 bombs, or three 500kg (1102lb) SC-500 bombs, or three 500kg (1102lb) AB-500 clusters of 2kg (4.4lb) SD-2 anti-personnel bomblets, or three 250kg (551lb) AB-250 clusters of 2kg (4.4lb) SD-2 anti-personnel bomblets

type. Thereafter the Ar 234 was used with such regularity as the worsening fuel supply situation permitted, and proved an effective type that could generally achieve its assigned mission without interference from Allied fighters. The primary variants of the Ar 234B-2 were the Ar 234B-2b reconnaissance model and the Ar 234B-2/1 pathfinder model. The two subvariants could also be fitted with the Patin PDS three-axis autopilot and/or drop tanks, these capabilities being noted in the suffix of the letters 'p' and/or 'r' in the designation.

A variant that did not reach full operational service was the Ar 234C with the revised powerplant of four BMW 109-003A-1 Sturm turbojets each rated at 7.845kN (1764lb st). Only 14 production aircraft were built, these representing small numbers of the Ar 234C-1 equivalent of the Ar 234B-1 and the Ar 234C-3 multi-role version with a pair of 20mm MG151/20 fixed forward-firing cannon. Variants projected but not built included the Ar 234C-2 equivalent to the Ar 234B-2, the Ar 234C-3/N night-fighter with two-seat accommodation, FuG 218 Neptun V radar and an armament

ABOVE *Seen in British markings before transfer to the UK for post-war evaluation, this is an Ar 234B-2 of the most important production variant. Interesting features are the fuselage-mounted landing gear, twin-turbojet powerplant, over-cockpit sight with rear-view mirror and gun sight.*

of two 30mm MK108 fixed forward-firing cannon and two 20mm MG151/20 fixed forward-firing cannon, the Ar 234C-4 armed reconnaissance model, the Ar 234C-5 bomber with side-by-side seating for a pilot and bombardier, the Ar 234C-6 two-seat reconnaissance model, the Ar 234C-7 night-fighter with two-seat accommodation and FuG 245 Bremen radar and the Ar 234C-8 single-seat bomber with a powerplant of two Jumo 109-004D turbojets each rated at 10.59kN (2381lb st). Models that did not reach even this stage were the Ar 234D reconnaissance and bomber variant with a powerplant of two Heinkel-Hirth HeS 011A turbojets each rated at 12.75kN (2866lb st), and the Ar 234P night-fighter with two-seat accommodation and a lengthened nose accommodating centimetric airborne interception radar equipment.

DORNIER DO 17

Generally known as the 'flying pencil' for its very slender fuselage, the Do 17 resulted initially from a civil transport and was only later transformed into a bomber. The type was modestly successful by the standards prevailing in 1939, but lacked the potential for development as a viable first-line warplane from 1941.

Designed in an effort to satisfy a Lufthansa specification of 1933 for a civil transport for the movement of six passengers and mail, the Dornier Do 17 was a shoulder-wing monoplane of basically all-metal construction with a very slender fuselage, retractable main landing gear units, a tail unit with a single centreline vertical surface, and the powerplant of two BMW VI Vee engines each rated at 492kW (660hp). The Do 17 V1 first of three initial prototypes made its maiden flight in 1934. The airline then decided as a result of its evaluation of the type in 1935 that the fuselage was too small in cross section for effective use in the passenger-carrying role, and all three prototypes were then returned to the manufacturer. When the military

LEFT *The final production variant of the Do 17 bomber series was the Do 17Z with a revised forward fuselage offering better operational capabilities at the expense of aerodynamic cleanliness. Grouping of the crew in the forward fuselage resulted in vulnerability to a single attack.*

potential of the design was appreciated, the Do 17 V4 (first of 12 military prototypes) was created with a shorter fuselage and a revised tail unit incorporating endplate vertical surfaces and a shorter fuselage. Evaluated from the late summer of 1935, this machine was soon joined by the other prototypes with an assortment of powerplant, armament and equipment options.

The first production model, intended for the high-speed light bomber role with 500kg (1102lb) of bombs, was the three-seat Do 17E-1 with a shortened and glazed nose, and this variant was powered by two BMW VI 7,3 engines each rated at 559 kW (750hp). The Do 17F-1 was basically similar but for its enlarged fuel capacity and weapons bay revised for the carriage of two cameras in the long-range reconnaissance role. Both types entered service at the beginning of 1937 and were built in only small numbers. Later development of the same basic airframe resulted in the Do 17L, of which two prototypes were created as

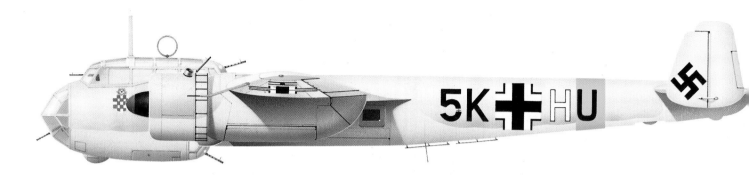

SPECIFICATIONS: Dornier Do 17Z-2

GENERAL
Type: medium bomber
Accommodation: pilot in an enclosed cockpit, and navigator/bombardier/ gunner, radio operator/gunner and gunner carried in the fuselage
Equipment: standard communication and navigation equipment, plus an optical bomb sight and optical gun sights
Weights: empty 5715kg (12,958lb); normal take-off 8587kg (18,931lb); maximum take-off 8837kg (19,481lb)

MOTIVE POWER
Powerplant: two BMW-Bramo 323P Fafnir radial piston engines each rated at 746kW (1024hp) for take-off and 701kW (940hp) at 4000m (13,125ft)
Fuel: internal fuel 1550litres (341Imp gal; 409.5 US gal) plus provision for 895 litres

(196.7Imp gal; 236.4US gal) of auxiliary fuel in a fuselage tank; external fuel none

PERFORMANCE
Maximum speed: 410km/h (255mph) at 4000m (13,125ft) declining to 345km/h (214mph) at sea level
Cruising speed: 300km/h (186mph) at 4000m (13,125ft)
Climb: to 1000m (3280ft) in 3 minutes 18 seconds
Service ceiling: 8200m (26,900ft)
Maximum range: 1500km (932 miles) with auxiliary fuel; typical radius 330km (205 miles) with maximum bomb load

DIMENSIONS
Wing span: 18.00m (59ft 0.66in)
Wing area: 55.00sq m (592.03sq ft)
Length: 15.80m (51ft 10.04in)

Height: 4.55m (14ft 11.14in)

ARMAMENT
Fixed armament: two 7.92mm MG15 fixed or trainable forward-firing machine-guns in the windscreen, one or two 7.92mm MG15 trainable forward-firing machine-guns in the nose position, two 7.92mm MG15 trainable lateral-firing machine-guns in the side windows, one 7.92mm MG15 trainable rearward-firing machine-gun in the dorsal position, and one 7.92mm MG15 trainable rearward-firing machine-gun in the ventral position
Disposable armament: up to 1000kg (2205lb) of disposable stores carried in a lower-fuselage weapons bay rated at 1000kg (2205lb), and generally comprising four 250kg (551lb) SC-250 bombs or 10 50kg (110lb) SC-50 bombs

conversions of earlier prototypes for the four-seat pathfinder role with two BMW-Bramo 323A-1 Fafnir radial engines each rated at 671kW (900hp), and the Do 17R, of which two new prototypes were built as engine test-bed machines.

The powerplant of two Fafnir engines provided a considerable fillip to overall performance, and a radial-engined powerplant was retained for virtually all later Do 17 production aircraft even through one of the three Do 17M prototypes (conversions of earlier prototypes) was completed with two Daimler-Benz DB 600A inverted-Vee engines each rated at 746kW (1000hp). The other two machines had BMW-Bramo 323A-1 radial engines and paved the way for the Do 17M-1 that was a medium bomber development of the Do 17E with a 1000kg (2205lb) weapons load and generally improved equipment. Preceded by a single prototype, the Do 17P-1 was the equivalent long-range reconnaissance version with an improved version of the Do 17F-1's operational equipment but the powerplant of two BMW 132N radial engines individually rated at some 652kW (875hp).

Production of the Do 17E, Do 17F, Do 17M and Do 17P totalled 565 aircraft, and while the Do 17M and Do 17P entered service in 1938, the Do 17M was soon replaced in first-line service by the Do 17Z. The Do 17P remained operational into the early part of World War II. Developed for Yugoslavia, the Do 17K was essentially similar to the Do 17M but powered by two Gnome-Rhòne 14N-1/2 radial engines each rated at 731kW (980hp) and built under licence in Yugoslavia: the three Do 17K subvariants were the Do 17Kb-1 bomber and the Do 17Ka-2 and Do 17Ka-3 reconnaissance aircraft with secondary bombing and attack capability. Production of the Do 17K totalled 20 German- and more than 50 Yugoslav-built aircraft.

The designation Do 17S-0 was used for three DB 600G-powered high-speed reconnaissance aircraft for trials with a four-man crew, a more extensively glazed nose, and a prone gunner's position in the underside of the forward fuselage for one MG15 rearward-firing machine gun. The Do 17U designation was used for 15 Do 17U-0 pre-production and Do 17U-1 production aircraft developed from the Do 17S with a five-man crew (including two radio operators) for the pathfinder/bomber role with DB 600A engines.

All these models led to the definitive Do 17Z, of which about 525 were completed for a service debut late in 1938 and a first-line bomber career that lasted to November 1942 (although conversions for the night reconnaissance and glider-towing roles lasted longer). Preceded by a single Do 17Z-0 pre-production machine, the Do 17Z series was in effect an improved Do 17U-1 with a four-man crew and BMW-Bramo 323 engines. The first two variants were the initial Do 17Z-1 with Bramo 323A-1 engines each rated at 671kW (900hp), four defensive machine guns, and a 500kg (1102lb) bomb load, and the Do 17Z-2 with Bramo 323P engines each rated at 746kW (1000hp) for the carriage of a 1000kg (2205lb) bomb load and up to six defensive machine guns: production of the Do 17Z-1 and Z-2 totalled 500 aircraft. The Do 17Z-3, of which 22 were completed, was a reconnaissance bomber with a reduced bomb load and two cameras, the Do 17Z-4 was dual-control conversion

trainer produced as conversions of older aircraft, and the Do 17Z-5 was long-range maritime reconnaissance model produced as Do 17Z-1 and Z-2 conversions with flotation bags in the fuselage and the rear of the engine nacelles.

The sole Do 17Z-6 Kauz I (Screech Owl I) conversion from Do 17Z-3 standard was a three-seat long-range intruder and night-fighter with the nose of the Junkers Ju 88C-2 equipped with one 20mm MG FF cannon and three 7.92mm MG17 machine guns. The Do 17Z-10 Kauz II, of which nine were created as conversions, was an improved model with a fixed forward-firing armament of four 20mm MG FF cannon and four 7.92mm MG17 machine guns as well as the Spanner-II-Anlage infra-red detection apparatus that was then replaced by Lichtenstein radar.

BELOW *Part of a Gruppe of Do 17Z bombers heads for its target in the dusk of a northern European day. The Do 17Z equipped nine Kampfgruppen in the Battle of Britain and the night 'Blitz' on London, and the type's obsolescence was reflected in comparatively heavy losses.*

CHAPTER 3

DORNIER DO 217

The Do 217 was a moderately radical development of the Do 17 via the Do 215, with an uprated powerplant as well as an enlarged and stronger airframe. It included a much more voluminous fuselage and was an altogether more effective bomber that served right to the end of the war, in varying roles that included a missile-launch platform.

In 1937 the German air ministry issued a requirement for a long-range warplane of considerably versatility but optimised for the heavy bombing role and capable of undertaking both level and diving attacks. Dornier responded with a design that was in basic conceptual terms a scaled-up version of its successful Do 17 bomber in its fully developed form as the Do 215 with a deepened forward fuselage section accommodating all four members of the crew in the fashion that was becoming standard for German bombers. Impressed with the basic design presented by Dornier in the summer of 1937, the German air ministry allocated the designation Do 217 and ordered the completion of the detailed design and the construction of an eventual 16 prototypes.

LEFT *The Do 217, here epitomised by a Do 217K, was a radical development of the basic concept embodied in the Do 17, but was an altogether superior machine able to accept either an air-cooled or a liquid-cooled powerplant.*

The Do 217 V1 prototype made its maiden flight in August 1938 with two Daimler-Benz DB 601A engines each rated at 801.5kW (1075hp), and there followed the Do 217 V2 and V3 with two Junkers Jumo 211A engines each rated at 708kW (950hp) for take-off, and the Do 217 V4 with full armament. Official trials began in 1939, and by this time Dornier was working on additional prototypes and a batch of pre-production aircraft that were criticised for their mechanical problems, lack of agility and indifferent performance. The manufacturer decided that neither the DB 601A nor Jumo 211A offered the prospect of adequate power, and opted instead for the BMW 139 radial engine that was under development as a comparatively small-diameter unit with a take-off rating of some 1156kW (1550hp). This engine was installed in two prototypes, but was then discontinued in favour of the more promising BMW 801 radial engine. The higher power expected from this engine led Dornier to undertake an extensive revision

of the Do 217's fuselage to provide additional volume for a heavier as well as larger weapons load and also extra operational equipment.

Reconnaissance variants

As this process was getting under way, the company completed production of two batches of pre-production aircraft with the DB 601A engine. The first of these comprised eight Do 217A-0 long-range reconnaissance machines with the line of the forward fuselage's lower bulge extended aft. This provided additional internal volume for two vertical reconnaissance cameras with the ventral gun position in the step at the rear end of this extension. The aircraft were delivered in spring 1940 to the Aufklärungsgruppe (reconnaissance wing) of the Luftwaffe high command and used for clandestine reconnaissance of the western USSR in preparation for the invasion in June 1941. Preceded by a Do 217C V1 prototype with a powerplant of two Jumo 211A engines, the four Do 217C-0 pre-production bombers had a powerplant of two DB 601A engines and introduced much improved armament. By the

spring of 1940, however, development was concentrated on the much improved Do 217E with BMW 801MA radial engines each rated at 1178kW (1580hp).

The Do 217E was placed in production during the early months of 1940, and deliveries of the Do 217E-0 pre-production and Do 217E-1 initial production models began respectively in the autumn and early winter of the same year. The Do 217E-1 was intended for the level bombing and anti-shipping roles with a typical complement of two 1000kg (2205lb) bombs, or four 500kg (1102lb) bombs or eight 250kg (551lb) bombs carried internally. The rest of the armament comprised a single 15mm MG151 fixed forward-firing cannon for the strafing role together with five 7.92mm MG15 trainable machine guns gimbal-mounted in the nose, ventral step, cockpit rear and two cockpit side positions.

The first 10 Do 217E-0 and Do 217E-1 machines were delivered in a reconnaissance configuration, and were used from January 1941 for clandestine coverage of the central and southern parts of the western USSR from a base in Romania. The first unit to fly the Do 217E-1 for armed

operations was II Gruppe (wing) of Kampfgeschwader 40, which converted in March 1941 for service in the anti-shipping role over the western Atlantic. These operations confirmed that the Do 217E-1 was generally effective, but needed greater offensive and defensive armament as well as a measure of armour protection for the crew. This led to Do 217E-3, in which an armoured seat was provided for the pilot, several panels of armour was added to the cockpit and fuselage, a trainable 20mm MG151/20 cannon was installed in the nose for use in the anti-ship roles, and another two gimbal-mounted 7.92mm MG15 machine guns were added in the cockpit side windows.

The versatility of the bomber was addressed in the creation of a number of Rästsätze (field conversion kits) whose use was indicated by the addition of the relevant designator: these included R1 for one external carrier for a 1800kg (3968lb) bomb, R2 for two external racks for 250kg (551lb) bombs, R4 for one external carrier for an LT F5 torpedo, R5 for one 30mm MK101 cannon in the lower port side of the forward fuselage, R6 for a weapons bay reconnaissance camera installation, R7 for a four-man dinghy pack installed in the fuselage above the weapons bay, R8 for an auxiliary fuel tank in the forward part of the weapons bay, R9 for an auxiliary fuel tank that could be installed in the rear part of the weapons bay, R10 for two external carriers for Henschel Hs 293 anti-ship missiles, R13 for a different auxiliary fuel tank in the forward part of the weapons bay, R14 for a different auxiliary fuel tank in the rear part of the weapons bay, R15 for two external carriers for Henschel Hs 293 anti-ship missiles, R17 for a different auxiliary fuel tank in the forward part of the weapons bay, R19 for one 7.92mm MG81z two-barrel machine gun that could be installed in the tail cone, R21 for a device to allow the carriage and jettisoning of external auxiliary fuel tanks, and R25 for a brake chute.

Although the early variants of the Do 217E series were developing into useful level bombers and anti-ship

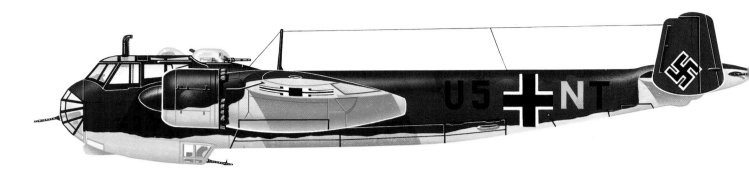

SPECIFICATIONS: Dornier Do 217E-2

GENERAL
Type: heavy bomber
Accommodation: pilot, navigator/bombardier/gunner, radio operator/gunner, and gunner in the enclosed forward-fuselage crew compartment
Equipment: standard communication and navigation equipment, plus an optical bomb sight, optical gun sights and, in aircraft equipped for carriage of the Hs 293A anti-ship missile, the FuG 203/230 Kehl/Strassburg guidance package
Weights: empty 10,535kg (23,225lb); normal take-off 15,000kg (33,069lb); maximum take-off 16,465kg (36,299lb)

MOTIVE POWER
Powerplant: two BMW 801ML radial piston engines each rated at 1178kW (1580hp) for take-off and 1029kW (1380hp) at 4600m (15,100ft)
Fuel: internal fuel 2920 litres (642.3Imp gal; 771.4US gal) plus provision for 750 litres (165Imp gal; 198.1US gal) of auxiliary fuel in a weapons bay tank; external fuel none

PERFORMANCE
Maximum speed: 515km/h (320mph) at 5200m (17,060ft) declining to 440km/h (273mph) at sea level
Cruising speed: maximum 360km/h (258mph) at 5200m (17,060ft) and economical 395km/h (245mph) at optimum altitude
Initial climb rate: 216m (740ft) per minute with maximum internal weapons load
Service ceiling: 9000m (29,530ft)
Maximum range: 2800km (1740 miles) with auxiliary fuel; typical range 2300km (1429 miles) with standard fuel

DIMENSIONS
Wing span: 19.00m (62ft 4 in)
Wing area: 57.00sq m (613.54sq ft)
Length: 18.20m (59ft 8.5in)
Height: 5.03 m (16ft 6 in)

ARMAMENT
Fixed armament: one 15mm MG151 fixed forward-firing cannon with 250 rounds in the lower port side of the nose, one 13mm MG131 trainable machine gun with 500 rounds in the power-operated dorsal turret, one 13mm MG131 trainable rearward-firing machine gun with 1,000 rounds in the ventral step position, one 7.92mm MG15 trainable forward-firing machine gun in the nose, one 7.92mm MG15 trainable lateral-firing machine gun in each of the cockpit side windows and, in the Do 217E-2/R19 subvariant, one remotely controlled 7.92mm MG81z rearward-firing two-barrel machine gun in the tail cone
Disposable armament: up to 4000kg (8818lb) of disposable stores carried in a lower-fuselage weapons bay rated at 2500kg (5511lb) and on up to two hardpoints (both under the wing with one unit rated at 1800kg (3968lb) or two units each rated at 1300 or 250kg (2866 or 551lb), and generally comprising an internal load of two 1000kg (2205lb) SC-1000 bombs and two 250kg (551lb) SC-250 bombs, or four 500kg (1102lb) SC-500 bombs, or eight 250kg (551lb) SC-250 bombs and an external load of one 1800kg (3968lb) SC-1800 bomb or LT F5 torpedo, or two Hs 293A anti-ship missiles, or two 250kg (551lb) SC-250 bombs

---

warplanes with or without the aid of the Rästsätze, the German air ministry was still eager to acquire a variant capable of the shallow dive-bombing role. In response Dornier completed the development of a variant as the Do 217E-2. This had first flown in Do 217 V11 prototype form during October 1940 and included an improved version of the original tail-mounted dive brake and an improved defensive armament with two 13mm MG131 weapons. The only other significant change was in the powerplant, which still comprised two easily changed 'power eggs' but in this instance containing BMW 801ML engines rated identically to the original BMW 801MA but driving a larger-diameter propeller with metal rather than wooden blades. The Do

217E-2 was built in parallel with the Do 217E-1, and the first aircraft were issued to the Stab (staff section) of Stukageschwader 2 for operational trials in the summer of 1941. This unit reported unfavourably on the capability of the Do 217E-2 as a dive-bomber, but considerably more development work followed before the German air ministry finally conceded that the dive-bomber concept was impractical for so large an aeroplane.

Anti-shipping attacks
As this was happening, Dornier was continuing deliveries of the Do 217E-2 and Do 217E-3 to KG 2 whose three Gruppen were based along the southern coast of the English Channel

for attacks on the UK and on shipping in the North Sea. Operations in this high-intensity arena revealed a need for improvements including heavier fixed forward-firing armament. By the end of 1941, some 300 Do 217E bombers had been delivered, about 100 of them being Do 217E-3 machines. Late in 1941 Dornier switched to production of the Do 217E-4 that entered service early in the following year with cable cutters in the wing leading edges and a powerplant of two BMW 801C radial engines. Production of the Do 217E-4 totalled about 500 aircraft, and of these a few late examples were completed to Do 217E-5 standard with provision for the R10 or R15 underwing kits to allow carriage of two Hs 293 anti-ship missiles. It was a Do 217E-5 of II/KG 100 that made the first operational attack with the Hs 293 missile in August 1943, when British destroyers operating in the Bay of Biscay were attacked.

The Do 217F and Do 217G designations were reserved for models that did not proceed past the project stage, and the Do 217H designation was applied to a single Do 217E-1 converted for high-altitude trials with a powerplant of two DB 601 engines fitted with turbochargers.

The next variant to enter production was therefore the Do 217K, which started its flight trials in March 1942. The primary changes in this model were a completely revised forward fuselage that eliminated the pilot's stepped windscreen to allow the incorporation of a rounded and more extensively glazed forward fuselage, a change in the powerplant from two BMW 801C engines to BMW 801D units each rated at 1700hp (1268kW) for take-off and 1440hp (1074kW) at 18,700ft (5700m), and a revised defensive gun armament. This comprised one 13mm MG131 trainable rearward-firing machine gun in the electrically operated dorsal turret, one 13mm MG131 trainable rearward-firing machine gun in the ventral step position, one 7.92mm MG81z trainable forward-firing machine gun (paired MG81 weapons) in the nose position, and two or later four 7.92mm MG81 trainable lateral-firing machine guns in the cockpit side windows.

Three prototypes paved the way for the Do 217K-1 that entered production in the early summer of 1942 and entered service in the autumn of the same year with KG 2 in the night bomber role. The Do 217K-1 was the first variant of the Do 217 series to enter production with the

BELOW *The Do 217E introduced the BMW 801 radial engine, and this illustration highlights the type's electrically operated dorsal turret, which offered excellent fields of vision and was fitted with a 13mm MG 131 heavy machine gun supplied with 500 rounds of ammunition.*

R25 tail fitting for a brake parachute, and other Rästsätze that could be applied to this and later variants included the R4 for external carriage of an LT F5 torpedo, R6 for a weapons bay reconnaissance camera installation, R7 for a four-man dinghy pack installed in the fuselage above the weapons bay, R10 for two outboard external carriers for Henschel Hs 293 anti-ship missiles, R13 for an auxiliary fuel tank in the forward part of the weapons bay, R14 for an auxiliary fuel tank in the rear part of the weapons bay, R15 for two inboard external carriers for Henschel Hs 293 anti-ship missiles, R17 for a different auxiliary fuel tank in the forward part of the weapons bay, R19 for one 7.92mm MG81z two-barrel machine gun that could be installed in the tail cone, and R21 for a device to allow the carriage and jettisoning of external auxiliary fuel tanks.

Entering service in December 1942, the Do 217K-2 was a development of the Do 217K-1 for the carriage of two FX-1400 Fritz-X guided bombs, a stand-off weapon designed to provide a heavyweight capability against capital ships and other major vessels. This variant introduced extended outer wing panels that increased the wing span to 24.80m (81ft 4.3in) with an area of 67.00sq m (721.218sq ft), and first used the Fritz-X operationally in August 1943 over the Mediterranean, sinking the Italian battleship Roma as she was steaming to Malta after the Italian armistice with the Allies. The Do 217K-3 differed only in having a revised electronic package allowing an operator to control either the Fritz-X guided bomb or Hs 293A anti-ship missile.

In the spring of 1943 Dornier flew the Do 217L V1 and Do 217L V2 prototypes with a rearranged cockpit and defensive armament scheme. In the event the Do 217L did not enter production, so the next and final operational development of the Do 217 in its pure bomber form was the Do 217M, built in parallel with the Do 217K with two Daimler-Benz DB 603A inverted-Vee engines each rated at 1305kW (1750hp) for take-off. The variant's performance and capabilities were similar to those of the Do 217K-1, and the sole model to enter service was the Do 217M-1. Developed versions were postponed and later cancelled so that Do 217 production could be concentrated on the Do 217N night-fighter derivative.

The ultimate development of the Do 217 bomber was the Do 217P high-altitude reconnaissance bomber. This was basically the Do 217E-2 revised with a four-man pressurised cockpit and the HZ-Anlage powerplant. This latter comprised two DB 603B engines installed in the wing-mounted nacelles and supercharged by a DB 605T engine in a semi-exposed installation under the rear fuselage and driving a two-stage compressor: the whole system offered 2610kW (3500hp) for take-off and 2147kW (2880hp) at 13,750m (45,110ft). The Do 217P V1 prototype made its maiden flight in June 1942 and revealed a ceiling of 13,400m (43,960ft). The test programme was later joined by the Do 217P V2 and Do 217P V3 prototypes with extended outer wing panels increasing the wing span to 24.50m (80ft 4.5in) with an area of 66.90sq m (720.13sq ft). The larger wing increased the service ceiling to 16,150m (52,985ft). There followed three Do 217P-0 pre-production aircraft but no true production machines.

Production of the Do 217 bomber was discontinued in June 1944 after the delivery of 1541 aircraft.

Night fighters

Although the Do 217 series provided the Luftwaffe with a very useful bombing capability, the type also mirrored the earlier Do 17 and Do 215 in drawing attention to itself as the basis for a specialised night-fighter to combat increasingly capable Allied bombers, most notably the Avro Lancaster four-engined heavy bomber, fielded by the Royal Air Force during the closing months of 1941 and early months of 1942. By this time considerable pressure was being exercised on Dornier to complete the development of the Do 217J night-fighter on which work had started in the summer of 1941. The Do 217J was a derivative of its Do 217E-2 in which the only major external change was the adoption of a solid nose accommodating a battery of four 20mm MGFF (Oerlikon) cannon and four 7.92mm MG17 machine guns. The task of this heavy night-fighter was visual acquisition and destruction of British bombers after the crew had been vectored into an interception position by ground-controlled radar, and long-range intruder sorties against British airfields with eight 50 kg (110lb) bombs in the rear half of the weapons bay. Other elements of the original armament that were retained were the single 13mm MG131 trainable machine guns installed in the electrically operated dorsal turret with 500 rounds and in the ventral step position with 1000 rounds.

The first Do 217J-1 conversion of a Do 217E-2 flew shortly before the end of 1941, and the first aircraft were delivered early in 1942. The Do 217J-1 was only an interim type, and most of the aircraft had been relegated to the training role by the summer of 1942 as the Do 217J-2 became available. This was a pure interception type in which the rear weapons bay was deleted and FuG 202 Lichtenstein BC airborne interception radar, using a nose-mounted Matratze (mattress) array of four Hirschgeweih (stag horn) antennae, was added. Agility was poor while the drum-fed MGFF cannon had a low rate of fire, but the

possession of radar made the Do 217J-2 an effective interceptor. The type was dimensionally identical to the later Do 217N-2, but differed in details such as its two BMW 801ML engines, maximum speed of 490km/h (304.5mph) at 5500m (18,045ft), empty weight of 9350kg (20,613lb) and maximum take-off weight of 13,180kg (29,056lb).

First flown in July 1942, the Do 217N was built in parallel as the night-fighter derivative of the Do 217M bomber, and differed from the Do 217J mainly in its powerplant of two DB 603A engines each rated at 1305kW (1750hp) for take-off. The type was delivered with the same gun armament as the Do 217J-2, but differed in a number of its electronic systems, which included the FuG 212 Lichtenstein or FuG 202 Lichtenstein radar. In some of the aircraft the MGFF cannon were later replaced by belt-fed 20mm MG151/20 cannon, which by comparison with the original weapons were lighter and more easily aimed. This modification was undertaken with the aid of an Umräst-Bausatz (factory conversion set) and resulted in the Do 217N-1/U1 that was also stripped of its dorsal turret and ventral gun position.

In the spring of 1943 the Do 217N-1 was replaced in production by the Do 217N-2 in which all the Do 217N-1/U1 alterations were incorporated as standard and

ABOVE *Despite its obsolescence from late 1943, the Do 217 remained in service up to the end of World War II. This is a Do 217E, and although the Do 217 operated with guided weapons, the type was most often associated with free-fall bombs.*

supplemented by provision for additional electronic equipment to counter the RAF's increasingly sophisticated electronic countermeasures equipment. Production of the Do 217N-2 was completed in the late summer of 1943, with 364 night-fighter aircraft completed.

This was not the end of the Do 217N-2 programme, however, for the type became the first to operate with the schräge Musik (shrill music, i.e. jazz) installation. This comprised a battery of 20mm obliquely upward/forward-firing cannon in the central fuselage. The installation allowed the night-fighter approach the target bomber from underneath, and then deliver a devastating burst of explosive shells into the crew area, weapons bay, engines and fuel tanks. The system was first tested in the spring of 1943 on three Do 217N-1 night-fighters each converted with two 20mm MG151/20 cannon and proved very successful. A Rästsätz was then produced to equip the Do 217N-2 with four MG151/20 cannon as the Do 217N-2/R22.

CHAPTER 4

FOCKE-WULF FW 189 EULE

Looking comparatively frail and possessing an unusual appearance, the Fw 189 was a highly effective tactical reconnaissance aeroplane that could double in the close support role. Despite its vulnerability to fighter interception, the Fw 189 was used operationally from 1940 to 1945, mainly on the Eastern Front.

The only two short-range or battlefield reconnaissance aircraft used in substantial numbers by the Luftwaffe in World War II were the Henschel Hs 126 parasol-wing monoplane and the more advanced and longer-lived Focke-Wulf Fw 189 Eule (owl) twin-boom monoplane that was often nicknamed Uhu (eagle owl). The latter resulted from a German air ministry requirement of February 1937 for an advanced tactical reconnaissance aeroplane to succeed the Hs 126, and its twin-engined configuration with two booms carrying the tail unit resulted from the determination of Dipl.-Ing. Kurt Tank to design an aeroplane offering the best possible fields of vision for the crew by the use of a central nacelle with very extensive

LEFT *This photograph reveals the Fw 189A in a typical operational setting, operating at low level for the tactical reconnaissance role right over the battlefield. The location of the crew in an extensively glazed central nacelle provided truly excellent fields of vision.*

glazing. The German air ministry was initially sceptical, but ordered the first three of an eventual six prototypes.

Focke-Wulf began work on detail design and prototype construction immediately after receiving the prototype order, and the Fw 189 V1 first prototype flew only 15 months later in July 1938 with two Argus As 410 engines each rated at 321kW (430hp). The three prototypes revealed an attractive combination of good performance, considerable low-level agility without any handling problems, and great structural strength. The type was ordered into production during the spring of 1940 in its initial Fw 189A form, Focke-Wulf starting with a batch of 10 Fw 189A-0 pre-production aircraft. Built at Focke-Wulf's main facility at Bremen, these aircraft were followed by aircraft of the first full-production standard, namely the Fw 189A-1 with further refinement of the engine nacelles, As 410A-1 engines, twin- rather than single-leg main landing gear units, full operational equipment including cameras,

SPECIFICATIONS: Focke-Wulf Fw 189A-2 Eule

GENERAL
Type: short-range operational and tactical reconnaissance aeroplane with limited close-support and night fighter capabilities
Accommodation: pilot, navigator/radio operator/gunner and flight engineer/gunner in the central nacelle
Equipment: standard communication and navigation equipment, plus a GV 219d optical bomb sight, optical gun sights, provision for one Rb 20/30, Rb 50/30, Rb 21/8 or Rb 15/18 reconnaissance camera and, in the night-fighter variant, FuG 212 Lichtenstein C-1 airborne interception radar
Weights: empty 3245kg (7154lb); normal take-off 3950kg (8708lb); maximum take-off 4170kg (9193lb)

MOTIVE POWER
Powerplant: two Argus As 410A-1

inverted-Vee piston engines each rated at 347kW (465hp) for take-off and 253.5kW (340hp) at 2100m (6890ft)
Fuel: internal fuel 220 litres (48.4Imp gal; 58.1US gal); external fuel none

PERFORMANCE
Maximum speed: 350km/h (217mph) at 2400m (7875ft)
Cruising speed: maximum 325km/h (202mph) at 2400m (7875ft)
Climb: to 4000m (13,125ft) in 8 minutes 18 seconds
Service ceiling: 7300m (23,950ft);
Maximum range: 670km (416 miles); endurance 2 hours 10 minutes

DIMENSIONS
Wing span: 18.40m (60ft 4.5in)
Wing area: 38.00 sq m (409.03sq ft)
Length: 12.03 m (39ft 5.6in)

Height: 3.10m (10ft 2in)

ARMAMENT
Fixed armament: two 7.92mm MG17 fixed forward-firing machine guns in the leading edges of the wing roots, one 7.92mm MG81z trainable rearward-firing two-barrel machine gun in the dorsal position replaced in the night-fighter role by one 15mm MG151 fixed upward/forward-firing cannon in a shräge Musik installation, and one 7.92mm MG81z trainable rearward-firing two-barrel machine gun in the power-operated Ikaria rotating tailcone turret
Disposable armament: up to 200kg (441lb) of disposable stores carried on four hardpoints (all under the wing with each unit rated at 50kg (110lb), and generally comprising four 50kg (110lb) SC-50 bombs

and armament standardised as two 7.92mm MG17 fixed forward-firing machine guns, one 7.92mm MG15 trainable machine-gun in each of the nacelle's dorsal and tail positions, and four 50kg (110lb) bombs. By the end of 1940 some 20 aircraft had been delivered for full operational evaluation, which resulted in very favourable reports.

Foreign production

Official demands for more aircraft delivered at a higher rate resulted in the creation of a second production line at the Aero works near Prague in occupied Czechoslovakia to take the burden off Focke-Wulf's main factory, which was increasingly committed to the final development and production of the Fw 190 fighter. During 1941 Focke-Wulf delivered 99 Fw 189A machines while the Aero factory produced 151 machines. Toward the end of the year, Focke-Wulf started to deliver the components for a third production line to factories in the south-western part of occupied France, where components were produced in

several locations for final assembly at Márignac near Bordeaux in Western France.

The only variants of the Fw 189A-1 were the Fw 189A-1/Trop for deployment to North Africa (and therefore adapted with dust/sand filters and desert survival equipment), and the Fw 189A-1/U command transport, of which a mere two were produced as Fw 189A-1 conversions. From mid-1941 the Fw 189A-1 was succeeded in production by the Fw 189A-2 that differed only in the adoption of MG81z two-barrel machine guns in place of the original MG15 one-barrel weapons. Produced in small numbers during the same period was the Fw 189A-3 trainer with the forward part of its central nacelle adapted to accomodate two pilots seated side-by-side with full dual flight controls.

The Fw 189A entered operational service in the autumn of 1940, initially with the 9(H)./Lehrgeschwader 2 that had received Fw 189B aircraft for conversion training in the spring of the same year. Rapid replacement of the older Hs

126 proved impossible because of the Fw 189's slow production rate. By the end of 1941, however, most Hs 126 units had completed at least a partial transition to the more advanced type, and from the spring of 1942 most existing Fw 189A units were operational on the Eastern Front, where the Eule was to see most employment. The production tempo increased markedly in 1942, largely as a result of the French factory coming on stream. In 1943 the French line became the primary source of the Fw 189A (194 aircraft) as Bremen and Prague ceased deliveries with a final 11 and three aircraft respectively. The last version of the Fw 189A, produced only in France, was the Fw 189A-4 intended for both the tactical reconnaissance and close support roles with the two 7.92mm fixed forward-firing machine guns supplemented by two 20mm MGFF cannon, and protection upgraded by the introduction of light armour on the underside of the engine nacelles, fuel tanks and parts of the central nacelle. Production of the Fw 189A ended in the first weeks of 1944 after the delivery of 828 aircraft.

When it ordered a second batch of Fw 189 prototypes, the German air ministry ordered that the second of these aircraft should be completed as the precursor of the planned trainer series, and the Fw 189 V5 was therefore developed with an entirely different central nacelle of more refined aerodynamic shape with a solid nose and stepped windscreen in place of the Fw 189A's multi-panel glazed nose. This prototype made its maiden flight early in 1939, and was also notable for its total lack of armament and for its side-by-side pilot accommodation with dual controls. The Fw 189B entered production before the Fw 189A, and was first seen in the form of three Fw 189B-0 pre-production aircraft and an initial batch of 10 Fw 189B-1 production aircraft all delivered by early 1940.

Close support

Late in 1938 the German air ministry had decided to investigate Focke-Wulf's proposal for a close support version of the Fw 189. The Fw 189 V1 prototype was thus removed from the flight test programme for conversion to Fw 189 V1b standard with an armoured nacelle of very angular lines and with just enough volume to accommodate the pilot and a rear gunner seated back to back. The fields of vision for both

crew members were limited; the pilot had to peer through small armoured glass panels in the armour cockpit hood, and the gunner was limited to a small opening in an armour visor to use his single 7.92mm machine gun. Flight tests on the Fw 189 V1b started in the first part of 1939 and proved disappointing, as did the Fw 189 V6 precursor of the planned Fw 189C production model. No further development of the Fw 189C concept was undertaken.

The Fw 189D was a proposed two-seat floatplane trainer, and the Fw 189E was a single conversion from Fw 189A-1 standard with two Gnome-Rhône 14M radial engines each rated at 522kW (700hp). Completed to the extent of just 17 aircraft before production in France ceased early in 1944, the Fw 189F was a development of the Fw 189A-2 with the revised powerplant of two As 411M-1 inverted-Vee piston engines each rated at 432kW (580hp) for take-off. The initial Fw 189F-1 was basically similar to the Fw 189A-2 apart from its revised powerplant, but the Fw 189F-2 introduced an electrically rather than hydraulically operated landing gear actuation system, increased fuel capacity, and additional armour protection. Another development, planned in 1942 but eventually stymied by the failure of its engine, was the Fw 189G with a powerplant of two As 402 inverted-Vee piston engines each rated at 708kW (950hp).

BELOW *On the Eastern Front, the three-man crew of an Fw 189A tactical reconnaissance aeroplane celebrate the 5000th operation sortie by their Nahaufklärungsgeschwader (short-range reconnaissance group). The vanes on the spinners controlled the automatic propeller pitch.*

CHAPTER 5

FOCKE-WULF FW 190

The Fw 190 was overshadowed by the rival Messerschmitt Bf 109, which was built in substantially larger numbers, but in essence was a superior and more versatile fighter that served as the mount of many leading aces, and was also built with an air-cooled radial engine or a liquid-cooled Vee unit. The Fw 190 was also an excellent fighter-bomber.

The Fw 190 vies with the Messerschmitt Bf 109 for the title of Germany's most important fighter in World War II. When it made its operational debut in the spring of 1941 it was without doubt the finest fighter in the world, comfortably superior to the Supermarine Spitfire Mk V that was its primary adversary. This superiority was maintained until the advent of the Spitfire MkIX almost exactly a year later. The Fw 190 proved capable of radical development with liquid-cooled engines of the inverted-Vee type as well as air-cooled engines of the radial type. This helped to maintain the capabilities of the Fw 190 as a true fighter, but enabled Focke-Wulfe to evolve the aircraft into an exceptionally potent fighter-bomber and dedicated

attack fighter. Even in these forms the Fw 190 never lost the superbly harmonised controls that made it one of the classic air combat fighters of World War II, combining with ease the often conflicting requirements of stability as a gun platform and agility as a dogfighter.

The origins of the type can be traced to a 1937 requirement issued by the German air ministry for a single-engined interceptor fighter to supplement the Messerschmitt Bf 109 that had already been selected as the Luftwaffe's standard fighter. Planned by Oberingenieur R. Blaser under the supervision of Dipl.-Ing. Kurt Tank, the new fighter was schemed with a choice of two powerplants, namely the Daimler-Benz DB 601 inverted-Vee piston engine with liquid cooling and the BMW 139 radial piston engine with air cooling. Somewhat to the surprise of all concerned, the German air ministry opted for the radial-engined version. Daimler-Benz was already hard pressed to meet demands for the DB 601, and as the BMW 139 was

LEFT *This photograph of virtually factory-fresh aircraft reveals Fw 190F-2 ground-attack aircraft of Schlachtgeschwader I as it prepared to leave Deblin-Irena in Poland for service on the Eastern Front. Several aircraft sport the 'Mickey Mouse' badge adopted by II/SG I in October 1943.*

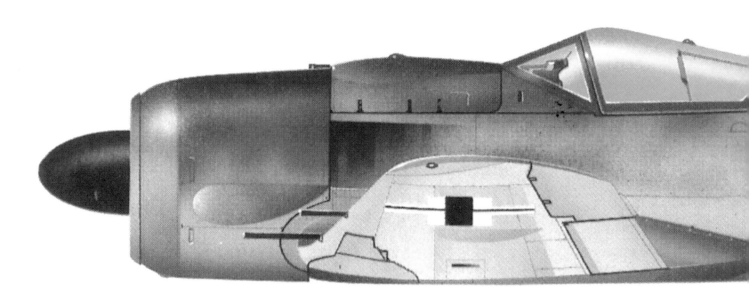

already offering a high power output at an excellent power/weight ratio it could be expected to offer significant improvements in both factors as development proceeded.

With the new fighter ordered in prototype form, Focke-Wulf began detail design work in the summer of 1938 to finalise the Fw 190 as an aggressive-looking monoplane fighter of cantilever low-wing configuration with a well streamlined engine installation. The Fw 190 V1 prototype made its maiden flight on 1 June 1939 with a powerplant of one BMW 139 radial engine rated at 1156kW (1550hp). Another prototype designated V2 followed before further work on the BMW 139 was terminated in favour of the BMW 801 radial engine rated at 1238kW (1660hp). This was installed in its BMW 801C-0 form in the Fw 190 V5k and Fw 190 V5g prototypes: these both had a restressed and strengthened airframe, and the cockpit was moved aft to help maintain the centre of gravity in the right location. The V5k (klein, or small) retained the original wing with a span of 9.50 m (31ft 2in) and area of 15.00sq m (161.46 sq ft), while the V5g (gross, or large) introduced an enlarged wing with a span of 10.50m (34ft 5.5in) and area of 18.30 sq m (196.99sq ft). These two prototypes made their maiden flights in the spring of 1940, and it soon became clear that the larger wing reduced speed only marginally but boosted climb rate, ceiling and agility considerably. The larger wing

was therefore adopted as the standard wing for the production model. By this time a pre-production batch of 30 Fw 190A-0 fighters had been ordered, and the first nine of these were delivered with the smaller wing. The larger wing therefore featured on the last 21 of the Fw 190A-0 pre-production aircraft and on the 102 Fw 190A-1 fighters. This was the first full production version to enter service even though the initial five were used for test work with the alternative designations Fw 190 V7 to Fw 190 V11.

Combat debut

The Fw 190A-1 was powered by the BMW 801C-1 engine, and was armed with four 7.92mm MG17 fixed forward-firing machine guns. The length of the A-1 was 8.80m (28ft 10.5in), and maximum take-off weight was 3205kg (7066lb). The first unit of the Luftwaffe earmarked for conversion to the new fighter was Jagdgeschwader 26 based in northern France. This unit started to convert in March 1941 for an operational debut in August 1941, soon revealed the Fw 190 to be a superb air combat fighter. The importance of the Fw 190 in German planning from this time forward is attested by the fact that while only 100 examples of the Fw 190A-1 were built, these were delivered from three different manufacturers – Focke-Wulf, AGO and Arado. These three were the first members of a widespread

production effort that was to grow dramatically in extent and rate as the war progressed.

The tactical consequences of the Fw 190A-1's poor firepower had already been foreseen, and the Fw 190A-1 was therefore regarded only as an interim type pending availability of the Fw 190A-2 with the two 7.92mm MG17

machine guns in the wing roots replaced by a pair of 20mm MGFF. The cannon certainly increased the Fw 190A-2's weight of fire, but were drum-fed weapons with a maximum of only 60 rounds per gun. Later aircraft were therefore fitted with supplementary armament in the form of two magazine-fed MG17 fixed forward-firing machine guns

SPECIFICATIONS: Focke-Wulf Fw 190A-8

GENERAL
Type: fighter
Accommodation: pilot in an enclosed cockpit
Equipment: standard communication and navigation equipment, plus a Revi 16/B reflector gun sight
Weights: empty 3470kg (7652lb); maximum take-off 4380kg (9656lb)

MOTIVE POWER
Powerplant: one BMW 801D radial piston engine rated at 1267.5kW (1700hp) for take-off and 1074kW (1440hp) at 5700m (18,700ft)
Fuel: internal fuel 524 litres (115.25Imp gal; 138.4US gal) plus provision for 115 litres (25.3Imp gal; 30.4US gal) of auxiliary fuel in an optional rear-fuselage tank; external fuel up to 300 litres (66Imp gal; 79.25US gal) in one drop tank

PERFORMANCE
Maximum speed: 656km/h (408mph) at 6300m (20,670ft) with GM 1 boost or 647km/h (402mph) at 5500m (18,045ft) without GM 1 boost declining to 571km/h (355mph) at sea level
Cruising speed: 298mph (480km/h) at 2000m (6560ft)
Initial climb rate: 1050m (3445ft) per minute; climb to 6000m (19,685ft) in 9 minutes 6 seconds
Service ceiling: 11,400m (37,400ft) with GM 1 boost or 10,300m (33,795ft) without GM 1 boost
Maximum range: 1470km (915 miles) with drop tank; typical range 1035km (644 miles) with standard fuel

DIMENSIONS
Wing span: 10.51m (34ft 5.8in)
Wing area: 18.30sq m (196.98sq ft)

Length: 8.95m (29ft 4.37in)
Height: 3.95 m (12ft 11.5in)

ARMAMENT
Fixed armament: two 20mm MG151/20E fixed forward-firing cannon with 250 rounds per gun in the leading edges of the wing roots with synchronisation equipment to fire through the propeller disc, two 20mm MG151/20E fixed forward-firing cannon with 140 rounds per gun in the leading edges of the wing, and two 13mm MG131 fixed forward-firing machine guns with 475 rounds per gun in the upper part of the forward fuselage with synchronisation equipment to fire through the propeller disc
Disposable armament: none

ABOVE *Compact, clean, powerful and moderately heavily armed, the Fw 190A entered operational service in the summer of 1941, and soon proved that it possessed superior performance and agility over the Spitfire Mk V that was currently the most capable British fighter.*

located farther outboard in the wing leading edges. The Fw 190A-2 was powered by the improved BMW 801C-2 engine, had additional radio equipment, and while dimensionally identical to the Fw 190A-1 had a maximum speed of 625km/h (388mph) at 5500m (18,945ft) and a maximum take-off weight of 3500kg (7716lb). The first Fw 190A-2 fighters were delivered in November 1941, and production of the Fw 190A-2 totalled 426 aircraft.

The Fw 190A-3 may be regarded as the first definitive production model of the Fw 190 series, and was basically similar to the Fw 190A-2 except in its powerplant and armament. The powerplant was one BMW 801D-2 engine rated at 1267.5kW (1700hp); the wing-mounted armament was revised to a quartet of 20mm weapons in the form of two MGFF cannon in the outboard positions and two faster-

firing and belt-fed MG151/20 cannon in the inboard positions. The size and extent of the Fw 190 production programme was now beginning to reveal itself more fully, and although deliveries of the Fw 190A-3 totalled only 509 aircraft, these were delivered in a comparatively short time from six Focke-Wulf factories, one AGO factory, two Arado factories, and one Fieseler factory. By the spring of 1942, the production rate for the Fw 190 was 250 fighters per month rising to 500 as all these facilities came on full stream.

Subvariants of the Fw 190A-3 included the Fw 190A-3/U1, Fw 190A-3/U3 and Fw 190A-3/U7 fighter-bombers, and the Fw 190A-3/U4 reconnaissance fighter. The first three were each stripped of their outboard MGFF cannon and fitted with a Umrüst-Bausatz (factory conversion set) in the form of an underfuselage rack. This was rated at 500kg (1102 lb) but actual capacity was a 1000kg (2205lb) load of one large bomb, or four small bombs or one drop tank. The Fw 190A-3 was dimensionally identical to the Fw 190A-8, but differed in details such as its maximum speed of 615km/h (382mph) at 6000m (19,685ft), cruising speed of

447km/h (278mph) at optimum altitude, initial climb rate of 865m (2838ft) per minute, service ceiling of 10,600m (34,775ft), maximum range of 800km (497 miles), and maximum take-off weight of 3800kg (8377lb).

Introduced during the summer of 1942, the Fw 190A-4 was basically the Fw 190A-3 with revised radio equipment and an uprated powerplant in the form of the standard BMW 801D-2 engine revised with the MW 1 methanol/water power-boost system. This system raised the maximum power rating to 1566kW (2100hp) for short periods, permitting an increase in maximum speed to 670km/h (416mph) at 6300m (20,670ft) after take-off at a maximum weight of 3800kg (8377lb). The Fw 190A-4 was also adapted for a number of alternative or supplementary roles by the installation of Umrüst-Bausätze and Rüstsätze indicated by a suffix to the basic designation: U1 indicated a heavy fighter-bomber with the gun armament reduced to just two MG151/20 cannon but a disposable armament of two 500kg (1102lb) bombs; U3 a medium fighter-bomber

with a fixed armament of two MG151/20 cannon and two MG17 machine guns as well as a disposable armament of one 500kg (1102lb) bomb; U4 a reconnaissance fighter with the same camera provision as the Fw 190A-3/U4; and U8 a long-range fighter-bomber with a maximum take-off weight of 4900kg (10,803lb) and armament that included a fixed component of two MG151/20 cannon and a disposable component of one 500kg (1102lb) bomb. The range of a fully-loaded U8 could be boosted by underwing carriage of two 300 litre (66Imp gal; 79.25US gal) drop tanks.

Desert aircraft

The only other variants of the Fw 190A-4 were the Fw 190A-4/Trop and Fw 190A-4/R6, the former a fighter-bomber

BELOW *This Fw 190A-3 is revealed as an Fw 190A-3/Trop by the sand filter incorporated in the air inlet for the engine. Although basically a fighter, the Fw 190A-3/Trop could also operate in the fighter-bomber role with a rack under the fuselage for up to 500kg (1102lb) of bombs.*

version tropicalised for use in North Africa and the latter having a maximum take-off weight of 4300kg (9480lb) with two underwing launchers for 210mm WGr.21 rockets for use in the bomber interception role. The Fw 190A-4 series, of which 894 were built, remained in production into 1943 and was followed by the Fw 190A-5, a version of the Fw 190A-4 with a revised engine mounting that positioned the BMW 801D-2 engine some 0.15m (5.9in) farther forward. This revision increased length to 8.95m (29ft 4.25in) and restored the centre of gravity to the location it had occupied before its alteration by the addition of extra equipment in the rear fuselage. Maximum take-off weight was 4300kg (9480lb) and provision was made for a larger assortment of Rüstsätze and Umrüst-Bausätze. The most important of these kits was the R6 that comprised a pair of underwing launchers for 210mm WGr.21 rockets. The range

of Umrüst-Bausätze was similar to that of the Fw 190A-4 but larger in number to reflect the increased number of fixed and disposable weapon options, which now included 30mm cannon and torpedoes. The only other variant of the Fw 190A-5 was the tropicalised Fw 190A-5/Trop. Production of the Fw 190A-5 series totalled 723 aircraft.

The Fw 190A-6 was the production-line version of the Fw 190A-5/U10 with a lightened wing structure. Nevertheless, this was able to accommodate a fixed armament of four 20mm MG151/20 cannon, supplemented by the two fuselage-mounted 7.92mm MG17 machine guns for a

BELOW *Seen while being prepared for gun-harmonisation tests, this is an Fw 190A fighter of a Jagdgeschwader's II Gruppe (indicated by the horizontal bar behind the fuselage cross), and a mount of the Geschwader staff flight (indicated by the chevron and bar ahead of the cross).*

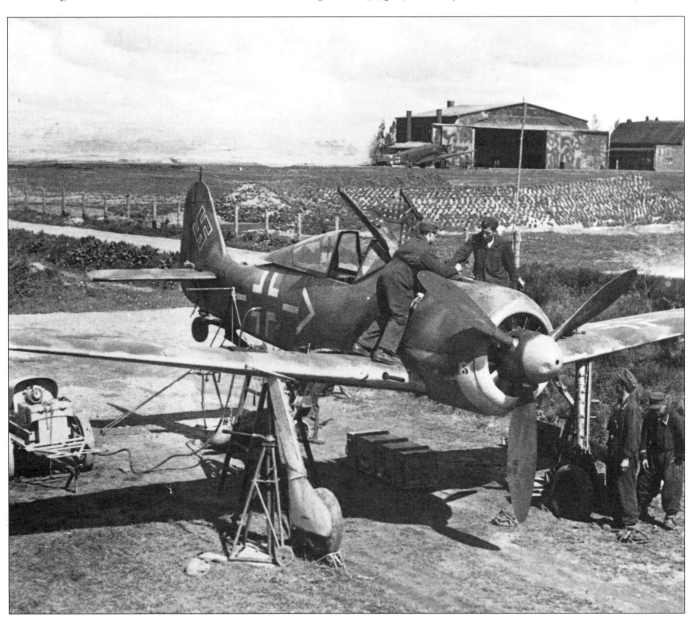

maximum take-off weight of 3900kg (8598lb). Production of the Fw 190A-6 fighter totalled 569 aircraft, and many of these were converted with Rüstsätze and Umrüst-Bausatz.

Entering production in December 1943, the Fw 190A-7 was the production derivative of the Fw 190A-5/U9 with a maximum take-off weight of 4000kg (8818lb) and the revised fixed armament of two 20mm MG151/20 cannon in the wing roots and two 13mm MG131 machine guns in the upper part of the forward fuselage, together with a new type of gun sight. Production totalled 80 aircraft; most were later converted with the R1, R2, R3 and R6 Rüstsätze.

The Fw 190A-8 was the final production model of the Fw 190A-series fighter, and was built from December 1943 in larger numbers than any other of the A-series fighters. Production totalled some 1,334 aircraft. The type was powered by the BMW 801D-2 engine in a form with the GM 1 nitrous oxide power-boost system. Other changes included a modest increase in internal fuel capacity through the introduction of a small auxiliary tank in the rear fuselage, different radio equipment, and the underfuselage rack moved 0.20m (7.9in) farther forward. Three of the aircraft were adapted as dual-control trainers with the designation Fw 190A-8/U1. These had the cockpit lengthened to the rear under a framed and somewhat angular rearward-sliding canopy section to provide

ABOVE *Seen in British markings for post-war evaluation, this odd-looking bird is an Fw 190A-8/U1, a dual-control conversion trainer of which a mere three were created in 1944. There were also Fw 190S-5 and Fw 190S-8 two-seaters used mainly for the liaison role.*

accommodation for the instructor's seat with dual controls and limited instrumentation, and the first aircraft made its maiden flight in January 1944.

Birth of the B-series

The advent in British service of the Spitfire MkIX in the autumn of 1942 threatened the superiority that had been enjoyed by the early variants of the Fw 190A-series. The Spitfire MkIX offered performance generally comparable to that of the Fw 190A-3 at altitudes below 7000m (22,965ft) but considerably better performance above that altitude as the BMW 801 began to lose power rapidly. This revelation spurred the efforts of the Focke-Wulf design team, which had already started work on the development of an Fw 190 model optimised for superior performance at high altitude. This optimisation was based on three features, namely a longer-span wing of increased area, a turbocharged version of the BMW 801 engine and a pressurised cockpit, and was intended to evolve an Fw 190B-1 production model of which only six were eventually completed with a wing increased in span to 12.30m (40ft 4.25in) with an additional 2.00sq m (21.53sq ft) of area. A parallel effort had been centred on another high-altitude model, the Fw 190C with an altogether different powerplant in the form of the Daimler-Benz DB 603 inverted-Vee piston engine. Four prototypes were built, but no production followed.

A third development programme undertaken in parallel with those for the Fw 190B and Fw 190C series led to the superlative Fw 190D fighter, equipped with the Junkers Jumo 213 inverted-Vee engine cooled by an annular radiator that allowed the retention of the earlier variants' radial-engined appearance, a pressurised cockpit, and the standard wing. It was only in 1943 that full-scale work on the Fw 190D began. The first prototype for the series was an Fw 190A-0 that was modified as the Fw 190 V17/U1 with a pressurised cockpit, the Jumo 213A-1 engine rated at 1305kW (1750hp) for take-off, and a fuselage that was

lengthened by some 0.60m (1ft 11.6in) in its forward section to accommodate the engine/radiator installation and by 0.50m (1ft 7.5in) in its rear section to improve directional stability even though a larger vertical tail surface was fitted. The Fw 190 V21 was the fourth and last Fw 190D prototype and introduced a new wing whose area was increased to 19.60sq m (210.98sq ft). By this time demand for the Fw 190D was urgent, and in August 1944 there appeared a pre-production batch of 10 Fw 190D-0 fighters that were produced as conversions from Fw 190A-7 standard. There were no Fw 190D-1 to Fw 190D-8 versions, for it had been decided that the Fw 190D should succeed the Fw 190A-8 on the various production lines scattered round Germany. The initial production model was therefore the Fw 190D-9 based on the airframe of the Fw 190A-8 with the powerplant of one Jumo 213A-1 engine with the MW 50 water/methanol power-boost system to raise short-term

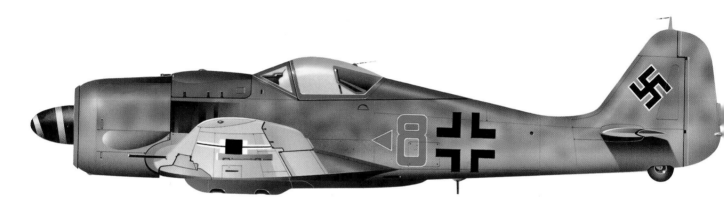

SPECIFICATIONS: Focke-Wulf Fw 190F-3

GENERAL
Type: ground-attack and close-support fighter
Accommodation: pilot in an enclosed cockpit
Equipment: standard communication and navigation equipment, plus a Revi 16/B reflector gun sight
Weights: empty 3325kg (7328lb); normal take-off 4400kg (9700lb); maximum take-off 4925kg (10,858lb)

MOTIVE POWER
Powerplant: one BMW 801D-2 radial piston engine rated at 1267.5kW (1700hp) for take-off and 1074kW (1440hp) at 5700m (18,700ft)
Fuel: internal fuel 524 litres (115.25Imp gal; 138.4US gal); external fuel up to 900 litres (198Imp gal; 237.75 US gal) in three

drop tanks

PERFORMANCE
Maximum speed: 635km/h (394.5mph) at 5500m (18,045ft) declining to 550km/h (342mph) at sea level
Cruising speed: not available
Initial climb rate: 642m (2,106ft) per minute
Service ceiling: 10,600m (34,780ft)
Typical range: 750km (466 miles)

DIMENSIONS
Wing span: 10.51m (34ft 5.8in)
Wing area: 18.30sq m (196.98sq ft)
Length: 8.95m (29ft 4.37in)
Height: 3.95m (12ft 11.5 in)

ARMAMENT
Fixed armament: two 20mm MG151/20E

fixed forward-firing cannon with 250 rounds per gun in the leading edges of the wing roots with synchronisation equipment to fire through the propeller disc, and two 13mm MG131 fixed forward-firing machine guns with 475 rounds per gun in the upper part of the forward fuselage with synchronisation equipment to fire through the propeller disc
Disposable armament: up to 1000kg (2205lb) of disposable stores carried on three hardpoints (one under the fuselage rated at 500kg (1102lb) and two under the wing with each unit rated at 250kg (551lb), and generally comprising one 500kg (1,102lb) SC-500 bomb and two 250kg (551lb) SC-250 bombs, or eight 50kg (110lb) SC-50 bombs

power to 1670kW (2240hp). This was fitted in a 'power egg' that was attached to the forward bulkhead of the fuselage by just four bolts.

The first Fw 190D-9 fighters were fitted with the original type of cockpit canopy, but later examples switched to the slightly bulged canopy that had been developed for the Fw 190F series and offered better visibility as well as improved aerodynamics. Despite the efforts made to improve the weight of the fighter's firepower in the second and third prototypes, the Fw 190D-9 carried a fixed armament of just two 20mm MG151/20 cannon in the wing roots and two 13mm MG131 machine guns above the forward fuselage, a rack being fitted under the fuselage for the carriage of a 250kg (551lb) bomb or a drop tank.

'Long-nosed Dora'

The Fw 190D-9 or 'Langnasen-Dora' (long-nosed Dora) entered service in the autumn of 1944. Such was the enthusiasm of pilots for the Fw 190A with which they had previously been equipped that they were initially distrustful of the new type with its liquid-cooled engine. Operational experience soon revealed that distrust to be wholly misplaced, and the Fw 190D-9 was soon regarded as a superb fighter, and indeed probably the best piston-engined fighter to serve with the Luftwaffe in World War II. The only subvariant of the Fw 190D-9 to enter service was the Fw 190D-9/R11, an all-weather fighter derivative.

The next model to enter production was the Fw 190D-12 ground-attack fighter that supplanted the Fw 190D-9 in production during February or March 1945 on the Arado and Fieseler production lines. The new model had the fixed armament of two 20mm MG151/20 cannon in the wing roots and one 30mm MK108 cannon between the cylinder banks of the Jumo 213F engine. This last was fitted with a three-stage supercharger, was rated at 1305kW (1750hp) for take-off or 1536kW (2060hp) with the MW HD high-pressure methanol/water power boost system, and was installed under a sheathing of armour designed to protect it from anti-aircraft fire during low-level missions. Only a very few aircraft were completed in the last stages of the war, and as far as is known none of these was used operationally for lack of fuel. A large number of variants was projected or developed only to prototype stage.

Total production of the Fw 190D series totalled 674 aircraft, all but a handful of them being Fw 190D-9 machines.

The versatility and adaptability of the basic Fw 190 fighter meant that the type was soon considered for alternative roles, and this led to the development of the Fw

190F dedicated close-support fighter and the Fw 190G long-range fighter-bomber. The Fw 190F had improved protection in the form of some 360kg (794lb) of armour for the pilot, engine and oil tank. This protection was intended to prevent the warplane's destruction as a result of anti-aircraft fire, and was therefore concentrated in the underside of the forward fuselage in the form of the lower part of the engine cowling, the lower fuselage and the wheel well covers. The initial model was the Fw 190F-1, of which some 25 to 30 examples were delivered on the basis of the Fw 190A-4 airframe.

The Fw 190F-2 was the first true production model, and was built to the extent of 271 aircraft up to April 1943. The type was based on the Fw 190A-5 but was generally similar to the Fw 190F-1 with the exception of its revised canopy and modified disposable armament capability. The revised canopy, which was adopted for most later developments of the Fw 190, was based on a single-piece sliding section of the blown type that was bulged upward slightly to provide the pilot with more headroom and also improve the aerodynamic shaping of the upper fuselage. This revised canopy was also fitted with suspended armour to enhance the pilot's protection. Provision for a supplementary rack to be installed on the primary underfuselage rack was made, allowing for the carriage of four 50kg (110lb) bombs as an alternative to a single larger store. Some of the aircraft were tropicalised as Fw 190F-2/Trop machines for service in Tunisia and then in southern Italy.

Built by Arado to the extent of some 250 aircraft based on the Fw 190A-6, the Fw 190F-3 introduced two ETC 250 racks in place of the four ETC 50 racks under the wings: these racks could each carry a single 250kg (551lb) bomb or drop tank. The type was also used in two subvariants as the Fw 190F-3/R1 with simplified bomb-release gear, and the Fw 190F-3/R3 (about 30 aircraft) with two 30mm MK103 fixed forward-firing cannon under the under wing panels for the specialised tank-busting role.

The next models were to have been the Fw 190F-4, Fw 190F-5 and Fw 190F-6, but these were later given the revised designations Fw 190F-8, Fw 190F-9 and Fw 190F-10 respectively. The Fw 190F-7 was designed with the original pair of 7.92mm MG17 fuselage-mounted machine guns replaced by 13mm MG131 weapons, but neither the basic Fw 190F-7 nor its Fw 190F-7/Trop tropicalised version was ever built.

The variant that entered service after the Fw 190F-3 was thus the Fw 190F-8 which, with a total of 385 built from March 1944, was numerically the most important variant of the F attack fighter series. The type had the fixed forward-firing armament of the planned Fw 190F-7 model, in place of the original 7.92mm MG17 weapons, an improved fuel-injection system, revised radio equipment, provision for an auxiliary rear-fuselage fuel tank, and a modified bomb-release system that improved the variant's tactical flexibility by permitting the dropping of the disposable weapons in a single salvo or a number of 'sticks'.

BELOW *This Fw 190A fighter-bomber was abandoned as the Germans pulled out of Monte Corvino airfield in southern Italy on 11 September 1943. Such was their haste to leave that the Germans left this aircraft completely intact and bombed up.*

Torpedo bombers

Production called for 30 of the aircraft from each month's production total to be completed as Fw 190F-8/U1 tandem two-seat conversion trainers, but it is uncertain if any of this model were in fact completed. Other variants on the Fw 190F-8 theme were the Fw 190F-8/U2 and Fw 190F-8/U3 torpedo-fighters with provision for one 400kg (882lb) BT 400, 700kg (1543lb) BT 700 or 1400kg (3086lb) BT 1400 torpedo-bomb, the Fw 190F-8/U14 and Fw 190F-8/U15 torpedo-fighters with provision for the LT F5b and 950kg (2,094lb) LT 900 torpedoes respectively, the Fw 190F-8/R1 with an armament of two 13mm MG131 fuselage-mounted

SPECIFICATIONS: Focke-Wulf Fw 190D-9

GENERAL
Type: fighter and fighter-bomber
Accommodation: pilot in an enclosed cockpit
Equipment: standard communication and navigation equipment, plus a Revi 16/B reflector gun sight
Weights: empty 3490kg (7694lb); normal take-off 4300kg (9480lb)

MOTIVE POWER
Powerplant: one Junkers Jumo 213A-1 inverted-Vee piston engine rated at 1320kW (1770hp) for take-off and 1670kW (2240hp) at altitude with MW 1 water/methanol power boosting
Fuel: internal fuel 524 litres (115.25Imp gal; 138.4US gal) plus provision for 115 litres (25.3Imp gal; 30.4US gal) of auxiliary

fuel in an optional rear-fuselage tank; external fuel up to 300 litres (66Imp gal; 79.25US gal) in one drop tank

PERFORMANCE
Maximum speed: 686km/h (426mph) at 6600m (21,650ft) declining to 574km/h (357mph) at sea level
Cruising speed: not available
Climb: to 6000m (19,685ft) in 7 minutes 6 seconds
Service ceiling: 10,000m (32,810ft)
Typical range: 835km (519 miles) with standard fuel

DIMENSIONS
Wing span: 10.51m (34ft 5.8in)
Wing area: 18.30sq m (196.98sq ft)
Length: 10.19m (33ft 5.18in)

Height: 3.36m (11ft 0.29in)

ARMAMENT
Fixed armament: two 20mm MG151/20E fixed forward-firing cannon with 250 rounds per gun in the wing roots with synchronisation equipment to fire through the propeller disc, and two 13mm MG131 fixed forward-firing machine guns with 475 rounds per gun in the upper part of the forward fuselage with synchronisation equipment to fire through the propeller disc
Disposable armament: up to 250kg (551lb) of disposable stores carried on one hardpoint under the fuselage rated at 250kg (551lb), and generally comprising one 250kg (551lb) SC-250 bomb

machine guns and four 20mm MG151/20 wing-mounted cannon as well as underwing bombs on four underwing racks, and the Fw 190F-8/R2 with the standard fixed armament of two 13mm MG131 fuselage-mounted machine guns and two 20mm MG151/20 wing-mounted cannon supplemented by two 30mm Mk108 cannon in underwing gondolas. There was also the Fw 190F-8/R3 with the standard fixed armament of two 13mm MG131 machine guns and two 20mm MG151/20 cannon supplemented by a pair of 30mm Mk103 underwing cannon for an added tank-busting capability, the Fw 190F-8/R5 (a projected long-range version of the Fw 190F-8/R3), the Fw 190F-8/R13 nocturnal ground-attack fighter with additional navigation equipment and an armament of two 13mm MG131 fuselage-mounted machine guns and up to 1500kg (3307lb) of disposable stores carried on one underfuselage and two underwing racks, the Fw 190F-8/R14 torpedo-fighter with the BMW

801TU radial engine rated at 1491kW (2000hp) for take-off, the PKS 12 radio navigation system and an armament of two 20mm MG151/20 cannon in the wing roots and one LT F5b torpedo carried under the fuselage. The final two aircraft in the series were the Fw 190F-8/R15 modelled on the Fw 190F-8/R14 but with the standard BMW 801D-2 engine and a 1400kg (3086lb) LT 1400 torpedo-bomb, and the Fw 190F-8/R16 modelled on the Fw 190F-8/R15 but with a 700kg (1543lb) LT 700 torpedo-bomb.

The Fw 190F-8 was also used with other weapon loads, the most important being 24 55mm R4M rockets, or 14 100kg (220lb) RBS B/F21 rocket bombs, or two clusters of three 280mm WGr.28 rockets, or Panzerblitz anti-tank rockets in 55, 78 and 130mm calibres, or large numbers of small anti-personnel bomblets.

The Fw 190F-9 was built in parallel with the Fw 190F-8, from which it was differentiated by its improved armour

protection and uprated powerplant, the latter comprising one BMW 801TS/TH turbocharged engine rated at 1491kW (2000hp) for take-off and 1692.5kW (2270hp) with the MW 50 methanol/water power-boost system. The type could be fitted with the same Rüstsätze and Umrüst-Bausätze (factory conversion sets) as the Fw 190F-8, but in practice not many of the aircraft were converted.

The Fw 190F-10 to Fw 190F-17 were unrealised projects except for the Fw 190F-15, which was powered by the BMW 801TS/TH engine, had much improved navigation and weapon-delivery systems, and an armament of two 13mm MG131 fuselage-mounted machine guns, two 20mm MG151/20 wing-mounted cannon and up to 1000kg (2205lb) of disposable stores on a single underfuselage rack. This variant was just entering production in May 1945.

Long-range FW190s

The Fw 190G long-range fighter-bomber was in essence the production version of the Fw 190A-4/U8 and Fw 190A-5/U3 and as a result of a simpler development task preceded the Fw 190F into production and service. The extra range required in this model was provided in part by sacrificing the two fuselage-mounted machine guns to leave the two cannon in the wing roots as the only fixed armament, and in part by the provision of attachments for two drop tanks under the wing. This concept was first realised in the Fw 190G-0 pre-production model that was built in small numbers with a rack under the fuselage for the carriage of one 1000kg (2205lb) or 500kg (1102lb) bomb.

The Fw 190G-1 was the first true production model, and 49 were built on the basis of the Fw 190A-4 airframe. This model was similar to the Fw 190G-0 except for strengthened main landing gear units to cope with a maximum take-off weight of 4750kg (10,472lb). The lower fin of the weapon had to be cropped to provide adequate ground clearance at take-off. The powerplant remained the standard BMW 801D-2 engine (rated at [1700hp] 1267.5kW for take-off) in the original type of short-nose installation resulting in an overall length of 8.80m (28ft 10.5in). This powerplant provided for a maximum speed of 565km/h (351mph) at optimum altitude, cruising speed of 465km/h (289mph) at optimum altitude, and range of 1050km (652 miles) with two drop tanks on Junkers underwing racks.

LEFT *Captured in Germany during April 1945, this is a Mistel 2 composite warplane comprising an explosives-filled and unmanned Ju 88G-1 twin-engined bomber and an Fw 190F-8 single-engined machine whose pilot controlled the composite until it was on final course for its ground target before detaching his machine for the return flight.*

The first unit to re-equip with this type, in its Fw 190G-1/Trop subvariant, was II/Schlachtgeschwader 2 in North Africa. The type proved useful between February 1943 and the final defeat of the Axis forces in May of the same year. While some of the aircraft were thereafter used in Italy against the Western Allies by SG 4, most of the Fw 190G-1 warplanes and their successors were used against the Soviets on the Eastern Front, where the type was first used in significant numbers by I and II/SG 1 in the decisive Battle of Kursk during July 1943.

Built to the extent of 468 aircraft, the Fw 190G-2 was a simple development of the Fw 190G-1 based on the airframe of the Fw 190A-5 with its longer nose section for an overall length of 8.95m (29ft 4.25in). The type also had Messerschmitt-designed racks for underwing drop tanks, which provided for a maximum range of 1550km (963 miles). The production total included a number of Fw 190G-2/Trop aircraft for use in the dusty climes of North Africa, Italy and the southern USSR.

The Fw 190G-3 variant, of which an unknown number was built from October 1943, differed from the Fw 190G-2 only in its incorporation of the PKS 11 autopilot, use of underwing racks designed by Focke-Wulf, and incorporation of balloon cable-cutters in the wing leading edges. A number of the aircraft were completed to Fw 190G-3/Trop standard with dust/sand filters, and the only known variant to be built was the Fw 190G-3/R5 that added four racks under the wings for the carriage of four 50kg (100lb) bombs.

The Fw 190G-4 was a development of the Fw 190G-3 with three racks, and was built in uncertain numbers of the basic and tropicalised Fw 190G-4/Trop subvariants. The Fw 190G-5 and Fw 190G-6 were unbuilt projects, and the Fw 190G-7 was used for trials with a torpedo-shaped centreline drop tank of 900 litres (198Imp gal; 237.75US gal) capacity.

The Fw 190G-8 was the last model to be built was based on the airframe of the Fw 190A-8 with its auxiliary fuel tank in the rear fuselage but was otherwise similar to the Fw 190G-3. Subvariants of this model were the Fw 190G-8/R4 with the GM 1 nitrous oxide power-boost system for the BMW 801D-2 engine, and the Fw 190G-8/R5 with the BMW 801TU engine rated at 1491kW (2000hp) for take-off and carrying four underwing racks in addition to the underfuselage rack. An uncertain number of aircraft being completed between September 1943 and February 1944.

Two other variants that were projected but not built with the BMW 801F engine were the Fw 190G-9 and Fw 190G-10 fighter-bomber counterparts of the Fw 190A-9 and Fw 190A-10 fighters.

CHAPTER 6

FOCKE-WULF FW 200 CONDOR

The Fw 200 was conceived as a transatlantic passenger and main transport, but was then pressed into military service as a long-range maritime reconnaissance bomber. Despite a structure that was really too weak for the task, and caused many operational accidents, the Fw 200 was a major force in the Atlantic War.

The Condor is best remembered as the long-range reconnaissance aeroplane that searched for Allied convoys in the North Atlantic during World War II and, having found such targets, either attacked them directly with bombs or, more importantly in the longer term, radioed the information that allowed packs of German U-boats to be vectored in for an interception. In this regard the Condor was one of the most important German warplanes of the conflict, but the type was also notable as a potent maritime reconnaissance bomber in its own right, and a warplane that might have achieved even more had it not possessed a structural weakness in the wing design, which resulted in many of the aircraft breaking their rear wing spars and then

LEFT *Operated mainly by Kampfgeschwader 40 from western France and Norway, the Fw 200C Condor was Germany's most important long-range maritime reconnaissance bomber of World War II, and in its heyday a potent weapon in Germany's campaign to cut the Atlantic convoy routes.*

their backs while landing. This weakness was not the result of an inherent design flaw, but rather of the fact that in its military form the Condor was not a purpose-designed warplane but an improvised development of a civil transport designed for a less rigorous operational life and landings at considerable lighter weights.

The Fw 200 resulted from a far-sighted 1936 requirement of Deutsche Lufthansa for an airliner able to carry mail and/or 26 passengers on the difficult North Atlantic route that was just beginning to be practical for land-based aircraft. Designed by Dipl.-Ing. Kurt Tank, the Fw 200 was a large, aesthetically attractive cantilever low-wing monoplane constructed entirely of metal with the exception of the fabric-covered control surfaces. The Fw 200 V1 prototype made its maiden flight on 27 July 1937 with four Pratt & Whitney Hornet radial engines each rated at 652kW (875hp) for take-off. There followed the Fw 200 V2 and Fw 200 V3 prototypes that differed from the first machine only in their powerplant of four BMW 132G-1 radial engines each rated at 537kW (720hp) for take-off. The Fw 200 V3 later became the personal transport of Adolf Hitler, the German dictator, and at later times other Condors were allocated to high-ranking members of the Nazi party. The three prototypes were followed by nine Fw 200A-0 pre-production aircraft that all carried prototype designations at some time. Of these aircraft, four were delivered to Deutsche Lufthansa, two to DDL Danish Air Lines, and two to the Syndicato Condor airline of Brazil.

Japanese involvement

The first steps toward the creation of a military version of the Condor resulted from a flight from Berlin to Tokyo by the Fw 200 V1 late in 1938. Impressed with the payload/range performance of this aeroplane, the Japanese ordered five aircraft as four Fw 200B civil transports and one maritime reconnaissance aeroplane. The Fw 200B transports were completed to two closely related standards as the Fw 200B-1 with four BMW 132Dc engines each rated at 634kW (850hp) for take-off, and the Fw 200B-2 with four BMW 132H radial engines each rated at 619kW (830hp) for

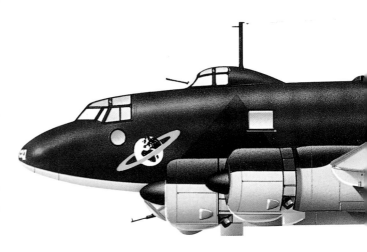

BELOW *The Fw 200C-3/U1 introduced structural strengthening, BMW-Bramo 323 Fafnir engines, and the HDL 151 forward dorsal turret carrying one 15mm MG 151 cannon. The turret was replaced in later models by the Fw 19 turret carrying one 7.92mm MG 15 machine gun.*

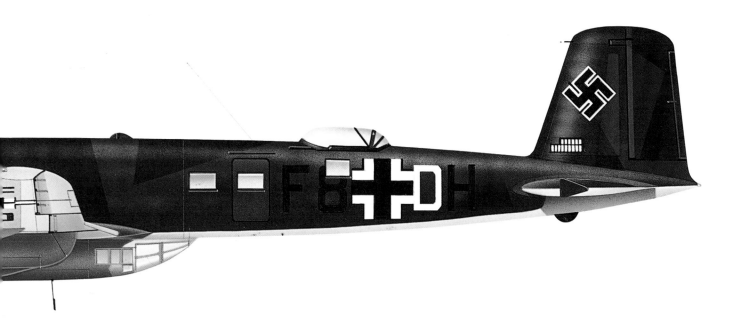

SPECIFICATIONS: Focke-Wulf Fw 200C-3/U4 Condor

GENERAL
Type: maritime reconnaissance bomber
Accommodation: pilot and co-pilot/bombardier side-by-side on the enclosed flightdeck, radar operator/gunner, radio operator/gunner, and two gunners
Equipment: standard communication and navigation equipment, plus FuG 200 Hohentwiel air-to-surface search radar, Lofte 7D bomb sight, and optical gun sights
Weights: empty 12,950kg (28,549lb); maximum take-off 22,700kg (50,044lb)

MOTIVE POWER
Powerplant: four BMW-Bramo 323R-2 Fafnir radial piston engines each rated at 895kW (1200hp) for take-off with MW 50 methanol/water injection and 701kW (940hp) at 4000m (13,125ft)
Fuel: internal fuel 8060 litres (1,773Imp gal; 2,129.25US gal) plus provision for up to 1895 litres (416.8Imp gal; 500.6US gal) of auxiliary fuel in fuselage tanks; external fuel up to 1200 litres (264Imp gal; 317US gal) in four drop tanks

PERFORMANCE
Maximum speed: 360km/h (224mph) at 4800m (15,750ft) declining to 306km/h (190mph) at sea level
Cruising speed: maximum 335km/h (208mph) at 4000m (13,125ft) and economical 255km/h (158mph) at optimum altitude
Initial climb rate: not available
Service ceiling: 6000m (19,685ft)
Maximum range: 4440km (2759 miles) with auxiliary fuel; typical range 3555km (2209 miles) with standard fuel; endurance 14 hours 0 minutes

DIMENSIONS
Wing span: 32.84m (107ft 9in)
Wing area: 118.00sq m (1,270.14sq ft)
Length: 23.46m (76ft 11.6in)
Height: 6.30m (20ft 8in)

ARMAMENT
Fixed armament: one 20mm MG151/20 trainable forward-firing cannon with 500 rounds in the forward ventral gondola position, one 13mm MG131 trainable rearward-firing machine gun with 500 rounds in the rear dorsal position, one 13mm MG131 trainable lateral-firing machine gun with 300 rounds per gun in each of the two beam positions, one 7.92mm MG15 trainable rearward-firing machine gun with 1,000 rounds in the rear ventral gondola position, and one 7.92mm MG15 trainable machine gun with 1000 rounds in the power-operated Fw 19 forward dorsal turret
Disposable armament: up to 2100kg (4630lb) of disposable stores carried in a ventral gondola weapons bay rated at 600kg (1323lb) and on four hardpoints (two under the outboard engine nacelles with each unit rated at 500kg (1102lb) and two under the outer wing panels with each unit rated at 250kg (551lb), and generally comprising two 500kg (1102lb) SC-500 bombs under the outboard engine nacelles, two 250kg (551lb) SC-250 bombs under the outer wing panels, and 12 50kg (110lb) SC-50 bombs in the ventral gondola weapons bay

take-off. The aircraft were never delivered to Japan, being taken on charge instead by Deutsche Lufthansa.

The maritime patrol type ordered by Japan was created as the Fw 200 V10 with a dorsal turret accommodating one 7.92mm MG15 trainable machine-gun, and two similar weapons in the forward and rear ends of the thin gondola that was added in a position offset to starboard under the fuselage. This provided (in addition to the two defensive gun positions) good downward fields of vision for the maritime observer. By this time the outbreak of World War II was imminent and Oberstleutnant Edgar Petersen, an experienced reconnaissance pilot, secured the approval of General Hans Jeschonnek, the Luftwaffe chief-of-staff, for the creation of a specialised maritime reconnaissance unit. The Luftwaffe had no landplane type suitable for long overwater flights, so Petersen had to select an aeroplane suitable for conversion to the role. Despite his reservations about its light structure, Petersen chose the Fw 200 for its proved payload/range capabilities, reliable four-engined powerplant, adequate internal volume, and the partial adaptation to military capability that had already resulted from the Japanese order.

Luftwaffe service

The militarised version for the Luftwaffe was first delivered in September 1939, in the form of the first of an eventual 10 Fw 200C-0 pre-production aircraft with a measure of structural strengthening: the first four aircraft were unarmed and, with four impressed Fw 200B aircraft, were operated in the transport role by KGrzbV 105 during the invasion of Norway that started in April 1940.

The other six aircraft were completed with armament and delivered in November 1939 to Petersen's Fernaufklärungsstaffel, which became operational in April 1940 and was redesignated as 1.Staffel (subsequently I Gruppe) of Kampfgeschwader 40 later in the same month. The success of the first aircraft confirmed to the Luftwaffe command that it had taken the right decision to persevere with the development and production of the Fw 200 as a maritime reconnaissance bomber. The type entered full production as the Fw 200C-1 with a crew of five, four BMW 132H radial engines each rated at 619kW (830hp) for take-off, fixed armament of one 20mm MGFF trainable forward-firing cannon in a position at the front of the lengthened ventral gondola as well as single 7.92mm MG15 trainable machine guns in the forward dorsal position, rear dorsal position and a position at the rear of the ventral gondola, and disposable armament of four 250kg (551lb) bombs. Two of these weapons or alternatively two 300 litre (66Imp gal; 79.25US gal) drop tanks were carried under the lengthened inboard engine nacelles, and the other two weapons on racks under the outer wing panels: the weapons were aimed with the aid of an optional 250kg (551lb) concrete bomb that had the same ballistic qualities as the real weapons and was carried in the ventral gondola. The Fw 200C-1 entered service in June 1940, and was used at that time as a conventional long-range bomber and aerial minelayer (with two 1000kg [2205lb] mines) in addition to its duties as a maritime reconnaissance bomber.

The Fw 200C-2 was the next production model, and was in essence the Fw 200C-1 with its outboard engine nacelles revised for semi-recessed carriage of one 250kg (551lb) bomb. This reduced the drag burden of the original underwing racks, which were retained but faired so that a larger bomb load could be carried when required.

Appearing in the summer of 1941, the Fw 200C-3 was the definitive version of the Condor, and featured a further strengthened airframe, four BMW-Bramo 323R-2 Fafnir radial engines each rated at 895kW (1200hp) for take-off, an additional crew member, the defensive firepower increased by the addition of two 7.92mm MG15 trainable machine guns in new beam positions, and the offensive armament boosted to a maximum of 2100kg (4630lb) in the form of two 500kg (1102lb) bombs under the inboard nacelles, two 250kg (551lb) bombs under the outboard nacelles, and up to 12 50kg (110lb) bombs in the ventral gondola.

Built in larger numbers than its predecessors, the Fw 200C-3 was improved by the addition of Umrüst-Bausätze (factory conversion sets). The use of such sets created subvariants such as the Fw 200C-3/U1 Condor with the original forward dorsal machine-gun position replaced by a hydraulically operated Fw 19 turret fitted with a 15mm MG151 trainable cannon and the MGFF cannon in the front of the ventral gondola replaced by a faster-firing 20mm MG151/20 cannon. The Fw 200C-3/U2 Condor had the original type of forward dorsal machine-gun position. The MG151/20 cannon on this variant was replaced by a 13mm MG131 trainable forward-firing machine-gun to provide space in the forward part of the ventral gondola for the Lofte 7D bomb sight, whose inclusion removed the need for

the concrete aiming bomb. The Fw 200C-3/U3 Condor had an electrically operated EDL 131 turret with a 13mm MG131 trainable machine-gun in the forward dorsal position and the 7.92mm MG15 machine-gun in the rear dorsal position was replaced by a 13mm MG131 machine-gun. Last of the C-3 variants was the the Fw 200C-3/U4 Condor in which the Fw 19 forward dorsal turret was restored and the two 7.92mm MG15s in the two beam positions were replaced by 13mm MG131s.

Radar

Manufactured from a time early in 1942, the Fw 200C-4 was a simple development of the Fw 200C-3 with improved equipment and armament. The primary equipment change was the adoption of FuG Rostock air-to-surface radar which was later replaced by the FuG 200 Hohentwiel series of air-to-surface search radars that allowed blind bombing attacks to be made, and which were also retrofitted in most of the surviving Fw 200C-3 aircraft. Other changes were the adoption as standard of the Fw 19 forward dorsal turret with its 15mm MG151 cannon, and provision in the forward position of the ventral gondola for the 13mm MG131 machine-gun to be replaced by a 20mm MG151/20 cannon if the Lofte 7D bomb sight was not required. The only subvariants of the Fw 200C-4, each built to the extent

ABOVE *The main features differentiating the Fw 200C military version of the Condor, in this instance an Fw 200C-1, from the original civil aircraft were the glazed excrescences for defensive guns and, most importantly, the ventral gondola for the bomb-aimer's position and the bomb load.*

of just one high-speed transport aeroplane with a shortened ventral gondola and a defensive armament of four 7.92mm MG15 machine guns carried in the two gondola positions and in Fw 19 and Fw 20 forward and rear dorsal turrets, were the Fw 200C-4/U1 with accommodation for 11 passengers and the Fw 200C-4/U2 with accommodation for 14 passengers.

The Fw 200C-6 designation was applied to Fw 200C-3/U1 and Fw 200C-3/U2 aircraft revised as launch platforms for two Henschel Hs 293 anti-ship missiles carried under the wings and controlled by means of the FuG 203b Kehl III transmitter unit.

The Fw 200C-8 was the new-build counterpart of the Fw 200C-6 conversion. The Fw 200/Hs 293 combination was not successful after its introduction in December 1943, and by June 1944 most of the surviving Fw 200 aircraft had were serving as transports, a few remaining operational to the last days of the war. Deliveries of military Condors amounted to 262 aircraft in all, supplemented by four impressed Fw 200B airliners.

HEINKEL HE 111

Created ostensibly as a high-speed transport, the He 111 was a capable medium bomber that served the Luftwaffe well in World War II. During this time the He 111 received a number of modest airframe improvements and engines of greater power, and despite obsolescence from 1943, was still in Luftwaffe service in a variety of roles in 1945.

In 1934 the German air ministry issued to Heinkel and Junkers a requirement for an aeroplane that could, with minimum structural change, operate in two roles: 10-passenger transport with Deutsche Lufthansa and medium bomber with the still-clandestine Luftwaffe. The results of this effort were the He 111 and Ju 86, the former designed by a team under the supervision of the twin brothers, Siegfried and Walter Günter, as a cantilever low-wing monoplane that was clearly a scaled-up and improved twin-engined development of the concept embodied in the Heinkel He 70 Blitz.

The He 111a (later He 111 V1) prototype made its maiden flight on 24 February 1935 with two BMW VI 6,0 Z

Vee piston engines each rated at 492kW (660hp) for take-off. There followed the He 111d (He 111 V4) civil prototype with a wing planform of semi-elliptical shape and greater area despite its reduction in span, and the He 111c (He 111 V3) and He 111d (He 111 V4) military prototypes with provision for a defensive armament of three 7.92mm machine-guns and a maximum bomb load of 1000kg (2205lb) stowed vertically in lower-fuselage cells: the He 111 V3 was presented to the public as a transport, the weapons cell area being a four-person 'smoking compartment'. The He 111 handled well in the air, and its clean design meant that it could show a clean pair of heels to most current fighters.

An evaluation of the He 111 V3 and He 111 V4 confirmed their potential in the bomber role, and in late 1935 the German air ministry authorised a pre-production series of 10 He 111A-0 bombers with a powerplant of two BMW VI 6,0 Z engines. The first of these aircraft were delivered for

LEFT *Seen as they depart for an attack on a target in England in August 1940, these Luftwaffe medium bombers are examples of the He 111H variant, which remained Germany's most important medium bomber up to the end of the war, with many variants.*

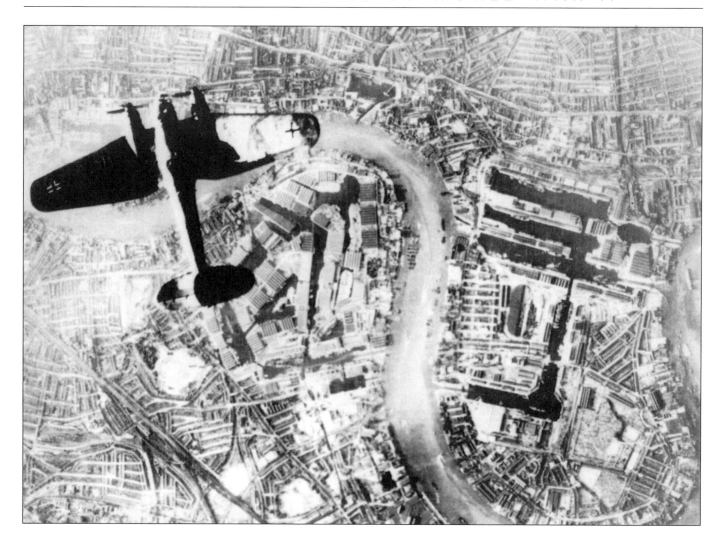

ABOVE *Seen as it flies over east London, this He 111H is typical of the medium bomber that bore the brunt of the German offensive effort in the Battle of Britain and 'Blitz', and was one of the few German types to emerge from the campaign with credit.*

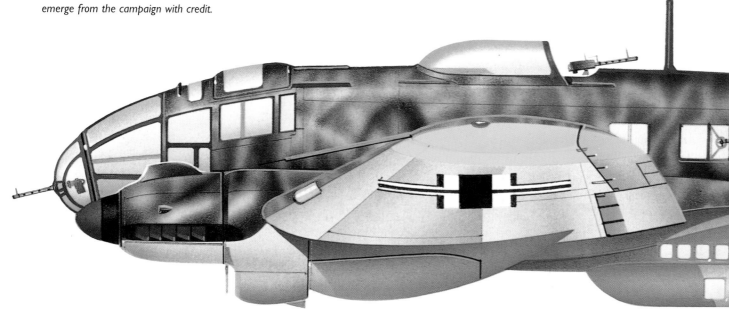

SPECIFICATIONS: Heinkel He 111P-4

GENERAL
Type: medium bomber
Accommodation: pilot and co-pilot side-by-side and bombardier/gunner in the forward crew compartment, and radio operator/gunner and gunner carried in the fuselage
Equipment: standard communication and navigation equipment, plus a Lofte optical bomb sight and optical gun sights
Weights: empty 8015kg (17,670lb); maximum take-off 13,500kg (29,762lb)

MOTIVE POWER
Powerplant: two Daimler-Benz DB 601A-1 inverted-Vee piston engines each rated at 820kW (1100hp) for take-off and 757kW (1015hp) at 4500m (14,765ft)
Fuel: internal fuel 4300 litres (945.9Imp gal; 1135.9US gal); external fuel none

PERFORMANCE
Maximum speed: 398km/h (247mph) at 5000m (16,405ft) declining to 362km/h (225mph) at sea level
Cruising speed: 373km/h (232mph) at 5000m (16,405ft)
Climb: to 4500m (14,765ft) in 31 minutes 18 seconds
Service ceiling: 8000m (26,245ft)
Maximum range: 2400km (1491 miles)

DIMENSIONS
Wing span: 22.60m (74ft 1.76in)
Wing area: 86.50sq m (931.07sq ft)
Length: 16.40m (53ft 9.7in)
Height: 3.40m (11ft 3in)

ARMAMENT
Fixed armament: one 7.92mm MG15 fixed forward-firing machine gun in the nose, one 7.92mm MG15 trainable forward-firing machine gun in the nose position, one 7.92mm MG15 trainable rearward-firing machine gun in the dorsal position, one 7.92mm MG15 trainable rearward-firing machine gun in the rear of the ventral gondola, two 7.92mm MG15 trainable lateral-firing machine guns in the two beam positions, and provision for one 7.92mm MG17 fixed rearward-firing machine gun in the tail cone
Disposable armament: up to 2000kg (4409lb) of disposable stores carried in a lower-fuselage weapons bay rated at 1000kg (2205lb) and on two hardpoints (both under the wing with each unit rated at 500kg (1102lb), and generally comprising four 250kg (551lb) SC-250 bombs carried internally, and one or two 500kg (1102lb) SC-500 bombs carried externally

trials in the spring of 1936, and proved a considerable disappointment as the addition of full military equipment had significantly increased weight and drag. The handling of the pre-production aircraft was still good, but their performance was decidedly sluggish. The Luftwaffe refused to accept the aircraft, which were then sold to China. The problem with the He 111A had been lack of power, and this resulted from the failure of the German aircraft manufacturing industry to evolve a modern Vee-type piston engine to replace the venerable BMW VI 6,0 and 7,3 series until the mid-1930s. However, in 1935 there appeared the Daimler-Benz DB 600 inverted-Vee piston engine that was destined to become important not only in its own right as the powerplant of a number of pioneering German warplanes, but also

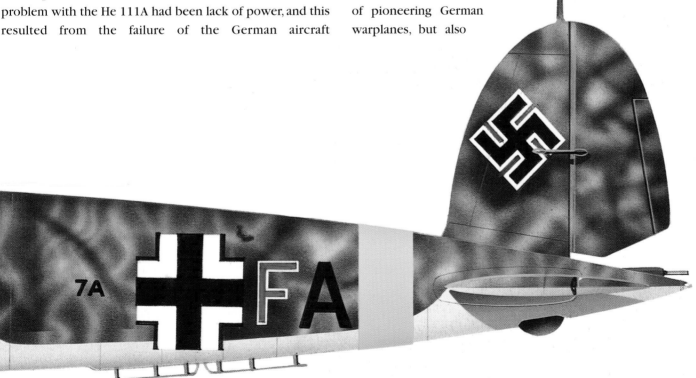

as the starting point for a series of increasingly powerful engines that were to serve the German war effort with enormous distinction in World War II. Rated at a nominal 1000hp (746kW), the DB 600 was the answer to the He 111's performance shortfall. Two such engines were installed in the He 111 V5 that served as the prototype for the He 111B series of bombers and paved the way for the early production models that had been largely supplanted in first-line service by the outbreak of World War II.

These models were the He 111B bomber, of which about 300 were built in the B-0, B-1 and B-2 variants with DB 600A or DB 600C engines in the B-1 and DB 600CG engines in the B-2, the He 111C civil model of which 10 were completed with provision for a crew of two and up to 10 passengers, the He 111D bomber of which a small number was completed with DB 600Ga engines each rated at 708 kW (950 hp) and cooled by a modified radiator system, the He 111E bomber of which about 190 were completed in E-0 to E-5 subvariants with Junkers Jumo 211A-1 engines each rated at 783 kW (1050 hp) and cooled by semi-retractable radiators, the He 111F bomber of which about 70 were completed in F-0, F-1 and F-4 subvariants with Jumo 211A-3 engines each rated at 820 kW (1100 hp), the He 111G civil model of which nine were completed, and the He 111J torpedo-bomber of which 90 were completed in the J-0 and J-1 subvariants with DB 600CG engines.

Early 'P' and 'H' series

Further development of the He 111 series resulted in the He 111P and closely related He 111H, the latter coming slightly later despite its earlier alphabetical designation. The two variants shared a common airframe (a ventral gondola and revised and a fully glazed forward fuselage with an unstepped cockpit), but differed in their powerplant: the He 111P was designed for the DB 601 engine while the He 111H was planned with the Jumo 211 piston engine.

The prototype for the He 111P and He 111H series was the He 111 V8 that introduced the shortened and broadened nose. This improved the aerodynamic cleanliness of the forward fuselage and eliminated the stepped cockpit windscreen. The forward fuselage section was almost completely glazed to provide the crew with much improved fields of vision, and the pilot was seated on the port side with the nose-mounted defensive machine gun offset to starboard so that it did not interfere with the pilot's forward field of vision. The result was an asymmetric nose that characterised all later variants of the He 111. An improved version of this forward fuselage section was then installed on the He 111 V7 that two years earlier had been used to

pioneer the revised and definitive semi-elliptical wing. The revised He 111 V7 also introduced the shallow underfuselage gondola that replaced the retractable 'dustbin' of earlier marks to provide low-drag accommodation for the ventral defensive machine gun, and was powered by two DB 601Aa engines each rated at 857kW (1150hp) for take-off.

The He 111P-0 was the pre-production model that paved the way for the He 111P-1 initial production variant. This entered service in the spring of 1939 with provision for a maximum bomb load of 2000kg (4409lb) and a maximum speed of 400km/h (249mph) at 5000m (16,405ft). The He 111P-2 differed from the He 111P-1 only in being fitted with different radio equipment. On the outbreak of World War II in September 1939, the Luftwaffe had some 349 He 111P-1 and He 111P-2 bombers on strength. The type was heavily involved in the Polish campaign, and suffered comparatively heavy losses because its combination of good performance and excellent handling was not sufficient to overcome the weakness of its defensive armament, which comprised just three 7.92mm MG15 trainable machine-guns located in single-gun nose, dorsal and ventral positions.

Later 'P' and 'H' series

The He 111P-3 was a trainer model produced by conversion of He 111P-0 and He 111P-1 aircraft, and the He 111P-4 was a development of the He 111P-2 with increased armour protection, heavier defensive armament, the port row of bomb cells revised for the carriage of an additional fuel tank but with two external hardpoints under it, and provision for two hardpoints under the starboard bomb cells.

Built in small numbers early in 1940 just before the He 111P series was phased out of production because of DB 601 production limitations, the He 111P-6 was a development of the He 111P-4 with internal bomb stowage and two DB 601N engines each rated at 876kW (1175hp) for take-off. Some of the aircraft were later revised to He 111P-6/R2 glider tug standard.

Introduced at the outbreak of World War II, the He 111H-2 was an improved version of the He 111H-1 with two Jumo 211A-3 engines each rated at 820kW (1100hp) for take-off and, soon after the start of the production run, the defensive armament doubled from three to six 7.92mm MG15 trainable machine-guns. The He 111H-3 was introduced in November 1939 as a development of the He 111H-2 for the bombing and anti-ship roles with two Jumo 211D-1 engines and the gun armament bolstered by a 20mm MGFF trainable forward-firing cannon in the ventral gondola. The disposable armament comprised 2000kg (4409lb) of bombs carried internally, and the weapons bay could alternatively be fitted

with an auxiliary fuel tank. Delivery of the He 111H-3 continued throughout 1940, and were complemented during the year by the arrival of the He 111H-4. This was a development of the He 111H-3, initially with the same powerplant but later with two Jumo 211F-1 engines each rated at 1044kW (1400hp) for take-off, and with a much revised disposable armament capability. The port side of the weapons bay was blanked off and strengthened for the external carriage of two 1000kg (2205lb) bombs or one 1800kg (3968lb) bomb. The He 111H-5 was an He 111H-4 variant with two Jumo 211D-1 engines, provision for both halves of the weapons bay to carry an auxiliary fuel tank, and the disposable armament limited to 2500kg (5511lb) of weapons carried on two external hardpoints at a maximum take-off weight of 14,055kg (30,985lb).

Both the He 111H-4 and He 111H-5 lasted in production long enough for a number of improvements to be added in stages, and all these improvements were incorporated as

ABOVE *Ground engineers of the Luftwaffe remove the covers from the Jumo 211 engines of this He 111H of the I Gruppe of KG 26, the Löwen-Geschwader. Aircraft of I Gruppe were identifiable by a white shield, II and III Gruppen machines having red and yellow shields respectively.*

standard in the He 111H-6 that entered production late in 1941. The He 111H-6 had two Jumo 211F-1 engines, a fixed armament of one 20mm MGFF cannon and six 7.92mm MG15 machine-guns supplemented in some aircraft by a remotely controlled 7.92mm MG17 fixed rearward-firing machine gun in the tailcone to deter attackers, and provision for the carriage of 765kg (1686lb) LT F5b air-launched torpedoes under the fuselage. The He 111H-6 quickly became the most extensively used version of the He 111H series. It had been planned to phase the He 111 out of production during 1942 in favour of the Heinkel He 177A Greif and Junkers Ju 288, but the failure of both these types meant that production of the He 111H-6 was maintained.

SPECIFICATIONS: Heinkel He 111H-16

GENERAL
Type: medium bomber
Accommodation: pilot and co-pilot side-by-side and bombardier/gunner in the forward crew compartment, and radio operator/gunner and gunner carried in the fuselage
Equipment: standard communication and navigation equipment, plus a Lofte optical bomb sight and optical gun sights
Weights: empty 8680kg (19,136lb); normal take-off 12,425kg (27,392lb); maximum take-off 14,000kg (30,865lb)

MOTIVE POWER
Powerplant: two Junkers Jumo 211F-2 inverted-Vee piston engines each rated at 1007kW (1350hp) for take-off and 790kW (1060hp) at 5300m (17,390ft)
Fuel: internal fuel 5750 litres (1264.85Imp gal; 1519US gal); external fuel none

PERFORMANCE
Maximum speed: 405km/h (252mph) at 6000m (19,685ft) declining to 330km/h

(217mph) at sea level
Cruising speed: 370km/h (230mph) at 2000m (6560ft)
Climb: to 4000m (13,125ft) in 23 minutes 30 seconds
Service ceiling: 8500m (27,890ft)
Maximum range: 2800km (1740 miles); typical range 1930km (1199 miles) with a 2500 kg (5511lb) weapons load

DIMENSIONS
Wing span: 22.60m (74ft 1.76in)
Wing area: 86.50sq m (931.07sq ft)
Length: 16.40m (53ft 9.7in)
Height: 3.40m (11ft 3in)

ARMAMENT
Fixed armament: one 20mm MGFF trainable forward-firing cannon with 180 rounds in the nose position, one optional 7.92mm MG15 trainable forward-firing machine gun in the nose position, one 13mm MG131 trainable rearward-firing machine gun with 1,000 rounds in the dorsal position, two 7.92mm MG81

trainable rearward-firing machine guns with 1000 rounds per gun in the rear of the ventral gondola, and one 7.92mm MG15 or MG81 trainable lateral-firing machine gun with 1000 rounds per gun, or two 7.92mm MG81 trainable lateral-firing machine guns with 500 rounds per gun in each of the two beam positions
Disposable armament: up to 2500kg (5511lb) of disposable stores carried in a lower-fuselage weapons bay rated at 2000kg (4409lb) and on two hardpoints (both under the wing with one unit rated at 2000kg (4409lb) and the other at 500kg (1102lb), and generally comprising eight 250kg (551lb) SC-250 bombs or 32 50kg (110lb) SC-50 bombs carried internally, or 16 50kg (110lb) SC-50 bombs carried internally and one 1000kg (2205lb) SC-1000 bomb carried externally, one 2000kg (4409lb) SC-2000 bomb and one 500kg (1102lb) SC-500 bomb carried externally

The He 111H-7 was a variant of the He 111H-6 with minor equipment changes, and the He 111H-8 was a development of the He 111H-6 that was produced to the extent of 30 aircraft converted from He 111H-3 and He 111H-5 standards with a balloon cable fender/cutter arrangement extending from a point ahead of the nose to both wing tips. This weighed some 250kg (551lb) and required the addition of ballast in the tail to preserve the centre of gravity in the right position, and the extra weight so affected performance and weapon load that the aircraft saw only the most limited of operational service before being relegated to use as glider tugs with the revised designation He 111H-8/R2. The He 111H-9 was a variant of the He 111H-6 with minor

equipment changes, while the He 111H-10 was a development of the He 111H-6 with two Jumo 211F-2 engines, balloon cable cutting devices in the wing leading edges, and the positions of the forward-firing 7.92mm machine gun and 20mm cannon reversed so that the MGFF cannon was installed in the nose and the MG15 machine gun in the ventral gondola.

The He 111H-11 was a development of the He 111H-10 with improvements to crew protection and defensive armament. The dorsal position was fully enclosed with screens of toughened glass, and was provided with a 13mm MG131 trainable rearward-firing machine gun in place of the original 7.92mm MG15 weapon. Ventral defence was boosted by the replacement of the single 7.92mm MG15 machine gun by two 7.92mm MG81 weapons and jettisonable armour plates were added over particularly vulnerable areas. Provision was also made for an improved offensive capability by the development of a carrier plate that could be added under the fuselage for five 250kg (551lb) bombs. The He 111H-11 proved successful within the limits of the basic airframe's increasing obsolescence, and the type's steadily worsening vulnerability to fighter attack was addressed by a number of front-line measures such as the replacement of the two 7.92mm MG15 trainable lateral-firing machine-guns by two 7.92mm MG81z two-barrel machine-guns in the He 111H-11/R1 with the R1 Rüstsätz (field conversion set). The

He 111H-11/R2 was another front-line conversion, in this instance with a glider-towing attachment.

Appearing early in 1943 and lacking the ventral gondola of all earlier He 111H models, the He 111H-12 was planned as a specialised platform for the carriage and launch of two Henschel Hs 293A air-to-surface missiles. The aeroplane carried the missiles under the inner parts of the wing, and only a few aircraft were produced. The He 111H-14 was a

BELOW *Armourers prepare to load the second of two LT F5b practice torpedoes under the fuselage of an He 111H-6, which was the standard multi-role version of this bomber adopted by the Luftwaffe as successor to the He 111H-3 from a time late in 1941.*

pathfinder development of the He 111H-10 with special radio equipment for use by KG 40 in its anti-shipping role over the eastern part of the Atlantic Ocean. Some 20 of the aircraft were modified before delivery to units on the Eastern Front as He 111H-14/R2 machines with the radio equipment removed and a glider-towing attachment added.

If the He 111H-3 and He 111H-6 were regarded as the first and second definitive models of the He 111H series, the He 111H-16 was the third model and in fact preceded a number of ostensibly earlier models. The He 111H-16 was a development of the He 111H-6 with two Jumo 211F-2 engines and a host of individually small but cumulatively important changes that had been introduced piecemeal on a number of earlier variants. The defensive armament and armour were those of the He 111H-11, and provision was made for a number of different disposable armament arrangements. Provision was also made for the addition of three Rüstsätze to provide the He 111H-16/R1 with an electrically operated dorsal turret carrying one 13mm MG131 machine gun, the He 111H-16/R2 with a boom-type glider towing attachment, and the He 111H-16/R3 with additional armour protection to operate in the pathfinder role with a reduced weapons load. The He 111H-18 was a nocturnal pathfinder based on the He 111H-16/R3 but with the special radio equipment of the He 111H-14.

Alternative roles

Although the He 111H had been planned as a bomber, the demands of operations on the Eastern Front had meant that many of the aircraft had been pressed into transport and glider-tug service during the first half of 1942. This capability was reflected later in the same year by the introduction of the He 111H-20, which was a development of the He 111H-16 optimised for adaptability in four main subvariants: the He 111H-20/R1 was a paratroop transport with a crew of three and provision for 16 paratroops who used a ventral jump hatch and could receive equipment dropped to them in two 800kg (1764lb) external supply containers; the He 111H-20/R2 was a freighter and glider tug with a crew of five, which included a gunner for the electrically operated dorsal turret armed with a 13mm MG131 trainable machine gun; the He 111H-20/R3 was a night bomber with provision for a 2000kg (4409lb) bomb load carried on external racks and a defensive armament of three 13mm MG131 trainable machine guns in the nose, dorsal and ventral positions plus two 7.92mm MG81z trainable two-barrel machine guns in the two beam positions; and the He 111H-20/R4 was a night harassment bomber with provision for a disposable load of 20 50kg (110lb) bombs carried externally.

The He 111H-21 had two Jumo 213E-1 engines each rated at 1305kW (1750hp), allowing the maximum weapons load to be increased to 3000kg (6614lb) at a maximum take-off weight of 16,000kg (35,273lb). The airframe was basically that of the He 111H-20/R3 with a measure of local strengthening, and as a result of delays in the delivery of the Jumo 213 engine the first 22 machines were completed with turbocharged Jumo 211F engines for improved high-altitude performance. The definitive model entered service in the later summer of 1944, and possessed a maximum speed of 480km/h (298mph) at optimum altitude.

It was clear as the He 111H-21 was entering service, however, that the days of the He 111's utility as a bomber were past. Most aircraft were adapted while still on the production line as He 111H-22 airborne launch platforms for the Fieseler Fi 103 pilotless bomb (the V-1 'doodlebug'). A number of He 111H-16 and He 111H-20 aircraft were also converted to the same standard.

The last aircraft of the He 111H series, completed in the autumn of 1944, were He 111H-21 machines completed to He 111H-23 standard as saboteur delivery aircraft with accommodation for a demolition team of eight men who were dropped by parachute. The powerplant of this model, of which some were adapted in the field as bombers, was two Jumo 213A-1 engines each rated at 1324kW (1776hp) for take-off. The number of He 111H aircraft built is no longer known, but certainly amounted to the bulk of the 6615 aircraft produced between 1939 and 1944 in the overall total of 7,300 or more He 111 aircraft delivered in all.

Final variants

The He 111R series was considered in 1943 and tested in He 111 V32 prototype form as an interim high-altitude bomber development of the He 111H-16 with two Jumo 211F engines in the He 111R-1 or turbocharged DB 603U engines, each rated at 1349.5kW (1810hp) for take-off and 1193kW (1600hp) at 12,800m (41,995ft), in the definitive He 111R-2. No production followed, and the final variant of the family was the He 111Z (Zwilling, or twin), which was in essence two He 111H-6 airframes connected by a constant-chord centre section carrying a fifth Jumo 211F-2 engine. The type was intended as a tug for heavy gliders such as the Messerschmitt Me 321 Gigant or Gotha Go 242 of which one and two respectively could be towed.

RIGHT *So satisfied were they with their first He 111 bombers (here He 111H-3 machines received from Germany from the autumn of 1940) that the Romanian Air Force ordered additional aircraft from Romanian licensed production. This machine is seen in Russia in the early 1943.*

CHAPTER 8

HEINKEL HE 177 GREIF

With the He 177, Germany hoped to re-enter the air war with a potent long-range heavy bomber, but intractable development problems with the powerplant, in which pairs of engines were coupled to drive single propellers, meant that the type was never wholly successful and also suffered heavy losses to in-flight fires.

The Heinkel He 177 Greif (griffin) resulted from the German air ministry's realisation in the middle of 1937 that its heavy bomber programme had lost impetus with the death in an air accident during June 1936 of Generalleutnant Walther Wever, the Luftwaffe's chief-of-staff and a chief proponent of strategic heavy bombing. In June 1937, therefore, Heinkel was ordered to proceed without delay on the development of its Projekt 1041 design, originally evolved to meet the 1936 'Bomber A' requirement for a type able to deliver a weapons load of at least 1000kg (2205lb) over a range of 6700km (4163 miles) at a maximum speed of at least 540km/h (336mph). The task of developing an improved version of the P.1041 design was

LEFT This is the nose section, complete with access hatch in the open position, of an He 177A-5 under evaluation by the British after the war. Each propeller was powered by a Daimler-Benz DB 610 engine that was in fact two DB 605 units coupled by a combining gearbox.

entrusted to a team supervised by Dipl.-Ing. Heinrich Hertel with Dipl.-Ing. Siegfried Günter as his prime deputy.

Development problems

Considerable delays, both technical and political, then intervened to slow the programme, and the resulting He 177 V1 prototype made its first flight only on 19 November 1939 as a large shoulder/mid-wing monoplane of all-metal construction. The design was very clean, and this was helped by the unusual powerplant, which appeared to be of the two-engined type but was in fact of the four-engined variety: each of the two large four-blade propellers was driven by two Daimler-Benz DB 601 inverted-Vee piston engines close-coupled to create a single DB 606 engine, which was bedevilled by problems throughout its life. The aeroplane had a number of other advanced features, and eight prototypes were used in the development programme.

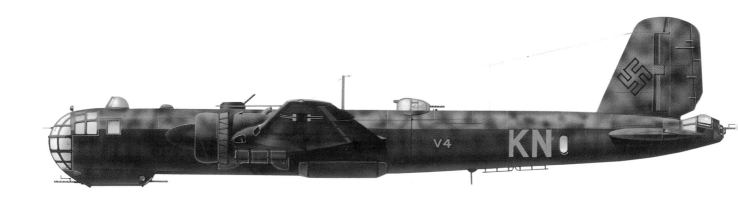

SPECIFICATIONS: Heinkel He 177A-1/R1 Greif

GENERAL
Type: heavy bomber
Accommodation: pilot, co-pilot/
bombardier/gunner, navigator/radio
operator/gunner and gunner in the
enclosed forward crew compartment, and
two gunners carried in the fuselage
Equipment: standard communication and
navigation equipment, plus an optical bomb
sight and optical gun sights
Weights: empty 18,040kg (39,771lb);
maximum take-off 30,000kg (66,139lb)

MOTIVE POWER
Powerplant: two Daimler-Benz DB 606
24-cylinder piston engines each rated at
2013kW (2700hp) for take-off and
1770kW (2360hp) at 5800m (19,030ft)
Fuel: internal fuel 12,820 litres (2820.1Imp
gal; 3386.7US gal); external fuel none

PERFORMANCE
Maximum speed: 510km/h (317mph) at
5800m (19,030ft)
Cruising speed: 430km/h (267mph) at
optimum altitude
Initial climb rate: not available
Service ceiling: 7000m (22,965ft)
Maximum range: 5600km (3480 miles);
Typical range: 1200km (746 miles) with
maximum weapons load

DIMENSIONS
Wing span: 31.44m (103ft 1.8in)
Wing area: 102.00sq m (1,097.92sq ft)
Length: 20.40m (66ft 11in)
Height: 6.39m (20ft 11.58in)

ARMAMENT
Fixed armament: one 7.92mm MG81J
trainable forward-firing machine-gun with
2000 rounds in the nose position, one

20mm MGFF trainable forward-firing cannon
with 300 rounds in the ventral gondola, two
7.92mm MG81 trainable rearward-firing
machine guns with 2,000 rounds per gun in
the ventral gondola, one 13mm MG131
trainable machine gun with 750 rounds in
the remotely controlled power-operated
dorsal barbette, and one 13mm MG131
trainable rearward-firing machine gun with
1,500 rounds in the tail position
Disposable armament: up to 6000kg
(13,228lb) of disposable stores carried in a
lower-fuselage weapons bay rated at
6000kg (13,228lb), and generally comprising
48 50kg (110lb) SC-50 bombs, or 12 250kg
(551lb) SC-250 bombs, or six 500kg
(1102lb) SC-500 bombs, or six 1000kg
(2205lb) SD-1000 bombs, or two 1000kg
(2205lb) SD-1000 and two 1800kg (3968lb)
SC-1800 bombs, or two LMA III mines and
two 1800kg (3968lb) SC-1800 bombs

Three of the prototypes were lost in fatal crashes, resulting mainly from engine fires and a structural weakness in the wing—both of these problems that were never fully cured. There followed 35 He 177A-0 pre-production aircraft before the first of 130 Arado-built He 177A-1 production aircraft entered service from July 1942. The He 177A-1 was produced in four variants as the He 177A-1/R1 basic bomber, He 177A-1/R2 with a bombing position replacing the two 7.92mm MG81 machine-guns in the rear of the ventral gondola, He 177A-1/R3 with a remotely controlled power-operated barbette under the rear fuselage with a single 13mm MG131 trainable machine-gun, and He 177A-1/R4 with one 13mm MG131 trainable rearward-firing machine-gun in the rear of the ventral gondola and one 13mm MG131 trainable machine-gun in a manned dorsal turret.

Airframe modifications

Built to the extent of 170 aircraft by Heinkel and Arado, the He 177A-3 differed from the He 177A-1 mainly in having the engines moved slightly farther forward, the fuselage lengthened by 1.60m (5ft 3in) behind the wing, and a manned dorsal turret added on the rear fuselage with an armament of two 13mm MG131 trainable machine-guns. The engine planned for this model was the DB 610, which comprised a pair of DB 605 engines close-coupled to provide 2199.5kW (2950hp) for take-off and 2311kW (3100hp) at 2000m (6560ft), but this engine suffered continued development problems and the He 177A-3 was powered like its predecessor with the DB 606 engine. Like the He 177A-1, the He 177A-3 was produced in a number of subvariants. These were the He 177A-3/R1; the He 177A-3/R2 with an improved electrical system, a modified gun position at the front of the ventral gondola with a 20mm MG151/20 cannon in place of the original 20mm MGFF cannon, and a redesigned tail position with a 20mm MG151/20 cannon in place of the original 13mm MG131 machine-gun; the He 177A-3/R3 launch platform for the Henschel Hs 193 air-to-surface missile, of which three were carried under the wings and fuselage; He 177A-3/R4 improved version of the He 177A-3/R3 with the ventral gondola lengthened by 1.19m (3ft 11in) to provide more volume for the missile controller and his FuG 203b Kehl III command transmitter; He 177A-3/R5 heavy attack model of which just five were made with a powerplant of two DB 610 engines and the gondola revised for the accommodation of a 75mm BK 7,5 anti-tank gun and its hand-loaded ammunition; and He 177A-3/R7 torpedo bomber of which a mere three were completed with provision for two Italian LT5 torpedoes

Later variants

The He 177A-4 was a planned high-altitude model that was later redesignated as the He 274 and completed after World War II in France as the AAS.01A.

The He 177A-5 was the DB 610-engined model optimised for the carriage of external loads such as the LT 50 torpedo, Hs 293 air-to-surface missile and FX-1400 Fritz X guided bomb, and thus featured a strengthened wing structure, shortened landing gear legs and the removal of the Fowler flaps along the inboard section of the wings in line with the weapon hardpoints. The basic model had the same armament as the He 177A-3/R2 and was thus designated as the He 177A-5/R2, and while this retained the original type of three-section ventral weapons bay, the doors of the forward section were locked in the closed position and fitted with external hardpoints. Subvariants of this model included the He 177A-5/R5 of which just one was completed with an additional remotely controlled power-operated barbette under the fuselage to the rear of the weapons bay with an armament of one 13mm MG131 trainable machine-gun, He 177A-5/R6 Greif derivative of the He 177A-5/R5 with the two forward parts of the weapons bay closed, He 177A-5/R7 with a pressurised cabin, and He 177A-5/R8 of which a single example was completed with remotely controlled chin and tail barbettes.

Production of the He 177A-5 series was undertaken only in 1944, and amounted to 565 aircraft. There were also other variants that reached only the prototype or development stages. Enormous effort was expended on the development and production of the He 177, but the type never achieved the reliability required on an effective operational warplane. However, it is worth noting that at the end of the war one example was under conversion as the delivery platform for the atomic weapon that the Germans had planned but not yet built.

BELOW *Among the unusual features of the He 177 (here the He 177A-03 pre-production aeroplane) was the four-legged main landing gear arrangement, the pair of units under each wing comprising separate port and starboard legs that retracted inboard and outboard respectively.*

CHAPTER 9

HEINKEL HE 219 UHU

The He 219 was developed largely in spite of, rather than for, the German air ministry, and as a result entered service somewhat belatedly. However, it was a superb nightfighter example of its type with excellent performance, potent firepower and a well-planned cockpit fitted with some of the world's earliest ejection seats.

The Heinkel He 219 Uhu (owl) was without doubt the finest night-fighter produced by Germany in World War II, but despite its exceptional capabilities was built only in very small numbers as a result of political antipathy to the Heinkel company, which had continued to develop and then to built the type despite orders not to do so. The origins of the type can be traced to 1940, when Heinkel submitted to the German air ministry a proposal for a high-performance warplane of the twin-engined heavy fighter type that could readily be adapted to the torpedo and short/medium-range level bombing roles. The air ministry was not impressed with Heinkel's display of private-venture enterprise, but late in 1941 began to change its mind after

the increasing weight and accuracy of the Royal Air Force's night bomber offensive on Germany began to make a real impact on German morale and war production.

The air ministry at this time asked Heinkel to develop its projected multi-role warplane as a dedicated night-fighter with a two-man crew, airborne interception radar and heavy forward-firing armament. As the project was already well advanced the company was able to start detail design and prototype manufacture almost simultaneously in January 1942. The programme received a considerable setback in March and April of that year when all the completed drawings were destroyed in RAF attacks on the Heinkel facility at Rostock. Further development was therefore entrusted to the company's facility near Vienna.

The result of this effort was an advanced warplane of very aggressive appearance and all-metal construction that made its maiden flight, in the form of the He 219 V1 (first of 10 prototypes), on 15 November 1942 with two Daimler-Benz

LEFT *The He 219 needed tall landing gear units because of the diameter of its propellers. Another feature evident in this nose view of the He 219 V5 are the four attachment points for the 'stag's horn' antennae for the FuG 212 Lichtenstein C-I airborne interception radar.*

ABOVE *The antennae on the nose of the He 219 generated considerable drag, but the aeroplane's high power and otherwise clean design ensured that performance was still very good.*

DB 603A engines each rated at 1305kW (1750hp). From the start of its flight trials and development programme, the He 219 revealed excellent performance and very good handling characteristics, and in December 1942 the type started armament trials with the comparatively light weapon fit of two 20mm MG151/20 fixed forward-firing cannon in a ventral tray and one 13mm MG131 trainable rearward-firing machine-gun in the rear cockpit. In February 1942 the Uhu was given more formidable fixed forward-firing armament when the two 20mm cannon were supplanted by four 30mm MK108 cannon.

In March 1943 the development programme was joined by three more prototypes: the He 219 V2 had an armament of six 20mm MG151/20 cannon (two in the wing roots and four in the ventral tray), the He 219 V3 had a similar armament but larger vertical tail surfaces, and the He 219 V4 was fitted with FuG 202 Lichtenstein airborne interception radar. By this time an initial order for 100 aircraft (which was placed even before the first prototype's maiden flight) had been increased to 300 aircraft. The development programme was further speeded by the arrival of another six prototypes. Several of these were used for operational trials of the Uhu with the revised designation He 219A-0. Fitted with an armament of four 30mm MK108 and two 20mm MG151/20 cannon or four 30mm MK103 and two 20mm MG151/20 cannon, the aircraft were more specifically designated He 219A-0/R1 or He 219A-0/R2 respectively.

First kill

It was a machine of the latter type that opened the type's account in a truly decisive fashion in June 1943 when in the course of a 30-minute engagement it intercepted and shot down five British bombers. Indeed, during their first six sorties, the He 219A-0 machines claimed the destruction of

20 British bombers, including six examples of the redoubtable de Havilland Mosquito.

As these prototype conversions were proving their worth, work had been proceeding on the first purpose-built pre-production model. This was designated He 219A-0/R3, with the fixed forward-firing armament limited to six 20mm MG151/20 weapons as there were inadequate supplies of the considerably more devastating 30mm MK103 and MK108 weapons. Production of this model totalled 130 aircraft including a number of aircraft that were used as pure prototypes with different powerplants and radar installations, and many others that were used for the evaluation of Rüstsätze (field conversion sets) between R1 and R6.

These allowed considerable variation in the armament, and the most important of them, in the longer term, was the R6. This added in the rear fuselage, immediately to the rear of the central-fuselage fuel tanks, two 30mm MK108 fixed upward/forward-firing cannon in the schräge Musik (shrill music, i.e. jazz) installation so that the He 219 could close up under the poorly protected and undefended belly of the target bomber and then pour a withering hail of fire into it without having to pull up the nose and so lose speed.

The pre-production aircraft were to have paved the way for the He 219A-1 production model with two DB 603 engines fitted with the GM 1 nitrous oxide power-boost system, but this model was cancelled and the first production model was therefore the He 219A-2, of which 40 were delivered with two DB 603A engines: the two subvariants were the He 219A-2/R1 with an armament of two 30mm MK108 cannon in the schräge Musik installation and a forward-firing armament of four 20mm MG151/20 cannon (two in the wing roots and the other two in the ventral tray), and the He 219A-2/R2 with the 20mm cannon in the ventral tray replaced by 30mm MK103 cannon. The He 219A-3 and He 219A-4 were unrealised projects for three-man bomber and reconnaissance bomber variants.

The A-5 variant

The He 219A-5 was therefore the next model to reach the production stage, and was an improved night-fighter based on the He 219A-2. The He 219A-5/R1 differed from the He 219A-2/R1 only in having the rear of the two engine nacelles modified for the carriage of additional fuel for a 650km (404 mile) increase in range. The He 219A-5/R2 differed from the He 219A-5/R1 in having two DB 603E engines each rated at 1342kW (1800hp) and replaced in the He 219A-5/R2-U2 subvariant by two DB 603G engines each rated at 1417kW (1900hp). The He 219A-5/R3 was powered by two DB 603Aa engines each rated at 1342kW (1800hp).

Finally, in the He 219A-5 series, the He 219A-5/R4 introduced a three-man crew, the additional man being accommodated in a raised, stepped cockpit section whose additional drag somewhat eroded performance. The He 219A-5/R4 had a powerplant of two DB 603E engines, and the armament was revised to include, once more, a 13mm MG131 trainable rearward-firing machine-gun in the rear cockpit. It was during the production of the He 219A-5 series that the He 219 programme was officially terminated, but such was the demand from units that a semi-clandestine effort resulted in further deliveries, including six aircraft assembled by the Luftwaffe from spare parts.

The He 219A-6 was planned specifically for the interception and destruction of high-flying Mosquito bombers, and was produced in unknown numbers as conversions from He 219A-2/R1 standard with two DB 603L engines each rated at 1305kW (1750hp) and fitted with the GM 1 nitrous oxide power-boost system, no schräge Musik installation, and no armour. The type entered service in August 1944.

The He 219A-7 was the last model to achieve production status, and differed externally from the He 219A-2 and He 219A-5 series in having larger inlets for the engine superchargers. The type was intended mainly for the high-altitude role, and other changes were two DB 603G engines each rated at 1417kW (1900hp), additional radar (including a tail-warning system), more armour protection, a number of armament Rüstsätze complementing the standard fit of two MK108 cannon in the schräge Musik installation and, in later aircraft, a different powerplant. The He 219A-7/R1 had two 30mm MK108 cannon in the wing roots and two 30mm MK103 and two 20mm MG151/20 cannon in the ventral tray. The He 219A-7/R2 differed in having two 30mm MK108 and two 20mm MG151/20 cannon in the ventral tray, the He 219A-7/R3 differed from the He 219A-7/R2 in having 20mm MG151/20 cannon in the wing roots, the He 219A-7/R4 had 20mm MG151/20 cannon in the wing roots and ventral tray and was also the first model with FuG 220 Neptun tail-warning radar, the He 219A-7/R5 had two Junkers Jumo 213E inverted-Vee piston engines each fitted with the MW 50 methanol/water power-boost system, and the He 219A-7/R6 had two Jumo 222A/B inverted-Vee piston engines each rated at 1864kW (2500hp) at optimum altitude.

Deliveries of the true production versions of the He 219A totalled 268 aircraft, and some 20 prototypes were also pressed into service.

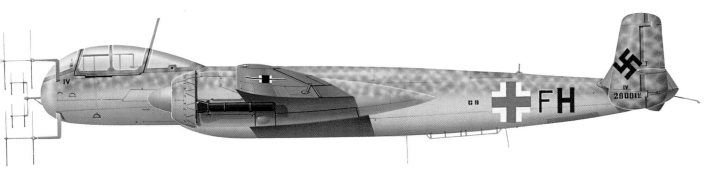

SPECIFICATIONS: Heinkel He 219A-7/R1 Uhu

GENERAL
Type: night-fighter
Accommodation: pilot and radar operator in tandem on ejection seats in a enclosed cockpit
Equipment: standard communication and navigation equipment, plus a Revi 16/B reflector gun sight, FuG 212 Lichtenstein airborne interception radar, FuG 220 Lichtenstein SN-2 airborne interception radar, and FuG 218 Neptun tail warning radar

MOTIVE POWER
Powerplant: two Daimler-Benz DB 603G inverted-Vee piston engines each rated at 1417kW (1900hp) for take-off and 1163kW (1560hp) at 7375m (24,200ft)

Fuel: internal fuel 2700 litres (593.9Imp gal; 13.25US gal); external fuel none
Weights: empty 11,200kg (24,692lb); maximum take-off 15,300kg (33,730lb)

PERFORMANCE
Maximum speed: 670km/h (416mph) at 7000m (22,965ft)
Cruising speed: maximum 630km/h (391mph) at optimum altitude and economical 540km/h (335.5mph) at optimum altitude
Initial climb rate: 552m (1810ft) per minute
Service ceiling: 12,700m (41,665ft)
Maximum range: 2000km (1243 miles); **Typical range:** 1545km (960 miles)

DIMENSIONS
Wing span: 18.50m (60ft 8.35in)
Wing area: 44.50sq m (478.99sq ft)
Length: 15.54m (50ft 11.81in)
Height: 4.10m (13ft 5.4in)

ARMAMENT
Fixed armament: two 30mm MK108 fixed forward-firing cannon with 100 rounds per gun in the wing roots, two 30mm MK103 and two 20mm MG151/20 fixed forward-firing cannon with 100 and 300 rounds per gun respectively in a ventral tray, and two 30mm MK108 cannon with 100 rounds per gun in an obliquely forward- and upward-firing installation in the upper part of the rear fuselage
Disposable armament: none

CHAPTER 10

HENSCHEL HS 129

The Hs 129 was a warplane that was excellent in concept but poor in execution. The aircraft offered potent anti-tank capabilities and first-class protection for the pilot, but only in an airframe that was cramped and lacking in adequate performance as a result of a powerplant that lacked adequate power and was vulnerable to ground fire.

The Henschel Hs 129 was Germany's only dedicated armoured single-seat close support and anti-tank warplane of World War II, but was never truly successful because of the poor fields of vision afforded to the pilot and its poor power/weight ratio, which resulted in decidedly sluggish performance even when carrying no disposable stores. The Hs 129 resulted from an April 1937 requirement that demanded the use of two low-powered engines, a fixed forward-firing armament of at least two 20mm MGFF cannon plus machine-guns and, as ways to reduce vulnerability to ground fire, small dimensions, 75mm (2.95 in) armoured glass glazing, and armour protection for

LEFT The Henschel Hs 129B had poor performance and agility as a result of its low power/weight ratio, which resulted from the combination of an inadequate powerplant with an airframe fitted with a mass of protective armour. The cockpit was also small and cramped, and provided its pilot with indifferent fields of vision.

the crew and powerplant. Created by a team under the supervision of Dipl.-Ing. Friedrich Nicolaus, the Hs 129 V1 prototype made its maiden flight in the spring of 1939 with a powerplant of two Argus As 410 inverted-Vee piston engines each rated at 347kW (465hp) for take-off and 309kW (415hp) at 2400 m (7875ft). By this time the original order for three prototypes had been supplemented by a contract for eight pre-production aircraft.

From the beginning of its flight trials, it was evident that the Hs 129 V1 was drastically underpowered even in lightly loaded condition, and that this poor power/weight ratio resulted in virtually non-existent manoeuvrability and sluggish performance, most notably under acceleration. Pilots' opinions of the view from the cockpit were equally unflattering. The Hs 129A-0 pre-production aircraft differed only in minor details from the prototypes, and so critical were the service test pilots that the Luftwaffe refused to order the planned Hs 129A-1 production model.

SPECIFICATIONS: Henschel Hs 129B-2

GENERAL

Type: close-support and anti-tank warplane

Accommodation: pilot in an enclosed cockpit

Equipment: standard communication and navigation equipment, plus a Revi C 12/C reflector gun sight

Weights: empty 4020kg (8862lb); maximum take-off 5250kg (11,574lb)

MOTIVE POWER

Powerplant: two Gnome-Rhône 14M-4/5 radial piston engines each rated at 522kW (700hp) for take-off and 507kW (680hp) at 4000m (13,125ft)

Fuel: internal fuel 610 litres (134.2Imp gal; 161.1US gal); external fuel none

PERFORMANCE

Maximum speed: 407km/h (253mph) at 3830m (12,565ft)

Cruising speed: 315km/h (196mph) at 3000m (9845ft)

Initial climb rate: 486m (1595ft) per minute

Service ceiling: 9000m (29,530ft)

Maximum range: 690km (429 miles); typical range 560km (348 miles) with an underfuselage pack carrying one 30mm MK103 cannon

DIMENSIONS

Wing span: 14.20m (46ft 7in)

Wing area: 29.00sq m (312.16sq ft)

Length: 9.75m (31ft 11.86in)

Height: 3.25m (10ft 8in)

ARMAMENT

Fixed armament: two 20mm MG151/20 fixed forward-firing cannon with 125 rounds in the upper sides of the central fuselage and two 13mm MG131 fixed forward-firing machine guns with 300

rounds per gun in the lower sides of the central fuselage, and provision under the fuselage for a pack accommodating one 30mm MK101 fixed forward-firing cannon with 30 rounds, or four 7.92mm MG17 fixed forward-firing machine guns with 250 rounds per gun

Disposable armament: up to 450kg (992lb) of disposable stores carried on three hardpoints (one under the fuselage rated at 250kg [551lb] and two under the wing with each unit rated at 100kg/220lb), and generally comprising one 250kg (551lb) SC-250 bomb, or four 50kg (110lb) SC-50 bombs, or four packs each carrying 24 2kg (4.4lb) SD-2 anti-personnel fragmentation bomblets carried under the fuselage (instead of the cannon or machine gun pack), and two 50kg (110lb) SC-50 bombs or two containers each carrying 48 2kg (4.4lb) SD-2 fragmentation bomblets carried under the wing

The Henschel design team had already decided that the Hs 129 was too small for practical employment, and had therefore planned a slightly enlarged model with revised and more extensively glazed cockpit together with a powerplant of two Gnome-Rhône 14M radial engines, of which Germany had plentiful stocks after the defeat of France. The Hs 129 production programme was too advanced for the larger type to be considered, however, so the German air ministry instructed Henschel instead to revise the Hs 129 with the uprated powerplant and an improved cockpit providing its pilot with improved fields of vision.

Two Hs 129A-0 aircraft were returned to the company for conversion, which was effected without undue difficulty despite the fact that the new engine type was

bulkier and heavier than the original Argus unit, as Hs 129B prototypes. Flight trials revealed that the revised aircraft had better performance with adequate acceleration, but handling still required considerable effort and the fields of vision from the cockpit had actually been worsened by the greater bulk of the radial engines. Even so, the type was ordered into production, and the first of 10 Hs 129B-0 pre-production aircraft was delivered in December 1940 with the revised armament of two faster-firing MG151/20 cannon and two MG17 machine guns as well as provision for the carriage of several types of Rüstsätze (field conversion sets) to improve the type's operational flexibility.

In March 1941 there appeared the first three examples of the Hs 129B-1 initial production model that differed from the Hs 129B-0 only in details and entered service over the

Eastern Front in April 1942 in the hands of 4./Schlachtgeschwader 1. Here serious criticism of the new warplane was soon voiced: it had already been appreciated that the Gnome-Rhône 14M was prone to sudden seizure, but to this problem was now added the news that it was also hopelessly vulnerable to battle damage. Such was the need for a close-support warplane, however, that the Luftwaffe decided to persevere with the type, and a number of Rüstsätze were issued: the R2 was a ventral pack carrying one 30mm MK101 cannon with 30 rounds, the R3 was a ventral installation of four 7.92mm MG17 machine guns with 250 rounds per gun in a port fuselage bay, the R4 was a rack for the underfuselage carriage of four 50kg (110lb) bombs, or four packs of 24 2kg (4.4lb) fragmentation bomblets or one 250kg (551lb) bomb, and the R5 installation added an Rb 20/30 reconnaissance camera.

Introduced in 1943, the Hs 129B-2 was a development of the Hs 129B-1 incorporating as standard all the improvements effected individually in the course of the Hs 129B-1 production run. Soon after the type's introduction, however, anti-tank operations became more important than close support, and provision for the Rüstsätze was replaced by underfuselage attachments for anti-tank weapons. This resulted in the Hs 129B-2/Wa (Waffenträger, or weapon

carrier) subvariant that could be fitted first with a 30mm MK103 cannon offering a higher muzzle velocity and therefore better penetration capability than the MK101, and then with the 37mm BK 3,7 cannon whose installation meant the deletion of the machine guns to provide volume for cannon ammunition. Several other anti-tank weapon types were evaluated but not adopted for the Hs 129B-2.

By the beginning of 1944, the 30mm and 37mm cannon were no longer effective against even the side or rear armour of Soviet tanks, and the designation Hs 129B-3/Wa was adopted for Hs 129B-2 warplanes adapted on the production line with an underfuselage 75mm BK 7,5 anti-tank gun, which was itself a conversion of the ordnance of the PaK 40L anti-tank equipment. Only some 25 such Hs 129B-3 aircraft were completed before production of the Hs 129B ended in the closing stages of 1944. The Hs 129B type was used mostly on the Eastern Front, but a number also found their way to the North African, Italian and French theatres.

BELOW *Seen here in North African markings, this Hs 129B-1 reveals the semi-external installation of one of the two 20mm MG 151/20 cannon in the fuselage above the wing root, and the external installation of the Revi C 12/C reflector gun sight ahead of the windscreen.*

CHAPTER 11

JUNKERS JU 87

Synonymous with the 'Blitzkrieg' campaigns in which Germany secured her initial victories, the Ju 87 was a first-class dive-bomber but could operate with success only under an umbrella of air superiority. When this umbrella was absent, the type suffered horrendous losses but nonetheless remained in service for lack of a successor.

Some aircraft are so indelibly associated with the wars in which they appeared that the mere mention of the war conjures them into the mind. One of the types that springs to mind at the mention of World War II must surely be the Junkers Ju 87 'Stuka'. The nickname is abbreviated from Sturzkampfflugzeug, the German word for dive-bomber, and the Stuka's task was to operate as 'flying artillery' in support of the fast-moving armoured forces that spearheaded the German army's offensive campaigns in the first stages of the war up to June 1941.

The origins of the Ju 87 can be traced to 1933 and the advent to power of the Nazi party, which immediately started to enlarge and improve Germany's armed forces. The

LEFT *The Ju 87, seen here in the form of an echelon of Ju 87D machines, was closely associated with 'Blitzkrieg' warfare in World War II. From 1940 it was largely obsolescent, but lack of any successor meant that the type was retained in production and service.*

Henschel Hs 123 biplane was designed as an interim dive-bomber for the close support role, allowing time for the creation of a definitive dive-bomber to meet a January 1935 requirement essentially written round the Ju 87 whose design had been started in 1933 under the leadership of Dipl.-Ing. Hermann Pohlmann. The construction of three prototypes had been started in the summer of 1934, and thus it was only three months after the issue of the requirement that the Ju 87 V1, the first of four prototypes, appeared for its maiden flight. This was an all-metal monoplane with a wing of the inverted-gull configuration, fixed tailwheel landing gear, and the powerplant of one Rolls-Royce Kestrel V Vee piston engine rated at 391kW (525hp) for take-off.

The Ju 87 V1 had a tail unit with endplate vertical surfaces, but in the Ju 87 V2 with the Junkers Jumo 210A engine rated at 455kW (610hp) this was changed to a single centreline surface. On the Ju 87 V4 production prototype

LEFT *Early examples of the Ju 87, such as this Ju 87A, were distinguishable from later variants by features such as their heavily framed canopies, strut-braced main landing gear units, and narrow-chord blades of a propeller driven by the Junkers Jumo 210C engine.*

this was increased in area for the Ju 87A series of which 210 were built in Ju 87A-0, A-1 and A-2 variants for an operational debut in the spring of 1937 in the Spanish Civil War.

Ju-87 'B'-series

The surviving Ju 87A warplanes had been retired before the outbreak of World War II, when the standard type was the Ju 87B with the more powerful Jumo 211 engine and a large measure of redesign that resulted in the retention of only the wing and horizontal tail surface of the Ju 87A. The remainder of the airframe was essentially new and embodied a combination of major aerodynamic and structural changes. The Ju 87B-0 pre-production type had the Jumo 211A engine rated at 746kW (1000hp) for take-off but replaced in the Ju 87B-1 initial production version by the Jumo 211Da with a fuel-injection rather than carburettor system, and a rating of 895kW (1200hp) for take-off. As well as improving performance to a tactically important extent, the uprated powerplant also meant that the Ju 87B-1 could carry a 500kg (1102lb) bomb with a

crew of two embarked, and this gave the heavily laden aeroplane at least a measure of defensive firepower that would otherwise have been lacking; the alternative weapon load was a single 250kg (551lb) bomb carried on the underfuselage crutch and four 50kg (110lb) bombs carried under the outer wing panels.

On the outbreak of World War II, all nine of the Luftwaffe's Stukagruppen were equipped with the Ju 87B-1, of which 336 were in the current inventory. Operating under conditions of local if not total air superiority, the Ju 87 proved a decisive weapon in the Polish campaign, but by the end of 1939 the Ju 87B-1 had been replaced in production by the Ju 87B-2 with individual ejection exhaust stubs for a measure of thrust augmentation, hydraulically operated radiator cooling gills, and an improved propeller. This model could lift a bomb load of 1000kg (2205lb) when flown as a single-seater, and subvariants produced by the incorporation of Umrüst-Bausätze (factory conversion sets) included the Ju 87B-2/U2 with improved radio equipment (also retrofitted on the Ju 87B-1 to create the Ju 87B-1/U2),

BELOW *The angular yet aggressive and oddly pleasing lines of the Ju 87 dive-bomber are readily apparent in this overhead view of a Ju 87A. The outward-canted pylons over the cockpit carried the forward ends of the radio antennae that extended back and out to the outer tips of the tailplane.*

Ju 87B-2/U3 with additional armour protection for the close-support role, and Ju 87B-2/U4 with ski rather than wheel landing gear. There was also a Ju 87B-2/Trop version for service in North Africa with sand filters and a pack of desert survival equipment.

Even before the outbreak of World War II there had been a camp within the German military establishment that argued for the Ju 87's retirement on the grounds that it was technically obsolete, and would therefore suffer heavy combat losses. This fact became indisputably clear only in the spring of 1941, and then lack of an adequate replacement type meant that the Ju 87B was succeeded only by the Ju 87D improved model that came after the Ju 87C and Ju 87R (Reichweite, or range) variants that were produced only in small numbers. The Ju 87C-0 was the pre-production model of a planned carrierborne Ju 87C-1 with catapult spools, an arrester hook, manually folding outer

wing panels and jettisonable main landing gear units, while the Ju 87R-1 to R-4 were variants of a long-range anti-shipping model with additional fuel capacity including drop tanks but the disposable weapons load limited to one 250kg (551lb) bomb.

Airframe redesign

By the spring of 1940, the new Jumo 211J-1 engine was ready for service, and the Junkers design team set about evolving a development of the Ju 87B to make the best possible use of this engine, which offered not only greater power but also the possibility of a considerably cleaner installation. This was achieved by the relocation of the oil cooler from its original position above the engine to a small chin radiator which assumed the position of the water cooling radiator that was divided into two sections which were relocated to the undersurfaces of the inner wing

SPECIFICATIONS: Junkers Ju 87D-1

GENERAL

Type: dive-bomber and close-support warplane

Accommodation: pilot and radio operator/gunner in tandem in an enclosed cockpit

Equipment: standard communication and navigation equipment, plus a Revi reflector weapons sight

Weights: empty 3900kg (8598lb); normal take-off 5842kg (12,880lb); maximum take-off 6600kg (14,550lb)

MOTIVE POWER

Powerplant: one Junkers Jumo 211J-1 inverted-Vee piston engine rated at 1059kW (1420hp) for take-off and 887kW (1190hp) for continuous running

Fuel: internal fuel 780 litres (171.6Imp gal; 206.1US gal); external fuel up to 600 litres (132Imp gal; 158.5 US gal) in two drop tanks

PERFORMANCE

Maximum speed: 410km/h (255mph) at 3840m (12,600ft)

Cruising speed: normal 320km/h (199mph) at 5090m (16,700ft) and economical 185km/h (115mph) at optimum altitude

Climb: to 5000m (16,405ft) in 19 minutes 48 seconds

Service ceiling: 7285m (23,905ft)

Maximum range: 1535km (954 miles) with drop tanks; typical range 820km (509.5 miles) with standard fuel

DIMENSIONS

Wing span: 13.80m (45ft 3.3in)

Wing area: 31.90sq m (343.37sq ft)

Length: 11.50m (37ft 8.75in)

Height: 3.90m (12ft 9.54in)

ARMAMENT

Fixed armament: two 7.92mm MG17 fixed forward-firing machine guns with 1000 rounds per gun in the leading edges of the wing, and one 7.92mm MG81z two-barrel trainable rearward-firing machine gun in the rear cockpit

Disposable armament: up to 1800kg (3968lb) of disposable stores carried on three hardpoints (one under the fuselage rated at 1800kg [3968lb] and two under the wing with each unit rated at 500kg [1102lb]), and generally comprising on the underfuselage crutch one 1800lb (3968lb) SC/PD-1800 bomb, or one 1400kg (3086lb) PC-1400 bomb, or one 1000kg (2205lb) SC-1000 bomb, or one 500kg (1102lb) SC-500 bomb, or one 250kg (551lb) SC-250 bomb and, with the underfuselage load limited to 500kg (1102lb), on the underwing hardpoints four 110kg (220lb) SC-50 bombs, or two 500kg (1102lb) SC-500 bombs, or two 250kg (551lb) SC-250 bombs, or two Waffenbehälter (weapon container) pods each carrying three 7.92mm MG81z two-barrel machine guns, or two 20mm MGFF cannon, or two packs of 92 2kg (4.4lb) SD-2 fragmentation bomblets

---

panels. Other changes effected in the new variant were a lower-drag cockpit enclosure, reduction in the size and complexity of the main landing gear fairings, increase in the internal fuel capacity through the adoption of the outer wing auxiliary tanks pioneered in the Ju 87R long-range version, improvement of crew protection through the introduction of more and thicker armour plate, doubling of the defensive firepower by the replacement of the 7.92mm MG15 one-barrel machine-gun by an MG81z two-barrel machine-gun of the same calibre, and strengthening of the lower fuselage and attached crutch for the carriage of one 1800kg (3968lb) bomb.

ABOVE *Ground crew work on the Jumo 211 engine of a Ju 87B, which differed from the original Ju 87A in a number of respects including heavier armament, revised canopy, cantilever main landing gear units with narrower-chord fairings, and a single-wire radio antenna.*

The first of the new breed was the Ju 87D-1, which began to replace the Ju 87B-2 on the 'Stuka' production line from the spring of 1942. At the time the D-1 was considered a low-priority, as the Luftwaffe considered it only an interim type pending the debut of more advanced warplanes better optimised for the Schlachtkampfflugzeug or close-support role (which was now replacing the Sturzkampfflugzeug dive-bomber role for which the Ju 87 had been conceived in the first half of the 1930s). Thus deliveries of the Ju 87 dropped from 70 per month in January 1941 to a mere two in November 1941 for a year total of 476 aircraft. When it became clear that new attack aircraft would not be available in the immediate future, production of the Ju 87 was boosted once more from January 1942. Deliveries in the course of this year totalled 917 aircraft. The Ju 87D-1 appeared in operational service in the spring of 1942 over the Eastern Front and, in its Ju 87D-1/Trop form with dust/sand filters and a pack of desert survival equipment, over North Africa.

The sharply rising pace of production meant that the Stukagruppen were able to convert from the wholly obsolete Ju 87B-2 to the more advanced Ju 87D in the course of the spring and summer of 1942. Many units received the Ju 87D-2 subvariant that was built in parallel with the Ju 87D-1 and from which it differed only in its strengthened rear fuselage and tailwheel unit, the latter incorporating a tow hook for cargo gliders. Toward the end of 1942, the Ju 87D-1 and Ju 87D-2 were phased out of production after suffering increasingly heavy losses.

Close-support variants

These two models were superceded by the Ju 87D-3. This was the first variant of the family fully optimised for the close support role with increased armour protection for the crew, engine and radiator. Despite its optimisation for this new low-level role, however, the Ju 87D-3 retained the dive brakes of its predecessors.

Consideration was also given to the use of the Ju 87D-1 and Ju 87D-3 in the torpedo role, but although a number of the aircraft were converted to this role with the revised designation Ju 87D-4, none of them was ever used operationally and the aircraft were later converted back to Ju 87D-3 standard.

Despite its heavy operational losses, the Ju 87D was retained in service for lack of any adequate replacement, and thought was given to a way of reducing the ever heavier wing loading that was degrading the warplane's manoeuvrability, which was in real terms was its only possible defence against fighter attack. This resulted, early in 1943, in the arrival of the Ju 87D-5 variant with extended outer wing panels, the jettisonable main landing gear units that had featured in the Ju 87C-0 and, in later aircraft, no dive brakes as these were now entirely superfluous to the D-5s revised role.

By now the Ju 87 was being forced to operate at night except in the areas in which the Luftwaffe could occasionally gain air superiority. The Ju 87D-5 was not well suited to this role, so there emerged the Ju 87D-7 with improved night-flying instrumentation and flame-damper tubes exhausting over the wing below and behind the pilot's normal fields of vision. The opportunity was also taken to improve the new variant with the Jumo 211P engine rated at 1118kW (1500hp), and the fixed forward-firing armament increased to two 20mm MG151/20 cannon. The Ju 87D-7 retained the larger wing and jettisonable main landing gear units of the Ju 87D-5 and was produced in parallel with the Ju 87D-8, which differed only in its lack of advanced night-flying instrumentation and flame-damper tubes. These were the final two variants to be built before production of the Ju 87 series finally ended in September 1944 after the delivery of more than 5700 aircraft including 1844 in 1943.

Tank-busters

In 1942 the growing strength and technical capability of the Soviet tank arm forced the Luftwaffe to consider an alternative to the bomb as its primary anti-tank weapon. The obvious solution was a high-velocity cannon firing a moderately large projectile. The Luftwaffe therefore ordered the conversion of the 37mm Flak 18 light anti-aircraft gun as the BK 3,7 for carriage in an underwing pod. The new armament system was evaluated with considerable success during the summer of 1942 on a Ju 87D-3 conversion, and the type was ordered into production as the Ju 87G-1 for full service from the autumn of that year. The type's success led to the creation of a dedicated anti-tank squadron in each of Schlachtgeschwadern 1, 2, 3 and 77, as Stukageschwadern 1, 2, 3 and 77 were redesignated in October 1943. Although the BK 3,7 cannon was effective against the Soviet tanks of the period, the Ju 87 was completely obsolete in the face of modern fighter opposition and was replaced as soon as possible for day operations by specialised Fw 190 variants.

Surviving aircraft were passed to the Nachtschachtgruppen, and by the autumn of 1944 only one Gruppe was still operating the Ju 87G-1 in the day role.

From 1943 a number of Ju 87D machines were adapted as Ju 87H dual-control trainers for use in the conversion of fighter and bomber pilots to the close support and anti-tank roles. The conversion involved the removal of all armament, the addition of dual controls, and the revision of the rear part of the cockpit canopy with side blisters so that the instructor in the rear seat could obtain a measure of forward view. Ju 87D-1, Ju 87D-3, Ju 87D-5, Ju 87D-7 and Ju 87D-8 aircraft converted in this way received the designations Ju 87H-1, Ju 87H-3, Ju 87H-5, Ju 87H-7 and Ju 87H-8.

ABOVE *Armourers work on one of the two 37mm BK 37 anti-tank cannon carried in podded installations under the wing of a Ju 87G-1. These cannon packed a considerable punch, but were heavy and generated considerable drag, thereby eroding performance and agility.*

CHAPTER 12

JUNKERS JU 88

One of the classic warplanes of all time, the Ju 88 was a stunning example of the aeroplane in which all the elements blended to create a highly effective operational weapon that was also capable of extensive development and, just as importantly, evolution into variants suiting the type for service in a multitude of first-line roles.

Rivalling the de Havilland Mosquito for the accolade of most versatile aeroplane of World War II, the Junkers Ju 88 was arguably the most important German warplane of its time and was used in a host of roles ranging from basic bombing to night-fighting via torpedo and dive bombing, heavy attack and reconnaissance. Yet the full potential of the machine had not been considered when the German air ministry issued its 1935 requirement for a three-seat fast bomber that could deliver a maximum weapons load of 800kg (1764lb) at a maximum speed of 500km/h (311mph). Junkers felt that the requirement would result in considerable orders for the winning design and expended great effort in the evolution of a far-sighted

design embodying the full spectrum of advanced features that had emerged in the last few years. Lacking the capability to design an advanced monoplane of the modern stressed-skin type, Junkers hired two American engineers, W. H. Evers and A. Gassner, who had considerable experience with this type of structural medium. Work began in January 1936, and the initial result was the Ju 88 V1 (first of 10 initial prototypes), which made its maiden flight on 21 December 1936 with two Daimler-Benz DB 600Aa engines each rated at 746kW (1000hp) for take-off. The engines each drove a three-blade metal propeller and were enclosed in nacelles that gave the impression of a radial-engined type as the engines were cooled by annular radiators located at the front of each nacelle.

The type immediately revealed the hallmarks of a thoroughbred warplane in its good performance, viceless handling characteristics and excellent tractability, and there followed 20 Ju 88A-0 pre-production aircraft delivered from

LEFT *A remarkable photograph reveals a moment before the crash of a burning Ju 88. The Ju 88 was arguably the finest multi-role warplane of World War II, and in every respect an excellent aircraft especially in the high-speed bomber role for which it had originally been designed.*

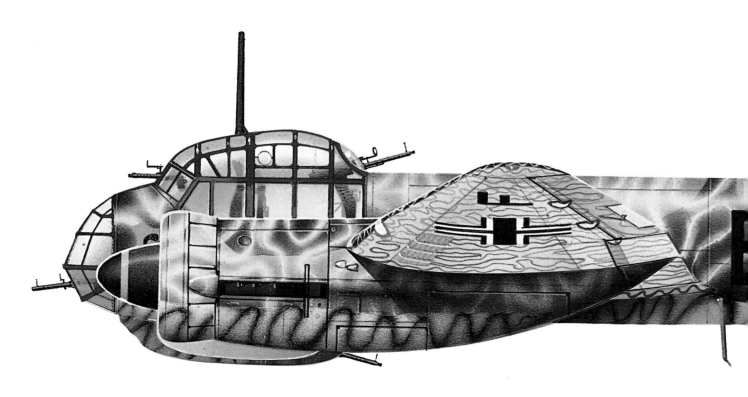

BELOW *The defensive armament of the Ju 88A-4 bomber was grouped round the forward compartment accommodating the four-man crew, and comprised three 7.92mm MG 81 machine guns and two 13mm MG 131 machine guns, which could be replaced by four more MG 81 weapons.*

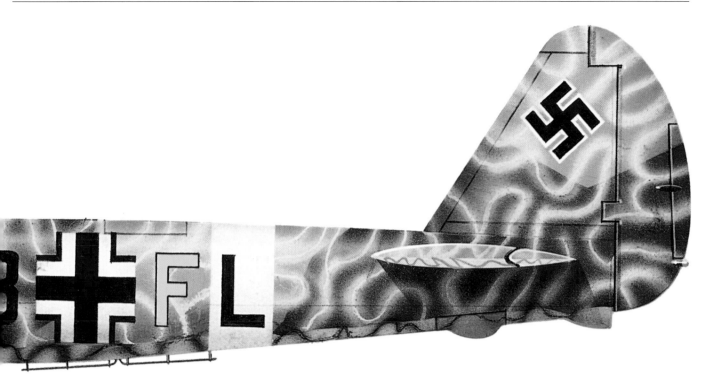

March 1939 to a revised standard with a four-man crew, dive-bombing capability, and heavier armament. The Ju 88A-1 initial production model flew its first operational sortie in the closing days of September 1939, and from that time onward the Ju 88 matured as one of the most formidable German warplanes of World War II even though there were a number of problems initially with the dive brakes, main landing gear units and loading limits. The Ju 88A-1 was powered by two Jumo 211B-1/G-1 engines each rated at 895kW (1200hp) for take-off. The standard internal bomb load was 1400kg (3086lb) in the form of 28 50kg (110lb) bombs, supplemented by 1000 kg (2205lb) of bombs carried on underwing hardpoints. The defensive armament was originally three 7.92mm MG15 machine-guns in the form of single trainable weapons in the windscreen, cockpit rear and undernose gondola: operations soon revealed the

SPECIFICATIONS: Junkers Ju 88A-4

GENERAL
Type: medium bomber
Accommodation: pilot, navigator/bombardier/gunner, radio operator/gunner and gunner in an enclosed forward-fuselage crew compartment
Equipment: standard communication and navigation equipment, plus an optical bomb sight and optical gun sights
Weights: empty 9860kg (21,737lb); normal take-off 12,105kg (26,686lb); maximum take-off 14,000kg (30,865lb)

MOTIVE POWER
Powerplant: two Junkers Jumo 211J-1/2 inverted-Vee piston engines each rated at 999kW (1340hp) for take-off and 790kW (1060hp) at 17,060ft (5200m)
Fuel: internal fuel 2900 litres (637.9Imp gal; 766.1US gal) plus provision for 1220 litres (268.4Imp gal; 322.3US gal) of auxiliary fuel in one fuselage tank and/or 680 litres (149.6Imp gal; 179.6US gal) of

additional auxiliary fuel in a weapons bay tank; external fuel up to 1680 litres (369.6Imp gal; 443.8US gal) in four drop tanks

PERFORMANCE
Maximum speed: 470km/h (292mph) at 5300m (17,390ft)
Cruising speed: maximum 400km/h (248.5mph) at 5000m (16,405ft) and economical 370km/h (230mph) at 6000m (19,685ft)
Climb: to 5400m (17,715ft) in 23 minutes 0 seconds
Service ceiling: 8200m (26,900ft)
Maximum range: 2730km (1696 miles); typical range 1790km (1112 miles)

DIMENSIONS
Wing span: 20.00m (65ft 7.4in)
Wing area: 54.50sq m (586.63sq ft)
Length: 14.40m (47ft 2.93in)
Height: 4.85m (15ft 11in)

ARMAMENT
Fixed armament: one 7.92mm MG81 fixed or trainable forward-firing machine gun in the windscreen, one 13mm MG131 or two 7.92mm MG81 trainable forward-firing machine guns in the nose position, two 7.92mm MG81 trainable rearward-firing machine guns in the rear of the cockpit, and one 13mm MG131 or two 7.92mm MG81 trainable rearward-firing machine guns in the rear of the undernose gondola
Disposable armament: up to 2500kg (5511lb) of disposable stores carried in a lower-fuselage weapons bay rated at 500kg (1102lb) and on six hardpoints (all under the wing with each unit of the inboard pair rated at 500kg [1102lb] and each unit of the two outboard pairs at 250kg [551lb]), and generally comprising 10 50kg (110lb) SC-50 bombs carried internally and two 500kg (1102lb) SC-500 bombs and four 250kg (551lb) SC-250 bombs carried externally

inadequacy of this arrangement, which was therefore boosted on the production line by the addition of a second MG15 in the rear of the cockpit, and in the field by the installation of two MG15 lateral-firing weapons in the sides of the cockpit glazing.

In other respects, the details of the Ju 88A-1 included a maximum speed of 450km/h (280mph) at 5500m (18,045ft), cruising speed of 350km/h (217mph) at 5500m (18,045ft), service ceiling of 9800 m (32,150 ft), range of 1700km (1056 miles) with one auxiliary fuel tank in the weapons bay, empty weight of 7700kg (16,975lb), maximum take-off weight of 10,360kg (22,840lb), wing span of 18.37m (60ft 3.25in), wing area of 52.50sq m (565.12sq ft), length of 14.40m (47ft 2.67in) and height of 5.33m (17ft 5.75in).

LEFT *The gunner accommodated in the gondola under the starboard side of the Ju 88A's nose protected the underside of the warplane from stern attacks. In addition to bombs carried internally in the lower fuselage, the Ju 88A could carry more weapons on racks inboard of the wing nacelles.*

The first definitive model was the Ju 88A-4 development of the Ju 88A-1 with the wing extended slightly in span and area, inset rather than trailing ailerons with metal rather than fabric skinning, strengthened main landing gear units, and two Jumo 211J-1/2 engines each rated at 999kW (1340hp) for take-off. Early aircraft were completed with two Jumo 211F-1 engines each rated at 999kW (1340hp) for take-off and also had the same defensive armament as the improved Ju 88A-1. The definitive version of the Ju 88A-4 switched to superior 7.92mm MG81 weapons that were often replaced by 13mm MG131 machine-guns. Other changes in the Ju 88A-4 were improved armour protection for the crew, the elimination of the forward weapons bay in favour of additional fuel tankage, and provision under the outer wing panels for two more hardpoints each rated at 250kg (551lb).

Battle of Britain duties

As there were delays in the final development of the Jumo 211J engine for the Ju 88A-4, the revised wing and strengthened landing gear units were fitted to the Ju 88A-1 airframe to create the Ju 88A-5 interim type. The variant appeared in the summer of 1940, and proved itself the most capable of the German bombers operating in the Battle of Britain. The Ju 88A-6 was a development of the Ju 88A-5 intended to clear the way for any main bomber force by cutting the cables of balloon barrages with a large forward-mounted fender that terminated at each wing tip in a cable-cutting device. The aircraft were soon withdrawn from the balloon cable-cutting role and adapted as standard bombers or, with the revised designation Ju 88A-6/U, for the long-range maritime role with the crew reduced to three, the undernose gondola removed, FuG 200 Hohentwiel air-to-surface search radar added, and provision made for the carriage of drop tanks.

The Ju 88A-7 was a Ju 88A-5 variant for the dual-control conversion trainer role, and the Ju 88A-8 was a Ju 88A-4 development with balloon cable cutters built into the wing leading edges and the crew reduced to three. The Ju 88A-9, A-10 and A-11 were the tropicalised versions of the Ju 88A-1, A-10 and A-4 respectively with sand filters, desert survival equipment and cockpit sun blinds. Ju 88A-4 aircraft adapted to the same standard by field maintenance units received the designation Ju 88A-4/Trop.

The Ju 88A-2 was a version of the Ju 88A-1 with attachment points for Rocket Assisted Take-Off units (RATO), which were designed to descend to the ground under parachutes after use. The Ju 88A-3 designation was used for the conversion trainer version of the Ju 88A-1 with dual controls, dual throttles and some measure of flight instrument duplication.

ABOVE *The Ju 88P represented an attempt to tackle the Soviet tank armies, and the Ju 88P-2 illustrated here was produced in small numbers as conversions of Ju 88A-4 airframes with two 37mm BK 3,7 cannon in a very large and 'draggy' ventral fairing.*

The Ju 88A-12 was the Ju 88A-4 adapted on the production line to dual-control trainer standard, while the Ju 88A-13 was the Ju 88A-4 rebuilt for the low-level attack role with the dive brakes and bomb sight removed, additional armour worked into the airframe to protect the crew, engines and fuel supply, provision made for a disposable load of 500kg (1102lb) of fragmentation bomblets, and fixed forward-firing armament provided in the form of up to 16 7.92mm MG17 machine-guns in pods carried on the underwing hardpoints. The Ju 88A-14 was an improved version of the Ju 88A-4 with increased armour protection, cable cutters in the wing leading edges and, in some aircraft, a 20mm MGFF forward-firing cannon in the forward part of the undernose gondola for improved firepower in the anti-ship role. The Ju 88A-15 was a development of the Ju 88A-4 with an enlarged weapons bay for the carriage of a 3000kg (6614lb) weapons load, the crew reduced to three, the undernose gondola removed, and the defensive armament restricted to two MG15 machine-guns. The Ju 88A-16 was the trainer version of the Ju 88A-14 with the undernose gondola and all armament removed.

Further development yielded the Ju 88A-17 development of the Ju 88A-4 for the torpedo bombing role with a three-man crew and the four racks inboard of the engine nacelles replaced by two racks each capable of carrying one 765kg (1686lb) LT F5b torpedo. The forward fuselage was revised to carry on its starboard side a large bulged fairing accommodating the gear to adjust the guidance mechanism of the torpedoes before release. The production model was preceded in 1942 by a number of field conversions to basically the same Ju 88A-4/Trop standard.

The exact number of Ju 88A aircraft built in this series is not known, but exceeded 7000 machines delivered by Junkers, Arado, Dornier, Heinkel, Henschel and VW.

Although conceived solely as a high-speed bomber, the Ju 88 revealed such performance, payload, agility and versatility in its prototype forms that the type was soon considered for a number of other roles. One of these alternative roles was that of heavy fighter, a type in which the German air ministry placed considerable faith for the bomber destroyer, anti-ship and intruder roles.

The first development in this direction was the Ju 88 V7, which was the Ju 88C V1 fighter prototype with the nose revised for the fixed forward-firing armament of one 20mm MGFF/M cannon with 120 rounds and three 7.92mm MG17 machine-guns with a total of 2800 rounds; the defensive armament comprised single 7.92mm MG15 trainable rearward-firing machine-guns in the rear of the cockpit and in the ventral step position. Trials with this converted prototype confirmed that the Ju 88 was also an excellent gun platform. Before this Junkers had also proposed a heavy fighter derivative of the Ju 88B with two Jumo 213 engines, a shallower fuselage, and a fixed forward-firing armament of two 20mm MG151/20 cannon with 800 rounds and one 7.92mm MG81z two-barrel machine-gun with 4,000 rounds in a ventral tray.

The German air ministry ordered no development of the Junkers heavy fighter concept, but the company continued limited design work on the type with a powerplant that was later changed to two BMW 139 radial engines that were finally replaced by BMW 801 radial engines. As this final version was basically similar to the Ju 88B attack bomber whose development was already under way, the German air ministry ordered the type as the Ju 88C-1 with two BMW 801MA engines and a fixed forward-firing armament of two 20mm MGFF cannon and two 7.92mm MG17 machine-guns. It was then decided that the Focke-Wulf Fw 190 fighter should have complete priority for the BMW 801 radial engine, and further development and production of the Ju 88C-1 were terminated.

Heavy fighter development

The air ministry was still interested in a heavy fighter development of the Ju 88, however, and ordered the Ju 88C-2 for evaluation in the form of a number of conversions from Ju 88A-1 bomber standard with the same gun armament as the Ju 88C V1 but a revised nose with an armoured bulkhead but no glazing. The Ju 88C-2 was powered by two Jumo 211B-1 engines each rated at 895kW (1200hp) for take-off, and among its other details were a disposable armament of 10 50kg (110lb) SC-50 bombs in the rear weapons bay, maximum speed of 475km/h (295mph) at 5500m (18,045ft), range of 1820km (1131 miles), maximum take-off weight of 11,000kg (24,250lb) and wing span of 18.37m (60ft 3.25in). The Ju 88C-2 entered service during the spring of 1940 in the day coastal anti-ship role before switching to the night intruder role during the following autumn. There followed a single Ju 88C-3 prototype with two BMW 801 radial engines.

The Ju 88C-4 was the first variant built as a heavy fighter, and was based on the Ju 88A-4 with its span increased to 20.00m (65ft 7.5in). Other changes were an increase in the fixed forward-firing armament by the addition of two more 20mm MGFF/M cannon with 120 rounds per gun in the ventral gondola, which could alternatively be revised for the carriage of two cameras to allow the warplane to operate in the armed reconnaissance role, and in the defensive armament boosted by the restoration of the single 7.92mm MG15 trainable rearward-firing machine-gun in the rear of the ventral gondola and the change of the armament in the rear of the cockpit to two 7.92mm MG81J trainable rearward-firing machine-guns. The inner wing panels were fitted with four hardpoints for the carriage of external loads, which could include two WB 81 pods each carrying six 7.92mm MG81 fixed downward/forward-firing machine-guns for the ground-attack role. The Ju 88C-4 entered service in the autumn of 1941 with two Jumo 211F-1 engines, but in the spring of 1942 these were replaced by a pair of Jumo 211J-1/2 engines each rated at 999kW (1340hp) for take-off. Under 100 of this variant were produced.

Introduced early in 1942, the Ju 88C-5 was a Ju 88C-4 development with two BMW 801D-2 engines each rated at 1267.5kW (1700hp) for take-off, the 20mm MGFF cannon replaced by faster-firing MG151/20 weapon of the same calibre, and the undernose gondola supplanted by a weapons tray projecting from the weapons bay and carrying two 7.92mm MG17 fixed forward-firing machine-guns. There was still an acute shortage of the BMW 801 engine, however, and production of the Ju 88C-5 was therefore limited to just 10 aircraft. The Ju 88C-6 was delivered from the spring of 1942 as the first variant of the Ju 88C series to be produced in large numbers, and was essentially a Ju 88C-4 development with additional armour. The type was delivered with and without the ventral gondola and its two 20mm cannon, and the defensive armament varied considerably according to the availability of weapons, crew preference and their theatre of operations.

The night-fighters

In the autumn of 1942 the first genuine night-fighter variant of the Ju 88C series appeared as the Ju 88C-6b (resulting in the redesignation of the Ju 88C-6 day fighter as the Ju 88C-6a), a derivative of the Ju 88C-6 with FuG 202 Lichtenstein BC or FuG 212 Lichtenstein C-1 radar and a fixed forward firing armament of three 20mm MGFF/M cannon and three 7.92mm MG17 machine-guns.

Early in 1944 this type was replaced in production by the Ju 88C-6c with the FuG 220 Lichtenstein SN-2 radar. Later aircraft of the Ju 88C-6c subvariant added to their electromagnetic armoury the FuG 227 Flensburg and FuG 350 Naxos Z radar homing systems, which were used to detect emissions from Royal Air Force bombers. Later the Ju 88C-6c also added a schräge Musik (shrill music, i.e. jazz) installation of two 20mm MG151/20 fixed upward/forward-firing cannon in the rear fuselage.

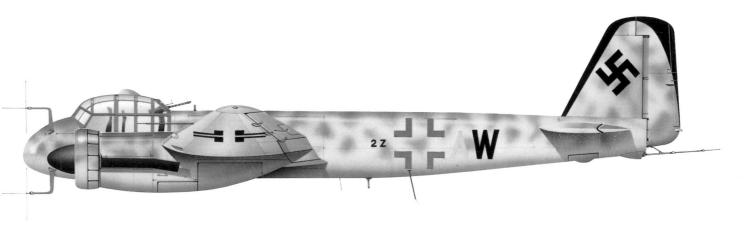

SPECIFICATIONS: Junkers Ju 88G-7b

GENERAL
Type: night-fighter
Accommodation: pilot, radar operator, radio operator/gunner and gunner carried in the enclosed crew compartment
Equipment: standard communication and navigation equipment, plus a Revi reflector gun sight, FuG 220 Lichtenstein SN-2, FuG 228 Lichtenstein SN-3 or FuG 218 Neptun VR airborne interception radar and, on some aircraft, FuG 227 Flensburg or FuG 350 Naxos radar homing system and tail-warning radar
Weights: empty not available; normal take-off 13,110kg (28,902lb); maximum take-off 13,825kg (30,478lb) standard or 14,765kg (32,352lb) overload

MOTIVE POWER
Powerplant: two Junkers Jumo 213E inverted-Vee piston engines each rated at 1286kW (1725hp) for take-off and 928kW (1245hp) at 9080m (29,970ft) or 1199kW (1608hp) with MW 50 power boost at 9080m (29,790ft)
Fuel: internal fuel 3200 litresl (7034.9lmp gal; 845.35US ga); external fuel up to 900 litres (198lmp gal; 237.75US gal) in one drop tank

PERFORMANCE
Maximum speed: 626km/h (389mph) at 9100m (29,855ft) with MW 50 power boost declining to 435km/h (270mph) at sea level
Cruising speed: not available
Initial climb rate: 504m (1655ft) per minute
Climb: to 9200m (30,185ft) in 26 minutes 24 seconds
Range: not available; endurance 5 hours 12 minutes with drop tank or 3 hours 43 minutes with standard fuel

DIMENSIONS
Wing span: 20.08m (65ft 10.6in)
Wing area: 54.50sq m (586.65sq ft)
Length: 15.55m (51ft 0.28in) or, with tail-warning radar, 16.36m (53ft 8in)
Height: 4.85m (15ft 11in)

ARMAMENT
Fixed armament: four 20mm MG151/20 fixed forward-firing cannon with 200 rounds per gun in the ventral tray, two 20mm MG151/20 fixed obliquely upward/forward-firing cannon with 200 rounds per gun in the rear fuselage, and one 13mm MG131 trainable rearward-firing machine gun with 500 rounds in the cockpit rear
Disposable armament: none

The Ju 88C-7 was the day fighter counterpart of the Ju 88C-6 first introduced in 1943 as the Ju 88C-7a with the undernose gondola replaced by a weapons tray carrying two 20mm MGFF/M cannon. The tray was installed in the forward weapons bay with the cannon muzzles projecting below the lower line of the fuselage; the rear weapons bay was retained for a disposable load of 500kg (1102lb), generally comprising 10 50kg (110lb) bombs. The Ju 88C-7b was generally similar except for its four underwing hardpoints so that the bomb load could be increased to 1500kg (3307lb). Production of the Ju 88C and closely related Ju 88R lasted to the closing stages of 1944, and amounted to some 3,200 aircraft in all.

The Ju 88P series resulted from the Germans' realisation in 1942 that the Soviets, far from being beaten, were beginning to gain strength in both quantitative and qualitative terms, especially in terms of armoured fighting vehicles, most notably the redoubtable T-34 medium tank.

Tank destroyers
One of the types considered for the newly important heavy attack role was the Ju 88C, which had already been evolved with an external weapon tray that could be adapted for the carriage of a tank-busting gun. The first such development was in fact a Ju 88A-4 conversion that was completed in the summer of 1942 as the Ju 88P V1 prototype with a 75mm KWK 39 tank gun in a large external mounting under the fuselage. This replaced the original undernose gondola and carried at its rear a position for one 7.92mm MG81z two-

ABOVE *The Ju 88G night-fighter prototype, converted from a Ju 88R and intended to provide a type more capable than the Ju 88C, had a larger and more angular vertical tail surface, Lichtenstein C-1 airborne interception radar, and four 20mm MG 151/20 cannon in a ventral tray.*

barrel trainable rearward-firing machine-gun for ventral defence. Trials confirmed that the type possessed considerable tank-busting potential, and there followed a small batch of Ju 88P-1 aircraft with a crew of three, a 'solid' nose, and the 75mm PaK 40 anti-tank gun with a larger muzzle brake to reduce the recoil forces. The weight and drag of the larger-calibre gun installation made the Ju 88P-1 extremely vulnerable to interception, so the whole installation could be explosively jettisoned in emergencies. The rest of the armament comprised three 7.92mm

machine-guns in the form of one MG15 fixed forward-firing weapon used to sight the PaK 40 gun, and two MG81z trainable rearward-firing two-barrel weapons in the rear cockpit and ventral positions. The Ju 88P-2 was a development of the Ju 88A-4 with two 37mm BK 3,7 cannon in a ventral tray that was offset to port of the centreline, the Ju 88P-3 was basically similar to the Ju 88P-2 but with additional crew protection, and the Ju 88P-4 had one 50mm BK 5 cannon in the ventral tray.

From a time early in 1943, the Ju 88C-6b was complemented by the Ju 88R that differed only in its two BMW 801 engines, in the form of the BMW 801MA and BMW 801D units each rated at 1193kW (1600hp) for take-off, in the Ju 88R-1 and Ju 88R-2 subvariants respectively. Although the Ju 88C-6 proved an effective night-fighter, it was appreciated from an early date that the inevitable addition of extra equipment would increase both weight and drag, resulting in a degradation of performance. Thus in the spring of 1943 there appeared the Ju 88 V58 prototype of a considerably improved night-fighter model. This prototype was a conversion from Ju 88R standard and was therefore fitted with two BMW 801D engines, but the more angular tail unit of the Ju 188 was fitted for improved directional and longitudinal stability, and the armament was considerably revised. The offensive fit was two 20mm MG151/20 fixed forward-firing cannon in the starboard side of the nose and four 20mm MG151/20 fixed forward-firing cannon in a ventral weapons tray offset to port, while the defensive armament comprised one 13mm MG131 trainable rearward-firing machine-gun in the rear of the cockpit. Trials revealed that the muzzle flash of the two nose-mounted cannon tended to blind the pilot, so the Ju 88G-1 initial production model had a fixed armament of four 20mm cannon with 200 rounds per gun in the weapons tray and carried as its primary sensors the FuG 220 Lichtenstein SN-2 radar and the FuG 227 Flensburg radar homing system.

The Ju 88G-1 was followed by the Ju 88G-4, which incorporated as standard all the improvements that had been added in piecemeal fashion on the Ju 88G-1. Later aircraft added a schräge Musik installation of two 20mm MG151/20 cannon in the rear fuselage. The Ju 88G-6 differed from the Ju 88G-4 primarily in its two BMW 801G rather than BMW 801D engines, and was introduced as the Ju 88G-6a. The Ju 88G-6b added the FuG 250 Naxos Z system to home on the emissions of the RAF's H2S nav/attack radar but was soon replaced in production by the similarly equipped Ju 88G-6c with two Jumo 213A engines each rated at 1305kW (1750hp) for take-off, and the schräge Musik installation shifted farther forward to keep the centre of gravity in the optimum position.

The last Ju 88G variant to enter production was the Ju 88G-7, and this was produced in three subvariants that differed in equipment details but all had the same two Jumo 213E engines with the MW 50 methanol/water power-boost system. The Ju 88G-7a had Lichtenstein SN-2 radar, the Ju 88G-7b had FuG 228 Lichtenstein SN-3 radar that was later replaced by FuG 218 Neptun VR radar, and the Ju 88G-7c had FuG 240 Berlin N-1a centimetric radar.

Final variants

By late 1942 the vulnerability of the Ju 88A to daylight interception was increasing dramatically and a major effort was started to increase the performance of the bomber model without introducing the type of major structural modifications that would delay production. The most

obvious solution to the problem of the Ju 88A's performance shortfall vis-á-vis the latest fighters was a major increase in the available power, and a Ju 88A-4 was accordingly re-engined with two BMW 801D engines each rated at 1267.5kW (1700hp) for take-off. At the same time much of the armour protection that had been added in successive Ju 88A variants was removed to save weight, the undernose gondola was removed to save weight and reduce drag, and the earlier glazed nose section was replaced by a 'solid' fairing to reduce drag. This created the Ju 88 V93 that was also known as the Ju 88S V1. The prototype revealed a marked improvement in flight performance compared with the Ju 88A series bombers, but in an effort to secure even better performance Junkers then reduced the crew from four to three, removed most of the defensive armament, sacrificed virtually all of the remaining armour, and adopted a still higher-rated powerplant.

As these plans were being made, the construction of a small batch of Ju 88S-0 pre-production aircraft was undertaken with two BMW 801D engines, a crew of four, a defensive armament of one 7.92mm MG81 machine gun in the windscreen, one 7.92mm MG81z two-barrel machine gun in the rear of the undernose gondola and one 13mm MG131 machine gun in the rear of the cockpit. Offensive armament consisted of 65kg (14 143lb) bombs in the forward weapons bay so that auxiliary fuel could be carried in the rear weapons bay. In the late autumn of 1943 there followed the Ju 88S-1 initial production model with two BMW 801G-2 engines fitted with the GM 1 nitrous oxide power-boost system, reduced armour and defensive armament, provision for more auxiliary fuel in the rear of the weapons bay, and the elimination of the dive brakes from under the outer wing panels. The first aircraft were delivered early in 1944.

The Ju 88S-2 was an improved Ju 88S-1 with two BMW 801TJ engines each rated at 1118kW (1500hp) at 12,200m (40,025ft) with the aid of a turbocharging system (which eliminated the need for the bulky and weighty GM 1 nitrous oxide power-boost system). The subvariant also introduced the wooden pannier tray of the Ju 88A-15 for a maximum internal weapons load of 3000kg (6614lb), and a pair of 7.92mm MG81 fixed rearward-firing machine guns was added in the rear of the pannier. A small number of these aircraft were delivered in the spring and summer of 1944. The Ju 88S-3 was a further Ju 88S-1 development with two Jumo 213A engines each rated at 1324kW (1776hp) for take-off but fitted with the GM 1 nitrous oxide power-boost system to increase the rating to 1585kW (2125hp). Only a few aircraft had been delivered before the Ju 88S programme was terminated in the late summer of 1944.

CHAPTER 13

MESSERSCHMITT BF 109

The Bf 109 was the most important German fighter of World War II and, with more than 30,000 examples, the warplane built in larger numbers than any other in history. The type was not without its poorer features, but possessed great 'developability' even if later variants lacked the excellent handling of their predecessors.

The Bf 109 was by any standards a classic fighter and, with more than 30,000 examples built before and during World War II, the type was of vital importance to the German war effort throughout that conflict. It is one of the few aircraft to remain in development and production right to the end of hostilities. The type was instrumental in the Luftwaffe's success in winning and then retaining air superiority over the Polish, Scandinavian and North-West European battlefields between September 1939 and June 1940, and it was only when the fighter was committed at longer range against the warplanes of the Royal Air Force in the Battle of Britain that the limitations of the Bf 109 began to be appreciated fully.

LEFT *British servicemen clear up the wreckage of a Bf 109E that made a diving pass against two Avro Anson aircraft, and then stalled and crashed in a steep turn. The Bf 109E was the most important early variant of the Bf 109 series, and the main type used in the Battle of Britain.*

Pre-war development

The Bf 109 was the first 'modern' fighter to enter German service with features such as stressed-skin construction in light alloy, a low-set cantilever wing fitted with trailing edge flaps, retractable tailwheel landing gear, and an enclosed cockpit, and was presaged by the Bf 108 two/four-seat touring and communications aeroplane that introduced these features.

Created under the supervision of Dipl.-Ing. Willy Messerschmitt and Dipl.-Ing. Walther Rethel in response to a 1934 requirement, the Bf 109 first took to the air in September 1935 in the form of the Bf 109a (later Bf 109 V1) the first of three initial prototypes with the powerplant, in the continued absence of the planned Junkers Jumo 210 engine, of one Rolls-Royce Kestrel V Vee engine rated at 518kW (695hp) for take-off. The type had good performance for its power, but had to overcome antipathy in official circles as well as from pilots used to slower biplanes with an

LEFT *The most modern Bf 109 version to serve in the Spanish Civil War was the Bf 109E-3. It was delivered in early 1939 but equipped only one German unit, 1/88 of the Condor Legion. The Bf 109E was basically the Bf 109D with the Daimler-Benz DB 601A engine.*

open cockpit, fixed landing gear and greater agility, before being ordered into production. There followed a pre-production batch of 10 Bf 109B-0 aircraft that were also the V4 to V13 prototypes with Jumo 210, or Daimler-Benz DB 600 or DB 601 engines before genuine production started. This started with the Bf 109B, Bf 109C and Bf 109D variants that were delivered only in modest numbers and had all disappeared from front-line service before the outbreak of World War II. The Bf 109B had B-1 and B-2 subvariants, the Jumo 210Da or Jumo 210G engine and an armament of two 7.92mm MG17 machine guns; the Bf 109C had C-1 and C-2 subvariants, the Jumo 210Ga engine driving an improved propeller, and an armament of four or five 7.92mm MG17 machine guns; and the Bf 109D had D-0 and D-1 subvariants, the DB 600A engine, and an armament of one 20mm MGFF cannon and two 7.92-mm MG17 machine guns.

The Bf 109D paved the way for the Bf 109E, generally known as the 'Emil', which was the first variant to enter large-scale production and was the most important version of the fighter in German service in the early years of World

War II. The key to the success of the Bf 109E was the switch from the DB 600 engine to the definitive DB 601 engine. The first prototypes to have this unit were the Bf 109 V14 and V15, which were each powered by the DB 601A-1 engine rated at 783kW (1050hp) for take-off and fitted with a fuel injection system in place of the DB 600's standard carburettor. The fuel-injection system allowed pilots to undertake negative-g manoeuvres without fear of the engine cutting out.

The 'Emil'

After the delivery of 10 Bf 109E-0 pre-production aircraft with the DB 601A-1 engine and an armament of four 7.92mm MG17 fixed forward-firing machine guns, the Bf 109E-1 entered service in February 1939 with the same powerplant and the armament revised to two 20mm MGFF cannon with 60 rounds per gun in the leading edges of the wing and two 7.92mm machine guns with 1000 rounds per gun in the upper part of the forward fuselage. The Bf 109E-1/B was a fighter-bomber conversion evolved in the

BELOW *A Bf 109F-2 of JG 2 is seen at readiness on an airfield located on the Channel coast in 1941. The Bf 109F had the best handling of the Bf 109 series, but lacked firepower and was soon replaced by the 'brute strength' Bf 109G with greater power and heavier armament.*

summer of 1940 with provision under the fuselage for one 250kg (551lb) bomb although, for range reasons, it was more common to carry just one 50kg (110lb) bomb. The Bf 109E-3 was a development of the Bf 109E-1 with the DB 601Aa engine rated at 876kW (1175hp) for take-off and including provision for the inclusion of one 20mm MGFF/M fixed forward-firing cannon in a Motorkanone installation if the machine-gun ammunition was reduced in quantity, a revised canopy and, for the first time in any Bf 109 variant, armour protection for the pilot.

Appearing late in 1939 for service from the summer of 1940, the Bf 109E-4 was a development of the Bf 109E-3 with all provision for the MGFF/M cannon removed and the MGFF cannon in the wings changed to a version with a higher rate of fire. The Bf 109E-4/B was the fighter-bomber version evolved in the summer of 1940 with provision for

BELOW *The Bf 109E had two 7.92mm MG 17 machine-guns in the upper cowling, and its subvariants had either two MG 17s or two 20mm MG FF cannon in the wing and, in some models, one 20mm MG FF/M cannon between the cylinder banks to fire through the propeller shaft.*

one 250kg (551lb) bomb or four 50kg (110lb) bombs; the Bf 109E-4N was a development with the DB 601N engine rated at 895kW (1200hp) for take-off, and the Bf 109E-4/Trop was the tropicalised version of the Bf 109E-4 with a dust/sand filter over the supercharger air inlet and a desert survival pack in the rear fuselage.

Later 'E' series

The Bf 109E-5 was the reconnaissance fighter derivative of the Bf 109E-4 with the two wing-mounted cannon removed and one Rb 30/50 camera in the fuselage, and its tropicalised version was the Bf 109E-5/Trop. The Bf 109E-6 was a development of the Bf 109E-5 with the DB 601N engine, and the Bf 109E-7 was the version of the Bf 109E-4/N with its underfuselage hardpoint revised for the carriage of bombs or alternatively one 300 litre (66Imp gal; 79.25US gal) drop tank. Some of the aircraft were tropicalised with the revised designation Bf 109E-7/Trop, others were fitted with undersurface armour protection (oil coolers, radiators and fuel pump) for enhanced survivability in the ground-attack role with the revised designation Bf

SPECIFICATIONS: Messerschmitt Bf 109E-4

GENERAL
Type: fighter
Accommodation: pilot in an enclosed cockpit
Equipment: standard communication and navigation equipment, plus a Revi C/12C reflector gun sight
Weights: empty 2125kg (4685lb); normal take-off 2510kg (5534lb); maximum take-off 2665kg (5875lb)

MOTIVE POWER
Powerplant: one Daimler-Benz DB 601Aa inverted-Vee piston engine rated at 876kW (1175hp) for take-off, 746kW (1000hp) at 3700m (12,140ft) and 760.5kW (1020hp) at 4500m (14,765ft)
Fuel: internal fuel 400 litres (88Imp gal;

105.7US gal); external fuel none

PERFORMANCE
Maximum speed: 560km/h (348mph) at 4440m (14,560ft) declining to 467km/h (290mph) at sea level
Cruising speed: maximum 483km/h (300mph) at 4000m (13,125ft) and economical 325km/h (202mph) at 1000m (3280ft)
Initial climb rate: 1000m (3280ft) per minute; climb to 6000m (19,685ft) in 7 minutes 45 seconds
Service ceiling: 10,500m (34,450ft)
Maximum range: 660km (410 miles)

DIMENSIONS
Wing span: 9.87m (32ft 4.5in)

Wing area: 16.17sq m (174.05sq ft)
Length 8.64m: (28ft 4.2in)
Height 2.50m: (8ft 2.42in)

ARMAMENT
Fixed armament: two 20mm MGFF fixed forward-firing cannon with 60 rounds per gun in the leading edges of the wing, one optional 20mm MGFF/M fixed forward-firing cannon with 200 rounds in a Motorkanone installation, and two 7.92mm MG17 fixed forward-firing machine-guns with 1,000 (or 500 if MGFF/M installed) rounds per gun in the upper part of the forward fuselage with synchronisation equipment to fire through the propeller disc
Disposable armament: none

109E-7/U2, and a few aircraft were given the GM 1 nitrous oxide power-boost system with the revised designation Bf 109E-7/Z. The Bf 109E-8 was the development of the Bf 109E-7 with the DB 601E engine rated at 1007kW (1350hp) for take-off. The Bf 109E-9 was the reconnaissance fighter derivative of the Bf 109E-8 with no wing cannon and a camera installation that could comprise one Rb 50/30 or two Rb 32/7 units. The last of these aircraft were completed early in 1942, ending production of the Bf 109E series after the delivery of some 4,000 or more aircraft.

The German carrier program
The Bf 109T (Träger, or carrier) was a Bf 109E development for Germany's planned force of two aircraft-carriers, and was basically the Bf 109E-1 with its wings increased in span and area by some 1.22m (3ft 11.75in) and 1.10sq m (11.84sq ft) respectively, upper-wing spoilers for a steepened approach angle to carrier landings, manually

folding outer wing panels, longer-span slots on the leading edges, interconnection of the ailerons and flaps, catapult attachment points, and an arrester hook. The variant was pioneered by 10 Bf 109T-0 pre-production aircraft to be followed by 60 Bf 109T-1 production fighters, but the cancellation of the carrier programme meant that the Bf 109T-1 machines were in fact completed to Bf 109T-2 standard with the DB 601N engine and no carrier capability. The aircraft were delivered from a time early in 1941 as fighter-bombers able to operate from short land airstrips. The machines had a ventral rack to carry one 250kg (551lb) bomb or four 50kg (100lb) bombs, or alternatively one drop tank, and in other respects the Bf 109T-2 differed from the Bf 109E-4 in details such as its DB 601N engine rated at 895kW (1200hp) for take-off, maximum speed of 575km/h (357mph) at 6000m (19,685ft) declining to 490km/h (304.5mph) at sea level, maximum cruising speed of 552km/h (343mph) at 5000m

ABOVE *The elegant lines of the Bf 109F are revealed in this head-on low-level photograph. By comparison with those of the Bf 109E, the engine installation was considerably cleaner, the depth of the underwing radiators was considerably reduced, and the tailplane-bracing struts were eliminated.*

(16,405ft), economical cruising speed of 355km/h (220mph) at 5000m (16,405ft), initial climb rate of 1020 m (3346ft) per minute, climb to 6000m (19,685ft) in 6 minutes 24 seconds, service ceiling of 10,500m (34,450ft), maximum range of 915km (568 miles) with drop tank, empty weight of 2253kg (4967lb), normal take-off weight of 2800kg (6173lb), maximum take-off weight of 3078kg (6786lb), wing span of 11.08m (36ft 4.23in), wing area of 17.50sq m (188.37sq ft), length of 8.76 m (28ft 9in) and height of 2.60m (8ft 6.36in). The Bf 109T-2 fighters were deployed to Norway as fighters until the summer of 1942, and the survivors were then used for the point defence of the island of Heligoland in the North Sea up to a time late in 1944.

The 'Friedrich'

The Bf 109F, or 'Friedrich', marked the apogee of the Bf 109 fighter's development in terms of its aerodynamic qualities and handling characteristics, but these refinements were achieved only at the expense of firepower, which was considered by virtually all pilots to be too light for genuine effectiveness. It was for this reason that production of the Bf 109F was terminated after the delivery of some 2200 aircraft. The Messerschmitt design team had decided as early as the first part of 1940, when the Bf 109E was still relatively new in operational terms, that the British and French would inevitably seek to counter this mainstay of the German fighter arm with improved versions of their Supermarine Spitfire, Bloch MB.151 and MB.152, and Dewoitine D.520. The design team therefore decided to offset the Allied response to the Bf 109E with an improved version. France was knocked out of the war in June 1940 before she could field any improved fighters, but the British responded to the Bf 109E by introducing the Spitfire Mk V with the Rolls-

Royce Merlin 45 engine using a two-stage supercharger. The Luftwaffe was ready for this development, however, and was able to start operating the upgraded Bf 109F from March 1941, initially in the hands of Jagdgeschwadern 2 and 26 flying out of bases on the French side of the Channel.

Aerodynamic refinements

The Bf 109F had been designed with the aerodynamic refinements that would allow the full exploitation of the greater power of the DB 601E engine. Research had shown that one of the main drag burdens suffered by the Bf 109E was associated with the two underwing radiators, so it was decided to recess these units farther into the wing on the Bf 109F with a boundary-layer bypass system to collect turbulent air from the undersurface of the wing ahead of the radiators, channel it over the top of the radiators, and then exhaust it through a duct in the the inboard flap section, which was split into upper and lower parts. Both parts acted together in conjunction with the outer flap section as conventional flaps, but the upper and lower parts of the inner section were also controlled separately by a

thermostat to move apart as the coolant temperature rose, the lower part then serving as a radiator flap. Other changes to the wing, which was reduced in span slightly, were a reduction in the span of the leading-edge slots and trailing-edge ailerons, although the latter were increased in chord for unaltered area, and the removal of the interlink between the flaps and ailerons.

Other aerodynamic improvements included a deeper and more symmetrical engine cowling whose lines were continued forward by the larger and more curved spinner for the improved propeller of reduced diameter, the movement of the supercharger air inlet farther out from the port side of the nose for greater ram effect, improved fin with a cambered rather than symmetrical section for reduced rudder demand in the climb, the reduction of rudder area, a strutless horizontal tail surface in a position

BELOW *Seen in company with a Ju 87B over North Africa, this is a Bf 109E-4/N Trop of the I Gruppe of JG 27. The Bf 109E-4 was a pure fighter, while closely related variants were the Bf 109E-5 reconnaissance fighter and the Bf 109E-7 fighter-bomber.*

SPECIFICATIONS: Messerschmitt Bf 109F-2

GENERAL
Type: fighter and fighter-bomber
Accommodation: pilot in an enclosed cockpit
Equipment: standard communication and navigation equipment, plus a Revi C/12C reflector gun sight
Weights: empty 2353kg (5188lb); normal take-off 2800kg (6173lb); maximum take-off 3066kg (6760lb)

MOTIVE POWER
Powerplant: one Daimler-Benz DB 601N inverted-Vee piston engine rated at 895kW (1200hp) for take-off and 947kW (1270hp) at 5000m (16,405ft)
Fuel: internal fuel 400 litres (88Imp gal; 105.7US gal); external fuel up to 300 litres

(66Imp gal; 79.25 US gal) in one drop tank

PERFORMANCE
Maximum speed: 600km/h (373mph) at 6000m (19,685ft) declining to 517km/h (321mph) at sea level
Cruising speed: maximum 560km/h (348.88mph) at 5000m (16,405ft) and economical 354km/h (220mph) at sea level
Initial climb rate: 1177 m (3860ft) per minute; climb to 5000m (16,405ft) in 5 minutes 12 seconds
Service ceiling: 11,000m (36,090ft)
Maximum range: 880km (547 miles) with drop tank

DIMENSIONS
Wing span: 9.92m (32ft 6.5in)

Wing area: 16.10sq m (173.30sq ft)
Length: 8.94m (29ft 3.9in)
Height: 2.60m (8ft 6.33in)

ARMAMENT
Fixed armament: one 15mm MG151/15 fixed forward-firing cannon with 200 rounds in a Motorkanone installation, and two 7.92mm MG17 fixed forward-firing machine-guns with 500 rounds per gun in the upper part of the forward fuselage with synchronisation equipment to fire through the propeller disc
Disposable armament: up to 250kg (551lb) of disposable stores carried on one hardpoint (under the fuselage rated at 250kg /551lb), and generally comprising one 250kg (551lb) SC-250 bomb

slightly lower and farther forward than on the Bf 109E, the introduction of a semi-retractable tailwheel, and the increase in the forward rake of the main landing gear units.

The result of these changes was to reduce the Bf 109F's drag burden by a significant degree by comparison with that of the Bf 109E, and in combination with the more powerful DB 601E engine this offered the promise of

significantly improved performance and well as better handling through all parts of the flight envelope.

Trials of two prototypes revealed that the reduction in span had a generally adverse effect on handling, so a third prototype was completed with detachable wing tips of semi-elliptical shape that restored all but 2.16sq ft (0.20sq m) of the previously deleted wing area, resulting in much

enhanced handling. The fourth prototype introduced a revised supercharger air inlet and a deeper oil cooler bath under the forward fuselage. From the beginning of the development programme it had been planned that the Bf 109F would switch to an armament scheme with the guns concentrated in the forward fuselage: thus the two 7.92mm MG17 machine guns with 500 rounds per gun were retained on the upper part of the nose, but the two 20mm MGFF cannon in the wing leading edges were replaced by a 15mm MG151/15 cannon with 150 rounds in a Motorkanone installation. The elimination of the wing-mounted guns certainly improved lateral agility by eliminating outboard mass, and the loss of notional firepower was considered to be more than offset by the fact that the MG151 was more reliable and faster-firing that the MGFF, and could be given a greater ammunition capacity as it was a belt-fed rather than drum-fed weapon.

As construction of the initial batch of Bf 109F-0 pre-

BELOW *Caught in a low-level reconnaissance photograph in its North Africa revetment, this is the Bf 109E of a Gruppe adjutant of JG 27. Aircraft of this unit carried a badge (a lion and a Negro) on the cowling which, with the propeller spinner, was painted bright yellow.*

production fighters was undertaken in the autumn of 1940, however, neither the DB 601E nor the MG151 was ready for service, so these first aircraft were completed with the DB 601N engine rated at 895kW (1200hp) for take-off, an armament of two MG17 machine guns and one 20mm MGFF/M cannon in the Motorkanone installation, and a

normal take-off weight of 2610kg (5754lb). Evaluation of the Bf 109F-0 resulted in a mixed reception: all pilots were enthusiastic about the new fighter's better performance and much improved combination of handling, but most were unhappy about the reduction in firepower. Even so, the advantages of the Bf 109F over the Bf 109E were very real

LEFT *Its combination of a cleaner airframe and uprated engine gave the Bf 109F thoroughbred fighter qualities in which high performance was matched by excellent handling and agility. The type was favoured by aces to whom these qualities were more important than heavier firepower.*

aircraft. The problem was caused by the elimination of the tailplane bracing struts: lack of rigidity in the new tail unit allowed vibration that overlapped with engine vibration at certain rpm to set up a sympathetic oscillation, resulting in structural failure. The problem was simply cured by the addition of external stiffener plates on the tail, and the Bf 109F-1 then entered service in February 1941.

'F' series developments

The Bf 109F-2 was a development of the Bf 109F-1 with the 15mm MG151 belt-fed cannon with 200 rounds in place of the 20mm MGFF/M drum-fed cannon and, as the first definitive variant of the 'Friedrich' series, this model was produced in a number of subvariants broadly analogous to those of the Bf 109E series. Thus there was the Bf 109F-2/Z with the GM 1 nitrous oxide power-boost system and the Bf 109F-2/Trop tropicalised version. The Bf 109F-3 was basically a Bf 109F-2 development with the DB 601E-1 engine rated at 1007kW (1350hp) for take-off. Produced virtually in parallel with the Bf 109F-3, the Bf 109F-4 introduced the 20mm MG151/20 version of the MG151 cannon in the Motorkanone installation. This required a reduction in ammunition quantity to 150 rounds. The opportunity was also taken in this model to make improvements such as better fuel tankage self-sealing capability, revised protection for the pilot in the additional toughened glass and armour plate for protection against lateral and stern attack, the Revi C/12D reflector gun sight, and a gun selector switch allowing the cannon and machine guns to be fired separately or collectively. In other respects, the Bf 109F-4 differed from the Bf 109F-2 in details such as its maximum speed of 625km/h (388mph) at 6500m (21,325ft) declining to 538km/h (334mph) at sea level, maximum cruising speed of 570km/h (354mph) at 5000m (16,405ft), economical cruising speed of 480km/h (298mph) at sea level, initial climb rate of 1310m (4300ft) per minute, climb to 3000m (9845ft) in 2 minutes 36 seconds, service ceiling of 12,000m (39,370ft), maximum range of 850km (528 miles) with drop tank, empty weight of 2390kg (5269lb), normal take-off weight of 2900kg (6393lb) and maximum take-off weight of 3117kg (6872lb).

The Bf 109F-4 and its Bf 109F-4/Trop tropicalised version replaced earlier Bf 109F models from a time late in 1941, and early in 1942 there appeared the Bf 109F-4/B fighter-

and the full production of the type was authorised. The first model to emerge from this programme was the Bf 109F-1 that differed from the Bf 109F-0 only in having a supercharger air inlet of round rather than square section. Production aircraft were available at the end of 1940, but full entry to service was delayed by the loss of several

bomber version with an underfuselage rack for one 250kg (551lb) bomb. It was at this point that differences in opinion about the Bf 109F's armament surfaced. A solution to these divergences of opinion was found in the evolution of Rüstsätze (field conversion sets). The first of these was the R1 set that added a pair of 20mm MG151/20 cannon with 120 rounds per gun in underwing gondolas, boosting firepower at the expense of performance and, more importantly, reducing agility in combat. Other Rüstsätze

BELOW *One of the aces who favoured the Bf 109F was Hans 'Assi' Hahn, whose aeroplane is seen here. Hahn scored 68 victories against the British before his January 1942 transfer to the Eastern Front, where he added another 40 Soviet aircraft before being shot down and captured.*

were developed, but the Bf 109F was on the verge of replacement by the Bf 109G and the only other set used was the R6 that added an underfuselage rack for one 250kg (551lb) bomb, or four 50kg (110lb) bombs, or one drop tank. The other Bf 109F-4 subvariant was the Bf 109F-4/Z with the GM 1 power-boost system for a higher emergency power rating at the expense of engine life.

The Bf 109F-5 was the tactical reconnaissance fighter version of the Bf 109F-4 with the engine-mounted cannon removed, a single vertical camera, and provision for a ventral drop tank. The Bf 109F-6 was a tactically more versatile derivative of the Bf 109F-5 with all armament removed and a special camera bay installed for the carriage of an Rb 20/30, Rb 50/30 or Rb 75/30 camera. Only a relatively small

number of the Bf 109F-5 and Bf 109F-6 variants was produced, and by the end of 1941 the Bf 109F series had been replaced in production by the Bf 109G series. The Luftwaffe flew the Bf 109F series only in small numbers by the end of 1942.

The Bf 109G or 'Gustav' was numerically and operationally the most important model of the Bf 109 series and was a highly capable type that with the aid of a number of kits could be adapted for virtually the full gamut of tactical fighter roles. Yet this capability was achieved only by the installation of an engine that many considered too powerful for the basic airframe, resulting in handling characteristics decidedly inferior to those of the Bf 109F. This was a penalty the pilots of the Luftwaffe were generally happy to pay after they had overcome initial misgivings when the first Bf 109G fighters entered squadron service early in 1942.

The 'Gustav'

The Bf 109G had been planned from a time early in 1941 as a Bf 109F development with a considerably more powerful engine and, in reflection of the fact that both cruising flight and combat were taking place at increasingly high altitudes, a pressurised cockpit. Evidence of the latter was discernible in the Bf 109G in the heavier framing of the cockpit and the

ABOVE *The Bf 109G, seen here in the form of a Bf 109G-6, marked the development of the Bf 109 past its aerodynamic prime. Additional power boosted performance and allowed heavier armament, but its handling and agility were inferior to earlier versions of the Bf 109F.*

elimination of the original type of quarter light. The pressurisation system inevitably added to the weight of the basic airframe, and this escalation of weight was exacerbated by the need for structural strengthening to cope with the additional mass and power of the new engine. This additional weight also dictated the adoption of stronger and therefore heavier main landing gear legs.

The engine selected for the new variant was the DB 605A unit, which was basically a development of the DB 601E with bored-out cylinders for a greater swept capacity: the result was an engine with basically the same exterior dimensions as the DB 601E but with a rating of 1098kW (1475hp) for take-off. Accommodation of the new engine required a modification to the cowling, which now possessed an upper line of virtually constant contour between the spinner and the windscreen; the lower contour was changed by the need to fit a larger oil cooler. It was felt that there was no need for prototypes, so the first Bf 109G machines were a small number of Bf 109G-0 pre-production fighters. The DB 605A engine was not ready in time for these machines, which

were built in the late summer of 1941, so they emerged with the DB 601E engine inherited from the Bf 109F. The same stricture did not apply to the Bf 109G-1 initial production model, which was delivered from the early spring of 1942 with the DB 605A-1 engine fitted as standard with the GM 1 nitrous oxide power-boost system. This added considerably to weight, the loaded weight being 3200kg (7055lb) with 115 litres (25.3Imp gal; 30.4US gal) of liquid nitrous oxide weighing some 180kg (397lb), but use of the power-boost system yielded a considerable dividend in a power rating of 932kW (1250hp) at 8500m (27,890ft).

The Bf 109G-1 was schemed as a pure air-combat fighter, and its fixed forward-firing armament was therefore restricted to one 20mm MG151/20 cannon in a Motorkanone installation and two 7.92mm MG17 machine guns in the upper part of the forward fuselage. The variant optimised for operation in hot and dusty areas was the Bf 109G-1/Trop, in which another change was the replacement of the two 7.92mm MG17 machine guns, standard in all Bf 109 fighters up to this time, by a pair of 13mm MG131 machine guns with 300 rounds per gun. This change was prompted by the frequent malfunction of the MG151/20 cannon when very hot, an occurrence that left the pilot with an offensive armament of just two rifle-calibre machine guns.

Produced in parallel with the Bf 109G-1 but entering service just a short time earlier as a result of its reduced complexity, the Bf 109G-2 differed from the Bf 109G-1 only in its lack of cockpit pressurisation. The variant could also be used in the reconnaissance role with the MG151/20 cannon removed and a single vertical camera installed in the rear fuselage. The Bf 109G-3 and Bf 109G-4 were versions of the pressurised Bf 109G-1 and unpressurised Bf 109G-2 with FuG 16z rather than FuG 7a radio equipment. The variants could also be used in the reconnaissance role with the MG151/20 cannon removed and a single vertical camera installed in the rear fuselage. These initial four variants of the Bf 109G series were produced virtually simultaneously, and first entered service in April 1942 with Jagdgeschwadern 2 and 26 located on coastal bases in Western France.

Late 'G' series

Although these first subvariants of the Bf 109G series proved more than adequate for the fighter tasks demanded of them, there was dissatisfaction with the GM 1 nitrous oxide power-boost system which, it was felt, was less effective than a more capable supercharging system. The Bf 109G-5 was fitted with the pressurised cockpit and was powered by the DB 605AS engine that used the larger

ABOVE *This Bf 109 E-3 of Jagdgeschwader 26 wears a pale-blue/black-green colour scheme that was gradually phased out from early 1940. The aircraft also carries the black 'Höllenhund' Staffel emblem on both sides of the fuselage.*

supercharger developed for the DB 603 and was rated at 895kW (1200hp) at 8000m (26,245ft). The Bf 109G-5/U2 subvariant was fitted with a wooden tail unit, the greater weight of this structure demanding the addition of a counterbalance weight in the engine bay, and the Bf 109G-5/R2 bomber interceptor was created when aircraft were retrofitted with the R2 Rüstsätze (a pair of underwing 210mm WGr.21 rockets) developed for the Bf 109G-6.

Delivered from the autumn of 1942, the Bf 109G-6 lacked the pressurised cockpit, introduced a Motorkanone installation of one 30mm MK108 cannon with 60 rounds, had full provision for Rüstsätze, was able to accommodate several variants of the DB 605A engine or, from a time early in 1944, the DB 605A engine, and had a tank for nitrous oxide or a methanol/water mixture so that either the GM 1 or MW 50 power-boost systems could be used. The DB 603AM engine with the MW 50 system had a normal take-off power of 1100kW (1475hp) that could be boosted to 1342kW (1800hp), and the boost system increased the power available at 4100m (13,450ft) to 1267.5kW (1700hp). A few examples of the Bf 109G-6 received the DB 603ASCM engine able to deliver a maximum of 1491kW (2000hp) for take-off and 1342kW (1800hp) at 5000m (16,405ft). Rüstsätze and Umrüst-Bausätze were used to create a series of important subvariants.

Complemented by small-scale Hungarian and Romanian production, Germany's production of the Bf 109G in 1943 amounted to 6379 aircraft, which was two-thirds of all German single-engined fighter production, and in 1944 to 13,942 aircraft. It was planned in the early part of 1943 to standardise an improved variant of the Bf 109G-6, but this notion was rendered impractical by the now thoroughly dispersed nature of Bf 109 production. The type was overtaken by the Bf 109G-8 that was built in only small numbers as a specialised reconnaissance derivative of the Bf 109G-6 with the DB 603A-1 or DB 603AS engine, a gun armament of one 30mm MK108 cannon sometimes replaced by one 20mm MG151/20 cannon, and a reconnaissance capability provided by one Rb 12.7/7 or Rb 32/7 camera in the rear fuselage.

The Bf 109G-10 was the result of a major effort to standardise a single model that could then be built in very large numbers. Introduced to production in the spring of 1944, the Bf 109G-10 was basically the Bf 109G-6 with the DB 605D engine with MW 50 methanol/water power boost for a rating of 13709kW (1850hp) for take-off. The Bf 109G-10 carried a fixed forward-firing armament of one engine-mounted 30mm MK108 cannon with 60 rounds or one 20mm MG151/20 cannon with 150 rounds, and two fuselage-mounted 13mm MG131 machine guns with 300

ABOVE *The Mistel composite attack warplane variant using the Bf 109 was the Mistel 1, which combined an old Ju 88A-4 bomber airframe fitted with an 8377lb (3800kg) warhead under the control of the pilot in the cockpit of the upper component, which was an obsolete Bf 109F fighter.*

rounds per gun; these were used with the Revi 16/B reflector sight. The Bf 109G-10 also had provision for a ventral drop tank, and was the fastest of all Bf 109 variants, its maximum speed at a weight of 3100kg (6834lb) being 685km/h (426mph) at 7400m (24,280ft) declining to 550km/h (342mph) at sea level. The climb rate was also excellent, an altitude of 6000m (19,685ft) being reached in 5 minutes 48 seconds. Fortunately for the Allies, however, the Bf 109G-10 was seldom encountered in 'clean' condition, for virtually every such fighter was fitted with a Rüstsätze on entry to service. Other changes effected without any change of designation included a fully retractable tailwheel and a less heavily framed canopy that in conjunction with an armour glass rather than armour plate panel behind the pilot's head did much to improve the pilot's fields of vision.

The Bf 109G-12 was the tandem two-seat conversion trainer member of the Bf 109G series. The need for such a type had been appreciated as early as 1940, but it was 1942 and the general acceleration of German pilot training that finally led to the creation of the Bf 109G-12, which was produced as conversion of Bf 109G-1, Bf 109G-5 and Bf 109G-6 single-seat fighters with a cockpit lengthened to the rear of the fuel tank with canopy sections that were bulged outward to port and starboard in an effort to provide the instructor in the rear seat with at least a modicum of forward and downward vision.

Although it had been decided in 1944 to concentrate on the standardised Bf 109K model, the gap before the new type could enter production was occupied by construction of the Bf 109G-14 that entered service in the late summer of 1944. This was basically the Bf 109G-10 with the DB 605AM engine, the improved canopy, an armament of one 20mm MG151/20 cannon and two 13mm MG131 machine guns, a fixed tailwheel, and provision for the R1 and R6 Rüstsätze. Some of the aircraft were completed with the wooden tail unit and the revised designation Bf 109G-14/U4. The Bf 109G-16 final version of the Bf 109G series was a development of the Bf 109G-14 with the DB 605D engine, armour protection for the oil cooler and coolant radiators, and the R1 and R6 Rüstsätze installed on the production line as permanent fixtures. More than 1,500 Bf 109G fighters were completed in 1945 before Germany's surrender to the Allies in May of that year.

'H' and 'K' series

The Bf 109H was a planned high-altitude model with the DB 605B engine rated at 1193kW (1600hp) for take-off, the wing enlarged to a span of 13.25m (43ft 6in) with an area of 21.90sq m (235.73sq ft), and an armament of one 30mm MK108 engine-mounted cannon and two 20mm MG151/20 wing-mounted cannon with 60 and 200 rounds per gun respectively. Prototypes revealed a maximum speed of 687km/h (427mph) at high altitude and a ceiling of 13,500m (44,290ft), but there were serious wing flutter problems in high-speed dives and further work on the type was discontinued.

The Bf 109K or 'Konrad' (otherwise 'Kürfürst') series was planned as a standardised type that could be built more rapidly than the plethora of variants and subvariants that had characterised the Bf 109G series. Based on the Bf 109G-10 airframe with the revised canopy, the Bf 109K included

as standard some of the progressive changes that had been introduced in that subvariant as Umrüst-Bausätze together with a number of aerodynamic improvements that were individually small but collectively significant. The first Bf 109K-0 pre-production aircraft appeared in September 1944 to a basic design that differed from that of the Bf 109G-10 most noticeably in the raised line of its cowling, longer propeller spinner, larger inset rudder tab supplemented by a large trailing tab, replacement of the two fuselage-mounted 13mm MG131 machine guns by two 15mm MG151 cannon to supplement the engine-mounted 30mm MK108 cannon as the fixed forward-firing battery, and the DB 605DB engine with the GM 1 nitrous oxide power-boost system. Operational trials with these pre-production aircraft revealed no major problems or deficiencies, so the type was authorised for production as the Bf 109K-2 with the DB 605ASCM engine or alternatively the DB 605DCM engine with the GM 1 power-boost system.

In its original form, the Bf 109K-4 differed from the Bf 109K-2 only in having a pressurised cockpit, but later examples were revised with the 30mm MK103 cannon in place of the MK108 weapon of the same calibre in the Motorkanone installation. The Bf 109K-6 was the heavy fighter version of the Bf 109K-4 intended for the bomber interceptor role with an armament of one 30mm MK103 cannon in the Motorkanone installation, two 13mm MG131 machine guns in the upper part of the forward fuselage, and two 30mm MK103 cannon in underwing gondolas. With a maximum take-off weight of 3595kg (7925lb), the Bf 109K-6 was distinctly unwieldy in the air, so it is perhaps fortunate for German fighter pilots that relatively few of the type were delivered after its service debut in January 1945.

Last in the line

Delivered only in very small numbers during the last two weeks before Germany's surrender at the end of World War II in Europe, the Bf 109K-14 was the ultimate version of the Bf 109 series, and was characterised by its DB 605L engine with a two-stage supercharger and the MW 50 methanol/water power-boost system: this engine delivered 1267.5kW (1700hp) for take-off, and its capabilities allowed the Bf 109K-14 to attain the same maximum speed as the Bf 109K-4 but at an altitude of 11,500m (37,730ft) rather than 6000m (19,685ft). The type's fixed forward-firing armament was somewhat lighter than that of the Bf 109K-4, however, and comprised one 30mm MK103 or MK108 cannon and two 13mm MG131 machine guns. The Bf 109 was licence produced by CASA in Spain after the war, and was operated by many countries, including Israel, well into the 1950s.

CHAPTER 14

MESSERSCHMITT BF 110

The Bf 110 twin-engined warplane was developed to provide the Luftwaffe with a 'maid of all work' heavy fighter, but was revealed by operations to lack the agility for successful daylight operations against fighter opposition. The type then came into its own as a limited yet effective night-fighter with nose-mounted radar.

Germany was one of many countries that in the mid-1930s acquired a considerable fascination with the concept of the heavy fighter that could undertake numerous long-range roles including that of the bomber-destroyer. To the Germans the heavy fighter was known as the Kampfzerstörer (battle destroyer), and the requirement for such a type was first issued in 1934 to AGO, Bayerische Flugzeugwerke (from 1936 Messerschmitt), Dornier, Focke-Wulf, Gotha, Heinkel and Henschel, calling for a twin-engined heavy fighter of monoplane configuration with a three-man crew, a heavy gun armament including trainable cannon, and provision for a disposable weapons load in an internal bay.

LEFT *The Bf 110 twin-engined heavy fighter was designed to provide the Luftwaffe with a potent bomber interceptor and long-range bomber escort, but was not successful against single-engined fighters and found more effective employment as a radar-carrying night-fighter.*

Dipl.-Ing. Willy Messerschmitt and his chief engineer, Dipl.-Ing. Walter Rethel, believed that the specification could result only in an indifferent warplane, and therefore opted to ignore many of the admittedly general requirements and concentrate their efforts on the design of a warplane offering the highest possible performance. Initially this did not meet with official approval but BFW, as the company was then known, then received an order for three Bf 110 prototypes that were completed to a revised specification after the German air ministry had divided its original multi-role Kampfzerstörer requirement into separate Schnellbomber (fast bomber) and Zerstörer (destroyer, or heavy fighter) types. BFW produced prototypes for the two types as the Bf 162 and Bf 110 respectively.

The Bf 110 V1 (first of three initial prototypes) made its maiden flight on 12 May 1936 with two Daimler-Benz DB 600A engines, and the type was ordered into production before the first flight of the Bf 110 V3 prototype in

December of the same year. This launched a production programme that saw the delivery of about 6,000 aircraft of all variants. The initial production model was to have been the Bf 110A with a fixed tailwheel and two DB 600Aa engines each rated at 735.5kW (986hp), but even as the first Bf 110A-0 pre-production aircraft were approaching completion this still-unreliable engine was being replaced in production by the DB 601 with a fuel-injection system in place of the DB 600's carburettor, a higher compression ratio and an improved supercharger.

Jumo power

The German air ministry decided that, pending the availability of DB 601, the four Bf 110A-0 aircraft should be completed with two Junkers Jumo 210Da inverted-Vee engines each rated at 507kW (680hp) for take-off. It was realised that the lower-rated powerplant would inevitably result in poorer performance, but it was thought that these aircraft would provide valuable experience in the operation

BELOW *The Bf 110C-4/B twin-engined warplanes of Erprobungsgruppe 210, which later became SG 210, operated largely non-operationally from Denain and Le Havre in northern France during the Battle of Britain; its primary task was the evaluation and development of the Bf 110.*

of the new type. It soon became clear that the DB 601 would not become available as soon as had been expected, so the next production model, the Bf 110B, was finalised round an uprated version of the Bf 110A's powerplant, namely two Jumo 210Ga engines each rated at 522kW (700hp) for take-off. The primary change in the Bf 110B was in the forward fuselage and fixed armament: the somewhat bulbous, drooped nose of the Bf 110A was now replaced by an aerodynamically refined nose without any droop and carrying four 7.92mm MG17 machine guns with 1000 rounds per gun. The fixed forward-firing armament was also bolstered by provision in the lower part of the forward fuselage for two 20mm MGFF cannon firing through blast tubes in the lower part of the nose: these cannon were installed on a pallet under the pilot, and their 60-round ammunition drums were changed by the navigator/radio operator. There was also one 7.92mm MG15 trainable rearward-firing machine gun in the cockpit rear.

The Bf 110B-0 pre-production aircraft were unarmed, but the full armament was provided in the Bf 110B-1 initial production model. This entered service in July 1938 with data that included a maximum speed of 455km/h (283mph) at 4000m (13,125ft), cruising speed of 319km/h (198mph) at 3000m (9845ft), service ceiling of 8000m (26,245ft),

SPECIFICATIONS: Messerschmitt Bf 110C-4

GENERAL
Type: heavy fighter
Accommodation: pilot, optional navigator/observer, and radio operator/gunner in tandem in an enclosed cockpit
Equipment: standard communication and navigation equipment, plus a Revi reflector gun sight
Weights: empty 5150kg (11,354lb); maximum take-off 6750kg (14,881lb)

MOTIVE POWER
Powerplant: two Daimler-Benz DB 601A-1 inverted-Vee piston engines each rated at 783kW (1050hp) for take-off

and 820kW (1100hp) at 3700m (12,140ft)
Fuel: internal fuel 1270 litres (279.4lmp gal; 335.5US gal); external fuel none

PERFORMANCE
Maximum speed: 560km/h (348mph) at 8000m (22,965ft) declining to 473km/h (294mph) at sea level
Cruising speed: maximum 489km/h (304mph) at 5000m (16,405ft)
Initial climb rate: 660m (2165ft) per minute; climb to 6000m (19,685ft) in 10 minutes 12 seconds
Service ceiling: 10,000m (32,810ft)
Maximum range: 1095km (680 miles)

DIMENSIONS
Wing span: 16.20m (53ft 1.8in)
Wing area: 38.50sq m (414.42sq ft)
Length: 12.10m (39ft 8.33in)
Height: 4.13m (13ft 6.5in) with the tail up

ARMAMENT
Fixed armament: two 20mm MGFF fixed forward-firing cannon with 180 rounds per gun in the nose, four 7.92mm MG17 fixed forward-firing machine-guns with 1000 rounds per gun in the nose, and one 7.92mm MG15 trainable rearward-firing machine-gun with 750 rounds in the cockpit rear
Disposable armament: none

range of 1720km (1069 miles), maximum take-off weight of 5698kg (12,562lb), wing span of 16.90m (55ft 5.33in), wing area of 38.90sq m (418.72sq ft), length of 12.60m (41ft 4in) and height of 3.47m (11ft 4.67in). Subvariants of this initial model were the Bf 110B-2 reconnaissance fighter with the cannon replaced by a camera installation, and the Bf 110B-3 conversion to trainer standard. Total production of the Bf 110B series was a mere 45 aircraft.

Daimler Benz power
The Messerschmitt design team now completed a limited but useful programme of aerodynamic refinement for the Bf 110's engine installation. This was available when the DB 601A-1 engine was finally delivered late in 1938 and made possible the production of the Bf 110C-1 that otherwise differed from the Bf 110B-1 only in its slightly revised wing with more angular tips that reduced span and area slightly. With a considerably more potent powerplant than the Bf 110B-1, the Bf 110C-1 had extremely good performance for the period of its service debut, including a maximum speed of 540km/h (335.5mph) at 6000m (19,685ft), but was already suffering criticism for its lack of agility. Prefaced by

a small number of Bf 110C-0 pre-production aircraft delivered from January 1939, the Bf 110C-1 entered service during the early summer of 1939, initially with the I (Zerstörer) Gruppe of Lehrgeschwader 1 and then with the I Gruppen of Zerstörergeschwadern 1 and 76. All three Gruppen were involved in the campaign against Poland that started World War II in September 1939, and acquitted themselves well in air combat against more agile but slower and distinctly less well armed Polish fighters.

Other than those revealed above, the details of the Bf 110C-1 included an armament of two 20mm MGFF fixed forward-firing cannon with 180 rounds per gun, four 7.92mm MG17 fixed forward-firing machine guns with 1,000 rounds per guns and one 7.92mm MG15 trainable rearward-firing machine gun with 750 rounds, maximum speed of 475km/h (295mph) at sea level, maximum cruising speed of 490km/h (304mph) at 5000m (16,405ft), economical cruising speed of 350km/h (217mph) at 4200m (13,780ft), initial climb rate of 660m (2165ft) per minute, climb to 6000m (19,685ft) in 10 minutes 12 seconds, service ceiling of 10,000m (32,810ft), range of 1095km (680 miles), empty weight of 4885kg (10,769lb), normal take-off

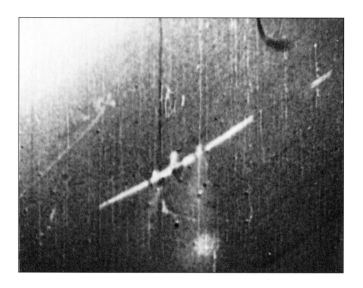

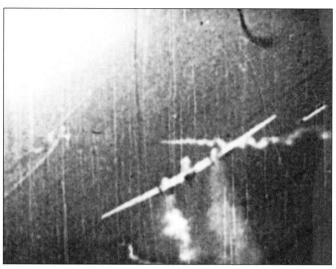

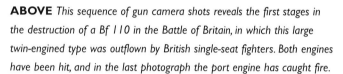

ABOVE *This sequence of gun camera shots reveals the first stages in the destruction of a Bf 110 in the Battle of Britain, in which this large twin-engined type was outflown by British single-seat fighters. Both engines have been hit, and in the last photograph the port engine has caught fire.*

weight of 6028kg (13,289lb), maximum take-off weight of 6750kg (14,880lb), wing span of 16.25m (53ft 3.75in), wing area of 38.40sq m (413.33sq ft), length of 12.07m (39ft 7.25in) and height of 4.13m (13ft 6.5in). When the Bf 110C-1 was withdrawn from operational service, a number of the aircraft were adapted for the glider-towing role with the revised designation Bf 110C-1/U1.

'C' series developments

The Bf 110C-2 differed from the Bf 110C-1 only in details of its radio equipment, and both the Bf 110C-1 and Bf 110C-2 were used in substantial numbers during the German invasion of Denmark and Norway that started in April 1940, then in the German campaign against the Low Countries and France beginning in May 1940. In both these campaigns the Bf 110C performed well when offered the right conditions of air superiority. Entering production in the early months of 1940 in succession to the Bf 110C-2, the Bf 110C-3 was a simple development of its predecessor with an improved version of the MGFF cannon whose smaller dimensions allowed the removal of the external fairings that had previously been required over the breeches. The Bf 110C-4 was basically the Bf 110C-3 with a modicum of armour protection for the pilot and gunner, and this accounted for part of the 222kg (490lb) increase in weight. By the time of the Bf 110C-4's development, the Luftwaffe had begun to appreciate that the Bf 110C was capable of more than just the basic Zerstörer role, and this realisation paved the way for the development of the Bf 110C-4/B

fighter-bomber version of the Bf 110C-4. This variant had side-by-side racks under the central fuselage for two 250kg (551lb) bombs. The considerable increase in maximum take-off weight thus produced was countered in part by the adoption of an uprated powerplant of two DB 601N engines each rated at 895kW (1200hp) for take-off. The model was built only in modest numbers.

The Bf 110C-5 was a specialised photo-reconnaissance model built in parallel with the Bf 110C-4/B. The type had its fixed forward-firing armament reduced to four 7.92mm MG17 machine guns, there was provision for an Rb 50/30 camera in the fuselage above a transparent panel, and the variant was produced in two forms as the basic Bf 110C-5 and Bf 110C-5/N with two DB 601A-1 or DB 601N engines respectively. Introduced during the course of the Battle of Britain in the summer of 1940, the Bf 110C-6 was a heavy fighter with the two 20mm MGFF cannon replaced by one 30mm MK101 cannon. The type was produced only in comparatively small numbers.

Convoy escorts

The Bf 110C-7 was the last model built before the end of Bf 110C production in the early part of 1941, and was a fighter-bomber with strengthened main landing gear units to allow the carriage of two 500kg (1102lb) bombs under the central fuselage. Only a small number of these aircraft were made.

During the fighting for Norway in April and May 1940, it became clear that while the Bf 110C had considerable range and endurance by comparison with contemporary single-

RIGHT *The inboard exhausts of the Bf 110C's Daimler-Benz DB 601A engines were curved down to reduce the glare that would affect the pilot's vision at night; the type's forward armament comprised four 7.92mm MG 17 machine-guns and two 20mm MG FF cannon in the nose.*

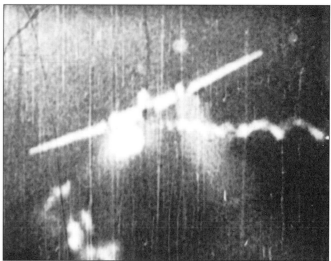

engined fighters, it lacked sufficient range and endurance for escorting German convoys plying up and down the coast of Norway. As a matter of great urgency, therefore, Messerschmitt evolved the Bf 110D with 1200 litres (264Imp gal; 317US gal) of auxiliary fuel in a fabric-covered plywood fairing under the fuselage. This bulged fairing was both dangerous and drag-producing, but was nonetheless used on the Bf 110D-0 pre-production model and Bf 110D-1/R1 initial production model. A far better solution to the range/endurance problem was adopted for the Bf 110D-1/R2, which had attachments outboard of the engine nacelles for the carriage of two 900 litre (198Imp gal; 237.75US gal) drop tanks.

The endurance of the basic type then prompted the suggestion that it could be used for night-fighting. Most of the surviving Bf 110D-1 long-range fighters were then adapted to the night-fighter role, some of them in the revised Bf 110D-1/U1 form with the Spanner-Anlage, an infra-red sensor used for target detection before the advent of radar. These revised aircraft were operated by I Gruppe of Nachtschlachtgeschwader 1, as I/ZG 1 was redesignated in July 1940.

The Bf 110D-2 was an extension of the long-range fighter philosophy embodied in the Bf 110D-1/R2, and was a fighter-bomber with underwing hardpoints for the carriage of two 500kg (1102lb) bombs and two 300 litre(66Imp gal; 79.25US gal) drop tanks. Built in parallel with the Bf 110D-2, the Bf 110D-3 was a long-range anti-shipping model with accommodation in the rear fuselage for a dinghy pack, racks under the fuselage for two 500kg (1102lb) bombs, and

LEFT *One of the main operators of the Bf 110 was Zerstörergeschwader 26 'Horst Wessel', which operated the Bf 110C, Bf 110E and Bf 110F heavy fighter variants in a number of roles, including that of coastal protection.*

ABOVE *The powerplant of earlier Bf 110s was two Daimler-Benz DB 601 inverted-Vee engines. This great engine occupied a vital position in the German armoury and, by comparison with the Rolls Royce Merlin, the unit had the advantage of fuel injection rather than normal carburation.*

hardpoints under the outer wing panels for two drop tanks. The Bf 110D-2 and Bf 110D-3 began to supplant the surviving Bf 110C fighters from the spring of 1941, and while the last Bf 110C fighters had disappeared from first-line service by mid-1942, the Bf 110D warplanes survived into the beginning of the following year.

After the indifferent performance of the Bf 110 in the Battle of Britain during the summer of 1940, the decision was taken to scale down production of this pioneering Zerstörer. Thus deliveries of the Bf 110C and Bf 110D models was steadily reduced from the early winter of 1940, but in the spring and early summer of the following year two new variants appeared as the Bf 110E and Bf 110F heavy fighter-bombers. The Bf 110E was a relatively simple development of the Bf 110D with updated equipment, improved crew protection, a measure of structural strengthening, and racks under the outer wing panels for

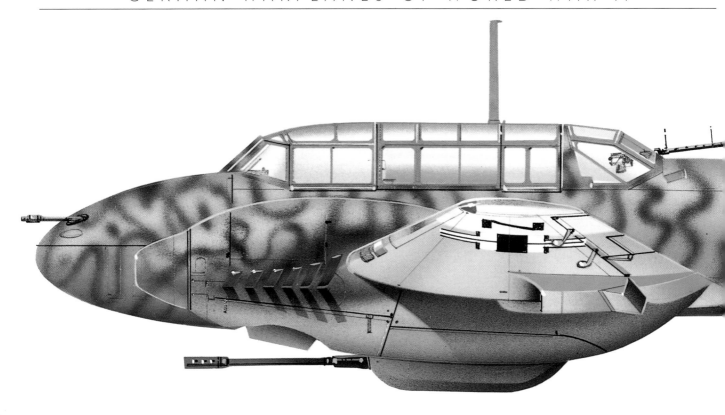

the carriage of four 50kg (110lb) bombs as well as the standard pair of 500kg (1102lb) bombs under the fuselage. This raised the maximum possible weapons load to 1200kg (2646lb), and provision was also retained for the carriage of two drop tanks under the wings in place of the four light 50kg (110lb) bombs.

'E' series production

The new model was pioneered by a small batch of Bf 110E-0 pre-production aircraft. There then followed the Bf 110E-1 initial production model with two DB 601A-1 engines that were replaced later in the production run by DB 601N engines. The subvariants of this model included the Bf 110E-1/R2 with provision for two 1000kg (2205lb) bombs, the Bf 110E-1/U1 night-fighter with the Spanner-Anlage sensor, and the Bf 110E-1/U2 night-fighter with provision in the cockpit for a control officer.

Produced in 1942, the Bf 110E-2 was a development of the Bf 110E-1 with the DB 601N powerplant and the Bf 110D-3's dinghy installation in the rear fuselage, while the Bf 110E-3 was a development of the Bf 110E-1 with the DB 601N powerplant for the long-range reconnaissance role with the MGFF cannon and ventral bomb racks replaced by a camera installation, the defensive armament increased by two 7.92mm MG17 fixed rearward-firing machine guns on

the sides of the rear fuselage, and provision under the outer wing panels for two drop tanks.

Appearing slightly later than the Bf 110E series and then built in parallel with it, the Bf 110F was introduced to take advantage of the greater power offered by the new DB 601F engine rated at 1007kW (1350hp) for take-off and requiring a larger oil cooler that was the only distinguishing feature of this engine. Deliveries of this variant started with a small batch of Bf 110F-0 pre-production aircraft that differed from the Bf 110E-1 only in their powerplant. In the Bf 110F-1 initial production model, however, protection for the crew was improved by the adoption of an external armour glass windscreen that was also applied retrospectively to the Bf 110D and Bf 110E, together with additional armour glass and armour plate in the cockpit and over the gunner's position. The Bf 110F-1 was fitted with racks for two 500 or 250kg (1102 or 551lb) bombs, or one AB-500 container for 500 incendiary or fragmentation bomblets, and these underfuselage loads could be supplemented by an underwing load of four 50kg (110lb) general-purpose or fragmentation bombs, or four AB-24 containers each carrying 24 2kg (4.4lb) fragmentation bomblets. The Bf 110F-2 was a heavy fighter derivative of the Bf 110F-1 with no provision for external loads, while the Bf 110F-3 was the reconnaissance derivative of the Bf 110F-1 with the MGFF

SPECIFICATIONS: Messerschmitt Bf 110G-4c/R3

GENERAL
Type: night-fighter
Accommodation: pilot, radar operator and optional radio operator/gunner in tandem in an enclosed cockpit
Equipment: standard communication and navigation equipment, plus Revi reflector gun sight and FuG 220B Lichtenstein SN-2 airborne interception radar, FuG 212 Lichtenstein C-1 airborne interception radar and FuG 227/1 Flensburg radar homing system
Weights: empty 5094kg (11,230lb); normal take-off 9390kg (20,701lb); maximum take-off 9888kg (21,799lb)

MOTIVE POWER
Powerplant: two Daimler-Benz DB 605B-1 inverted-Vee piston engines each rated at 1100kW (1475hp) for take-off and 1010kW (1355hp) at altitude

Fuel: internal fuel 1270 litres (279.4Imp gal; 335.5US gal); external fuel up to 600 litres (132Imp gal; 158.5 US gal) in two drop tanks

PERFORMANCE
Maximum speed: 550km/h (342mph) at 6980m (22,900ft) declining to 500km/h (311mph) at sea level
Cruising speed: maximum 510km/h (317mph) at 6000m (19,685ft)
Initial climb rate: 661m (2170ft) per minute
Service ceiling: 8000m (26,245ft)
Maximum range: 1300km (808 miles) with drop tanks; typical range 900km (560 miles) with standard fuel

DIMENSIONS
Wing span: 16.25m (53ft 3.77in)
Wing area: 38.40sq m (413.33sq ft)

Length: 13.05m (42ft 9.78in) including antennae and 12.07m (39ft 7.2in) excluding antennae
Height: 4.18 m (13ft 8.5in) with the tail up

ARMAMENT
Fixed armament: two 30mm MK108 fixed forward-firing cannon with 135 rounds per gun in the nose, two 20mm MG151/20 fixed forward-firing cannon with 300 rounds (port) and 350 rounds (starboard) in the ventral tray, and one 7.92mm MG81z trainable rearward-firing two-barrel machine-gun with 800 rounds in the cockpit rear or, in the alternative shräge Musik installation, two 20mm MG151/20 or MGFF fixed obliquely upward/forward-firing cannon in the rear fuselage
Disposable armament: none

cannon and ventral bomb racks replaced by a camera installation and provision under the outer wing panels for two drop tanks.

Neither the Bf 110F-2 nor the Bf 110F-3 had been built in more than very small numbers before the decision was taken to end Bf 110 production, deliveries from the two main sources ending in October and December 1941. Almost immediately it became clear that there were major problems with the Messerschmitt Me 210, the Bf 110's designated successor, and production of the Bf 110 was resumed in February 1942 as Messerschmitt undertook to improve the basic design for continued tactical viability

RIGHT *A notable unit in the German conquest of France in May and June 1940 was Zerstörergeschwader 76, whose II Gruppe operated Bf 110C heavy fighters with aggressive 'shark's mouth' marking on the nose and yellow 'eyes' at the forward tips of the propeller spinners.*

under current and foreseeable operational conditions. At this time there was a rapidly growing need for heavy day and night fighters with which to combat the Western Allies' growing bomber campaign. An early result was the Bf 110F-4, which was basically a three-seat night-fighter development of the Bf 110F-2 with the standard fixed forward-firing armament supplemented by two 30mm MK108 cannon in a ventral tray; the only other major change was the enlargement of the rudders and their trim tabs to improve controllability in single-engined flight. From the summer of 1943, however, a number of Bf 110F-4 night-fighters were modified to create the Bf 110F-4/U1 subvariant: the two 30mm cannon in the ventral tray were replaced by two 30mm MK108 fixed obliquely upward/forward-firing cannon in a schräge Musik (shrill music, i.e. jazz) installation in the rear cockpit.

Radar-equipped 'F' and 'G' series

Another change to the Bf 110F-4 introduced in the summer of 1942 was radar. This was the FuG 202 Lichtenstein BC equipment using a four-pole antennae array on the nose, and the addition of this FuG 202 equipment to the Bf 110F-4 created the Bf 110F-4a subvariant that also had its 20mm MGFF drum-fed cannon replaced by 20mm MG151/20 belt-fed cannon with 300 and 350 rounds for the port and starboard weapons respectively. The changes increased the maximum take-off weight of the Bf 110F-4a to 9287kg (20,474lb), and in conjunction with the drag of the Matratze (mattress) antenna array this reduced maximum speed to 510km/h (317mph) at 5600m (18,370ft) and range to 840km (522 miles) with internal fuel, although the provision for two drop tanks allowed this range to be increased at the expense of a further reduction in speed. Production of the Bf 110F-4a continued on both production lines to a time late in 1943.

With the Bf 110G variant, the Bf 110 series found its most effective employment as a night-fighter even though its performance was somewhat hampered by the weight and drag of the radar needed for this task. The variant was planned from the summer of 1941 with two DB 605B-1 engines each rated at 1100kW (1475hp) for take-off, which allowed the maximum take-off weight to be increased to 9390kg (20,700lb). The new model was prefaced by a small batch of Bf 110G-0 pre-production fighters, and plans were

made for the Bf 110G-1 to be the initial production model as a heavy day fighter with a fixed forward-firing armament of two 20mm MG151/20 cannon with 650 rounds and four 7.92mm MG17 machine guns with 1000 rounds per gun. It was soon decided, however, that even with the uprated powerplant the Bf 110G was obsolete in the pure fighter role, and the decision was therefore taken to drop the Bf 110G-1 in favour of the Bf 110G-2 heavy fighter with fighter-bomber capability made possible by provision for the carriage of several Rüstsätze (field conversion sets). The Bf 110G-2 was delivered from May 1942, and differed from the

Bf 110G-0 in having the revised vertical tail surfaces introduced by the Bf 110F-4 for improved single-engined handling, beefed-up main landing gear units, rearward defence improved by the adoption of the 7.92mm MG81z trainable two-barrel machine gun with 800 rounds in the rear cockpit, and a number of detail changes including two racks under the fuselage for 500kg (1102lb) bombs and provision under the outer wing panels for the carriage of four 50kg (110lb) bombs or two drop tanks. The Bf 110G-2 was soon modified for more specialised roles by the adoption of Rüstsätze that variously added different types of heavier armament and, to offset the performance loss resulting from the greater armament weight, the GM 1 power boost system.

Produced in parallel with the Bf 110G-2 from a point early in 1943, the Bf 110G-3 was a long-range reconnaissance fighter with one Rb 50/30 or Rb 70/30 camera, a fixed forward-firing armament of four 7.92mm MG17 machine guns, a fixed rearward-firing armament of one 20mm MG151/20 cannon under the rear fuselage with 350 rounds, a trainable rearward-firing armament of one 7.92mm MG81z two-barrel machine gun, and provision for

two drop tanks. Some of the aircraft were modified in service to Bf 110G-3/R3 standard with the fixed forward-firing machine guns replaced by two 30mm MK108 cannon. The Bf 110G-3 had a maximum speed of 560km/h (348mph) at 5800m (19,030ft), and its normal range was 900km (559 miles).

Later 'G' series

Another type produced in parallel with the Bf 110G-2 but in fact appearing before the Bf 110G-3, the Bf 110G-4 was a night-fighter that entered service in the late summer of 1942 with additional armour protection for the pilot, and was designed for the carriage of radar added in the form of Umrüst-Bausätze. The variant's standard armament was a fixed forward-firing battery of two 20mm MG151/20 cannon with 650 rounds and four 7.92mm MG17 machine guns with 4000 rounds together with a trainable rearward-firing armament of one 7.92mm MG81z two-barrel machine gun with 800 rounds, although some aircraft had a shräge Musik installation. The first type of radar installed in the Bf 110G-4 was the FuG 212 Lichtenstein C-1 equipment to produce the Bf 110G-4/U5 with a single-pole antenna array producing considerably less drag than the

ABOVE *The Bf 110G had a number of different radar equipments, the Bf 110G-4a having the Lichtenstein C-1 radar. The type was also available with armament upgrades adding one 37mm BK 3,7 cannon and replacing the machine-guns with two 30mm MK 108 cannon.*

four-pole Matratze (mattress) array of the Bf 110F-4. There were also a number of subvariants with different armament and radar installations as well as provision for drop tanks. The most important of these were the Bf 110G-4a introduced in the autumn of 1943 with the four-pole antenna array, and the Bf 110G-4b introduced later in the same year with FuG 212 Lichtenstein C-1 radar using the single-pole antenna array and complemented by the FuG 220 Lichtenstein SN-2 with a four-pole Hirschgeweih (stag's horn) antenna array to provide the ability to 'see' through the clouds of 'Window' metal foil strips dropped by RAF bombers. By a time early in 1944, the minimum-range capability of the FuG 220 Lichtenstein SN-2 radar had been improved to the point at which it was feasible to discard the FuG 212 Lichtenstein C-1 equipment and so reduce the number of drag-producing antennae sprouting from the nose. This resulted in the Bf 110G-4c night-fighter with the FuG 220b Lichtenstein SN-2 radar. The last Bf 110G was delivered in March 1945, by which time the Bf 110 could be considered at best as an obsolescent type even in the night-fighter role.

Produced in parallel with the Bf 110G up to the middle of 1944, the Bf 110H had been planned from mid-1941 with a number of differences from the Bf 110G. Many of its features had then been adopted for the Bf 110G, however, so that the Bf 110H differed significantly from the Bf 110G only in its two DB 605E engines, a measure of local strengthening in the rear fuselage, stiffened fins, stronger main landing gear units, and a retractable tailwheel. The Bf 110H was built only

in modest numbers, and its variants included the Bf 110H-2 heavy fighter, Bf 110H-3 reconnaissance fighter with the same mission equipment as the Bf 110G-3 but with the quartet of 7.92mm MG17 fixed forward-firing machine guns replaced by two 30mm MK108 cannon, and the Bf 110H-4 night-fighter equivalent to the Bf 110G-4.

BELOW *This night-fighter is a Bf 110G-4d/R3 with Lichtenstein SN-2 radar (using the Hirschgeweih antenna array) and the R3 Rüstsatze in which the standard arrangement of four 7.92mm MG 17 machine-guns in the nose was replaced by two 30mm MK 108 cannon with 135 rpg.*

CHAPTER 15

MESSERSCHMITT ME 163 KOMET

Wholly radical in the conception of its aerodynamics and powerplants, the Me 163 rocket-powered interceptor was an expedient forced on Germany by its worsening position in World War II, and offered phenomenal climb performance only in combination with an airframe/powerplant combination fraught with danger.

The Messerschmitt Me 163 Komet (comet) was truly one of the most remarkable aircraft of World War II, but was forced on Germany only by its worsening military situation and lack of modern interceptors, the latter stemming from the German air ministry's belief up to 1942 that the war would be short and therefore not require the development of a new generation of advanced warplanes. The type also revealed the German flair for bringing toward practical use an apparently far-fetched concept.

Germany was one of the few countries that during the 1930s believed it was worth pursuing the concept of a rocket-powered aeroplane for manned use, and from 1936 placed contracts with the Hellmuth Walter company for the

LEFT *With its swept wing and tailless design the Me 163 was certainly a harbinger of the future, but its liquid-propellant rocket propulsion was fraught with operational difficulties and also provided only the shortest of powered durations.*

development of liquid-propellant rockets applicable to an existing range of tasks. With the advent of the Walter R I-203 unit rated at 3.92kN (882lb st), the feasibility of rocket-powered aircraft increased dramatically, and a complex sequence of events led to the commissioning of the design for a rocket-powered tailless aeroplane from the Deutsches Forschungsinstitut fär Segelflug (German Gliding Research Institute). Dr. Alexander Lippisch, one of the scientists engaged at this facility, suggested a development of the DFS 39 Delta IVc tandem two-seat research machine currently powered by a Pobjoy radial piston engine rated at 60kW (75hp) and driving a two-blade pusher propeller. Lippisch believed that this basic design could readily be adapted for use with the Walter rocket motor and at speeds up to 500km/h (311mph).

Lippisch had already been investigating the possibility of a tailless aeroplane offering very high performance through the use of a rocket motor, and the possibilities inherent in such a type were so great that the German air ministry ordered the design to be undertaken in very great secrecy as the Projekt X. The use of a liquid-propellant rocket necessitated that the fuselage be made of metal rather than wood, and as the DFS lacked the capability for construction in metal the construction of the fuselage was passed to Heinkel while DFS constructed the wooden flying surfaces. Wind-tunnel tests suggested that a change be made from the DFS 39's combination of a straight wing with endplate vertical surfaces to a moderately swept wing and a central vertical surface for improved directional stability and yaw/roll characteristics. The implementation of these changes resulted in a considerably changed design, and at the end of 1938 Lippisch and his 12-man team moved to Messerschmitt, where Projekt X became the Me 163.

As all this was happening, Heinkel was completing its He 176 rocket-powered aeroplane that in July achieved a maximum speed of only 350km/h (217.5mph) rather than the estimated 1000km/h (621mph). In the wake of this disappointing trial the German air ministry lost much of its

BELOW *This side view of an Me 163B-1 taken to the USA after World War II reveals the excellent siting of the cockpit, the mid-set swept wing and the deep fuselage that carried the liquid propellants, as well as the landing skid above the anchorage for the take-off trolley.*

limited enthusiasm for a rocket-powered warplane, but this was rekindled when the DFS 194 with the R I-203 rocket motor revealed a maximum speed of 342mph (550km/h) as well as a phenomenal rate of climb. The DFS 194's success revitalised the Me 163 programme, which was further assisted by Walter's development of the R II-203b motor rated at 7.355kN (1653lb st) and intended primarily as a RATO unit, and his continuing work on a throttlable rocket intended to deliver 14.71kN (3307lb st). The revitalisation of the programme saw the enlargement of the original Me 163 experimental model effort from two to six Me 163A prototypes with the R II-203b motor, and the decision to proceed as a matter of urgency with an operational interceptor development as the Me 163B with the Walter rocket motor currently under development.

Early flight trials

The Me 163A V1 first of six prototypes started its trials as a glider in the spring of 1941, and immediately revealed excellent gliding performance together with a measure of rudder and aileron flutter that was cured by a rebalancing of these surfaces. The other prototypes were soon involved in the trials, and in the summer of 1941 the first and fourth prototypes were transferred to Peenemünde for revision with the R II-203b motor. These two aircraft undertook a

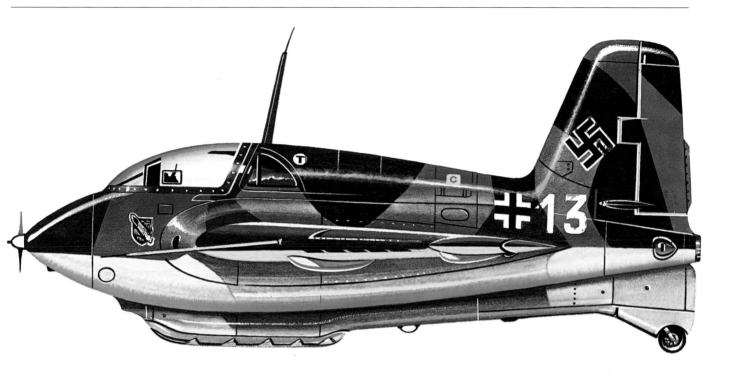

SPECIFICATIONS: Messerschmitt Me 163B-1a Komet

GENERAL
Type: point interceptor
Accommodation: pilot in an enclosed cockpit
Equipment: standard communication and navigation equipment, plus a Revi 16/B reflector gun sight
Weights: empty 1908kg (4206lb); maximum take-off 4310kg (9502lb)

MOTIVE POWER
Powerplant: one Walter HWK 109-509A-1/2 rocket motor rated at 16.67kN (3748lb st)

Fuel: internal fuel 1530 litres (336.6Imp gal; 404.2US gal); external fuel none

PERFORMANCE
Maximum speed: 955km/h (593mph) at 3000m (9845ft) and above declining to 830km/h (516mph) at sea level; cruising speed not available
Initial climb rate: 4862m (15,951ft) per minute; climb to 9145m (30,003ft) in 2 minutes 36 seconds
Service ceiling: 12,000m (39,370ft) typical radius of action 35.5km (22 miles); powered endurance 7 minutes 30 seconds

DIMENSIONS
Wing span: 9.33m (30ft 7.33in)
Wing area: 18.50sq m (199.13sq ft)
Length: 5.85m (19ft 2.33in)
Height: 2.76m (9ft 0.67in) on take-off dolly

ARMAMENT
Fixed armament: two 30mm MK108 fixed forward-firing cannon with 60 rounds per gun or two 20mm MG151/20 fixed forward-firing cannon with 100 rounds per gun in the wing roots
Disposable armament: none

comprehensive series of trials between July and October 1941, and were clocked at maximum speeds in the order of 885km/h (550mph). The trials also revealed that the maximum speed was not limited by aerodynamic or structural factors, but by the powered endurance of the motor, which consumed its fuel and oxidant at an extraordinarily high rate.

In an effort to assess the Me 163A's limiting speed, the Me 163A V4 was towed to altitude behind a Messerschmitt Bf 110C tug before the pilot released the tow and fired the motor. The Me 163A V4 attained a speed of 1004km/h (624mph) before the aeroplane became unstable as a result of high subsonic compressibility effects. The pilot then shut down the engine and regained full control as the Me 163 V4 decelerated. Assessment of this compressibility factor

resulted in modification of the wing planform being planned for the Me 163B. The changes included a constant leading-edge sweep angle, reduced trailing-edge sweep, and the inclusion of fixed slots over the outer 40% of each wing leading edge forward of the elevons used for control in pitch and roll. Longitudinal trim was provided by trailing-edge flaps inboard of the elevons. The R II-203b motor operated on the basis of the 'cold' reaction of its two antipathetic fuels, which comprised 530 litres (116.6Imp gal; 140US gal) in total of T-stoff (80% hydrogen peroxide stabilised by oxyquinoline or phosphate) and Z-stoff (aqueous solution of calcium permanganate). This quantity of fuels was sufficient for a powered endurance of 4 minutes 30 seconds at a maximum take-off weight of 2400kg (5291lb). Problems with the Z-stoff catalyst, which could result in truly

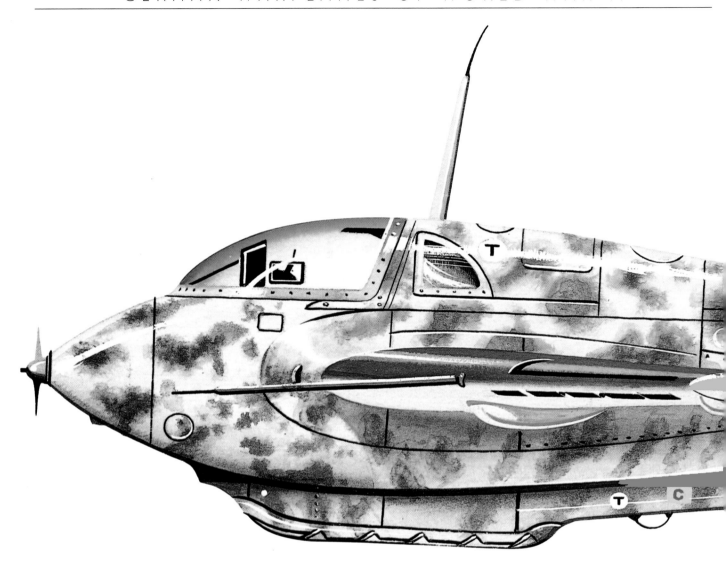

ABOVE *Though it was planned to deploy the Me 163 around Germany, the only airfields to be equipped with the special facilities needed to operate the aircraft were to be Peenemünde, Bad Zwischenahn, Wittmunhafen, Stargard, Udetfeld, Brandis, Venlo, Deelen and Husum.*

catastrophic explosions, led to its replacement by C-stoff (mixture of 57% methyl alcohol, 30% hydrazine hydrate and 13% water) for the R II-211 throttlable development of the R II-203b motor that entered production as the HWK 109-509A for the Me 163B interceptor.

The six Me 163A prototypes were complemented by 10 Me 163A-0 pre-production aircraft that were used as training aircraft for Me 163B pilots.

'B' series

Although it was clearly a close relative of the Me 163A, at least in basic construction and configuration, the latter including a jettisonable take-off dolly and an extendible landing skid, the Me 163B interceptor was in reality a completely different aeroplane in its basic details and included fixed forward-firing armament in the leading edges of the wing roots. The powerplant was one HWK 109-509A rocket motor, which was estimated at a rating of 16.67kN (3748lb st) and a powered endurance of 12 minutes from 306.4US gal (255.2Imp gal; 1160 litres) consumed at the rate of about 2.75 kg (6.06 lb) per second and complemented by 492 litres (108.25Imp gal; 130US gal) of C-stoff. It was calculated that this would provide a three-minute climb at full throttle to 12,000m (39,370ft), whereupon the engine would be throttled back to turn the remaining nine minutes of full-throttle power into 30 minutes of throttled-back cruising power at 950km/h (590mph) for a tactical radius of 240km (149 miles). As it transpired, the HWK 109-509A motor's T-stoff consumption rate was in fact 5kg (11.02lb) per second and powered endurance was thus considerably shorter than planned.

1943 that the first flight-cleared but still temperamental and indeed basically experimental engines became available. By this time more than half of the Me 163A-0 pre-production aircraft had been completed, and it was only in August 1943 that the Me 163B finally made its first powered flight.

The pre-production aircraft not used in the development programme were operated as service evaluation and training types with the revised designation Me 163Ba-1 and a fixed forward-firing armament of two 20mm MG151/20 cannon in the wing roots, while the first true production aircraft had the designation Me 163B-1a Komet and had the heavier fixed forward-firing armament of two 30mm MK108 cannon in the same positions. The task of getting the Me 163B-1a operational was formidable, for supervision of the type's production had been transferred from Messerschmitt to Klemm, which was faced with the problem of co-ordinating component manufacture by companies that were generally unused to operating to the fine tolerances required and were also scattered at points all over Germany.

Luftwaffe service

Thus it was only in February 1944 that the Me 163B-1a made its first flight, and the Luftwaffe accepted its first aeroplane in May 1944. Operational trials revealed problems, the two most serious involving a premature shut-down of the engine at high altitude as the Me 163B levelled out after the climb (traced to the creation of a air-lock in the fuel system as the remaining quantity of fuel sloshed around) or immediately after take-off (traced to turbulence in the fuel outlet as the aeroplane accelerated after releasing the take-off dolly). Problems were also encountered with the 30mm MK108 cannon, with the poor quality of new pilots, and with the general shortage of materials as a result of Allied bombing.

The highest monthly production total was achieved in December 1944, when 90 aircraft were delivered to bring the year's total to 237 machines. In the following period of slightly more than four months only another 42 aircraft were delivered. It is estimated that only 279 aircraft actually reached Luftwaffe service, and their successes were few and far between because of the Me 163B's very short endurance. The only unit to attain full operational status was I Gruppe of JG 400, and this achieved only nine 'kills' for the loss of 14 of its own number, several of these following heavy landings that caused residual fuel to detonate.

Produced in very small numbers in 1944, the Me 163S was a two-seat training glider version of the Me 163B for the training of pilots. The instructor's raised cockpit was installed in place of the main T-stoff tank in the fuselage, and the C-stoff tanks in the wings were used for water ballast.

The radical nature of the new interceptor was reflected in the fact that despite the Me 163A programme, orders were placed for six Me 163B prototypes and 70 Me 163B-0 pre-production aircraft, although in the event only 30 of the latter were actually used for development work with Versuchs (experimental) numbers. The six Me 163B prototypes were completed within a short time from April 1942, but there had been problems with the HWK 109-509A motor that was now expected to start bench-running trials only in the autumn of 1942. It was therefore decided that the Me 163B should undertake its first trials in glider mode. These flight and weapons trials, carried out in the summer of 1942 and including flights with water ballast to raise the type to its maximum take-off weight, revealed that the Me 163B had exceptional flying and handling characteristics, and was also a first-class gun platform.

Problems with the HWK 109-509A motor continued to delay the programme, and it was not until the summer of

CHAPTER 16

MESSERSCHMITT ME 210

The Me 210 was intended as successor to the Bf 110 in the heavy fighter role but incorporated provision for an internally carried bomb load so that the type could operate in the dive-bomber task. The type suffered from major problems, however, and only became 'right' when revised as the Me 410.

Despite its purposeful appearance and apparently thoroughbred lines, the Messerschmitt Me 210 was a very poor warplane that was beset by technical and aerodynamic problems, and as such was a severe disappointment to the Luftwaffe in its search for a type to supplant the Bf 110 in the heavy fighter role. This was a major blow to German war-making capability, for although the country had been generally remiss in planning for a war of anything but short duration, one of the few exceptions to this tendency had been the Zerstörer (destroyer) heavy fighter in which the political leadership of the Luftwaffe placed such faith. Thus it was early in 1938, even before the Messerschmitt Bf 110 entered service as the

LEFT *The Me 210, seen here in the form of two Me 210A aircraft, was designed as successor to the Bf 110 with significantly better operational capability through the incorporation of an uprated powerplant and advanced features such as remotely controlled rearward-firing guns.*

Luftwaffe's first Zerstörer, that Messerschmitt was asked to start work on a successor type to ensure that the Luftwaffe did not lose the operational advantage that would accrue, it was believed, from deployment of the Bf 110. The requirement for this successor type was couched in general terms, and demanded performance that was substantially better than that of the Bf 110, together with greater mission versatility and improved defensive armament. Added to this basic specification was the demand that the new type should be a multi-role type able to undertake the heavy fighter, reconnaissance, attack and dive-bombing roles: in short, the requirement for the new Zerstörer had turned the wheel full circle to return to the demands originally made of the Kampfzerstörer concept, from which the Zerstörer notion had been evolved as a more practical way of ensuring at least a moderate mission capability.

Messerschmitt considered a number of alternative designs, all of them drawing on its experience with the

Bf 110, and submitted its chosen type to the German air ministry in the summer of 1938. The basic design was approved, and in the autumn of the same year Messerschmitt was ordered to start on the detail design on the Me 210 and to begin work on the industrial requirements for an initial 1000 production aircraft.

In terms of its aerodynamics and basic configuration, the Me 210 was basically an improved version of the Bf 110. The earlier fighter's elegant forward fuselage and cockpit contours were replaced by a shorter and more compact arrangement with a short nose that offered the pilot very good fields of vision, and an advanced defensive suite remotely controlled from the rear cockpit via two reflector sights and comprising two FDL 131 barbettes on the sides of the fuselage just to the rear of the wing trailing edges. These barbettes each carried a single 13mm MG131 machine-gun that could be traversed through an arc of 40° independently of the weapon on the other side of the fuselage, and were installed on the ends of a drum extending through the fuselage: this drum carried 450 rounds of ammunition for each machine-gun, and was controlled by a 1.12kW (1.5hp) electric motor for collective movement of the two barbettes through an elevation/depression arc of 70°.

BELOW *One of the best features of the Me 210A was the siting of the cockpit high on the extreme forward part of the fuselage in a position that gave both the pilot and the radio operator/gunner to his rear excellent fields of vision.*

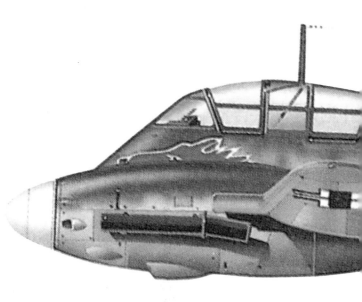

The Me 210 V1 (first of 15 prototype and service test aircraft) was completed in the summer of 1939 and made its maiden flight on 2 September with two Daimler-Benz DB 601A-1 engines each rated at 783kW (1050hp) for take-off and cooled by means of shallow radiators installed on the wing undersurfaces outboard of each engine. Excellent results had been expected of the type, so the disappointment was acute when the prototype revealed very poor handling characteristics including major

SPECIFICATIONS: Messerschmitt Me 210A-1

GENERAL
Type: heavy fighter and fighter-bomber
Accommodation: pilot and radio operator/gunner in tandem in an enclosed cockpit
Equipment: standard communication and navigation equipment, plus a Revi C/12D reflector gun sight and a remote sighting system for the lateral barbettes
Weights: empty 7070kg (15,586lb); maximum take-off 9706kg (21,397lb)

MOTIVE POWER
Powerplant: two Daimler-Benz DB 601F inverted-Vee piston engines each rated at 1007kW (1350hp) for take-off
Fuel: internal fuel 2420 litres (532.3Imp gal; 639.3US gal); external fuel none

PERFORMANCE
Maximum speed: 563km/h (350mph) at 5430m (17,820ft) declining to 463km/h (288mph) at sea level
Cruising speed: not available
Climb: to 4000m (13,125ft) in 7 minutes 30 seconds
Service ceiling: 8900m (29,200ft)
Maximum range: 1820km (1131 miles)

DIMENSIONS
Wing span: 16.34m (53ft 7.31in)
Wing area: 36.20sq m (389.66sq ft)
Length: 12.12m (39ft 9.17in)
Height: 4.28m (14ft 0.5in)

ARMAMENT
Fixed armament: two 20mm MG151/20

fixed forward-firing cannon with 350 rounds per gun in the nose, two 7.92mm MG17 fixed forward-firing machine guns with 1,000 rounds per gun in the nose, and one 13mm MG131 trainable lateral/rearward-firing machine gun with 450 rounds in each of the two remotely controlled power-operated FDL 131 barbettes on the sides of the fuselage
Disposable armament: up to 1000kg (2205lb) of disposable stores in a lower-fuselage weapons bay rated at 1000kg (2205lb), and generally comprising two 500kg (1102lb) SC-500 or 250kg (551lb) SC-250 bombs, or eight 50kg (110lb) SC-50 bombs

---

instability in the directional and longitudinal planes. The problem was diagnosed as the tail unit, and the prototype was therefore revised with a completely different tail with a single vertical surface of considerable size and a larger tapered rather than constant-chord horizontal surface of greater span. The revised Me 210 V1 was tested in comparison with the Me 210 V2, which initially retained the original type of tail unit with endplate vertical surfaces, and was found to possess better handling characteristics.

Flight trials and modifications continued through the winter of 1939-40 without major improvement of the type's handling, which was still inadequate and, perhaps more

disturbingly, unpredictable: the prototypes had bad stall characteristics, displayed a tendency to flick into a spin at high angles of attack, suffered from tailplane buffet as a result of fuselage turbulence, and under certain conditions were prone to elevator flutter. By this time another two prototypes had become available, and the decision had been taken to use the first 11 aircraft off the production line as additional Versuchs (experimental) aircraft.

The problems seemed to be insuperable, and the delay to the programme was soon a major concern for the German air ministry, but so desperate was the German air ministry that nothing should further delay the service entry of the type that

Messerschmitt's suggestions for major remedial changes were all refused. Work was now well advanced on the large batch of Me 210A-0 pre-production aircraft, numbering 94 in all, and deliveries of these aircraft were made from April 1941. The Me 210A-0 was a heavy fighter with secondary dive-bombing capability, and was powered by two DB 601F engines each rated at 1007kW (1350hp) for take-off. Service evaluation of the Me 210A-0 began in the autumn of 1941, and was marred by a spate of accidents resulting from the type's dismal handling qualities, which had been deemed bad by test pilots but were considered downright vicious by service pilots. The German air ministry still refused to accept that the Me 210 was unsuitable for service, but by the end of 1941 the Luftwaffe had decreed the type unsuitable for service and abandoned plans to issue the type to Schnellkampfgeschwader 210.

Luftwaffe service

The reluctance of the German air ministry to recognise the obvious was signalled by the ordering of two production models, namely the Me 210A-1 heavy fighter with secondary fighter-bomber capability, and the Me 210A-2 dive-bomber with secondary heavy fighter capability. Thus the Luftwaffe had to accept the Me 210A-1 from January 1942. Meanwhile an official commission had been assessing the Me 210, and finally concluded that production of the type should be halted immediately and that production of the Bf 110 should be reinstated. Production ended in April 1942 after the delivery of 94 Me 210A-0 pre-production and 90 Me 210A-1 production aircraft; at this time there were another 370 aircraft at various stages of the production process.

This did not end the Me 210 programme, however, for development work continued in an effort to cure the basic type's handling characteristics. The solution to these problems was finally found in the adoption of automatic leading edges slots and a rear fuselage that was deepened and increased in length by 0.95m (3ft 1.4in). The solution of the Me 210's problems did not result in any reinstatement of production in Germany, but rather development of the acceptable type into the Me 410 'Hornisse', with further work on the Me 210 now devoted to the development of features required for the Me 410.

As the Me 410 would not be available for some time and the Bf 110 was at best obsolescent in its original form with DB 601 engines, Messerschmitt was instructed to revise a number of stored Me 210A-1 aircraft to a partial Me 410 standard with slotted outer wing panels, the revised rear fuselage and air brakes on the upper and lower surfaces of the outer wing panels. The modified aircraft were issued to the Versuchsstaffel 210 that became operational in August 1942 as the 16.Staffel of Kampfgeschwader 6. The unit suffered moderately heavy losses in the course of offensive operations over the UK, but numbers were bolstered after Messerschmitt was authorised to complete a number of nearly completed Me 210A-1 and Me 210A-2 aircraft that had been placed in store. This yielded another 85 aircraft before the programme was finally halted in June 1942.

Hungary production

In June 1941, the month that saw the start of the German invasion of the USSR, Germany reached agreement with Hungary for production of the Me 210 by the Danube Aircraft Factory with the revised powerplant of two DB 605B engines built under license in Hungary by Manfred Weiss. The model planned for Hungarian production was the Me 210C with the slotted outer wing panels and rear fuselage finally evolved to cure the Me 210A's problems. This was delivered from the beginning of 1943 in two subvariants as the Me 210C-1 long-range reconnaissance type with secondary heavy fighter capability, and the Me 210Ca-1 heavy fighter with secondary dive-bombing capability. Hungarian production was allocated in the ratio of 2/1 to the Luftwaffe and Hungarian air force. The data for the Me 210C-1 included two DB 605B engines each rated at 1100kW (1475hp) for take-off, maximum speed of 555km/h (344mph) at 6300m (20,670ft) declining to 450km/h (280mph) at sea level, range of 1370km (851 miles), maximum take-off weight of 10,705kg (23,601lb), wing span of 16.34m (53ft 7.33in), wing area of 36.20sq m (389.66sq ft), length of 12.15m (39ft 10.33in) and height of 4.28m (14ft 0.5in). The Me 210Ca-1 differed in details such as its maximum speed of 578km/h (359mph) at 6500m (21,325ft) declining to 478km/h (297mph) at sea level, service ceiling of 8900m (29,200ft), range of 1730km (1075 miles) empty weight of 7283kg (16,055lb) and maximum take-off weight of 9745kg (21,482lb).

Production of the Me 210C was slow to gather pace, and when the factory ceased production of the type in March 1944 deliveries had reached only 267 aircraft of which 108 had been delivered to the Luftwaffe. Variants that did not reach the full production stage were the Me 210B-1 reconnaissance version of the Me 210A-1, and the Me 210D-1 version of the Me 210B-1 for production in Hungary with the DB 605B powerplant.

RIGHT *The Me 210A-1 was the first production version of the Me 210 series, and was a heavy fighter with the fixed forward-firing armament of two 20mm MG 151/20 cannon and two 7.92mm MG 17 machine guns but without the Me 210A-2 dive-bomber's 1000 kg (2205lb) of bombs.*

CHAPTER 17

MESSERSCHMITT ME 262

The Me 262 was the most advanced warplane to enter service in World War II and also the first turbojet-powered fighter to enter operational service anywhere in the world, but the significance of the part it could have played in the air war had been compromised by a combination of development delays and political antipathy.

The Messerschmitt Me 262 was undoubtedly the most far-sighted warplane to enter production during World War II. It was a turbojet-powered interceptor fighter of extremely advanced design, fully optimised in airframe terms for its radical powerplant of two slim axial-flow turbojets. Germany had made considerable strides with such engines during the later 1930s and on 27 August 1939, less than a week before the outbreak of World War II, had flown the Heinkel He 178 as the world's first turbojet-powered aeroplane. By the time this experimental type flew, Messerschmitt was already at work on an operational warplane intended to exploit the capabilities of the new type of engine.

LEFT Looking remarkably shabby without any paint, this Me 262A-1a nonetheless reveals the advanced nature of its lines, with the tricycle landing gear, the well-sited cockpit, and the fixed forward-firing armament of four 30mm Mk 108 cannon (with 100 rounds per gun) in the nose.

Projekt 1065

In the autumn of 1938 Messerschmitt started design work on an aeroplane to meet a German air ministry requirement for a warplane-type machine to be powered by two examples of the BMW P 3302 axial-flow turbojet. This engine was intended to be available in December 1939 at a rating of 5.88kN (1323lb st). From the outset the Messerschmitt design team planned the new type for possible development as an interceptor, and when it submitted its Projekt 1065 design to the air ministry in June 1939 the company stressed this aspect of the basic design even though no such capability had been demanded in the original requirement. As originally conceived, the P.1065 design was a cantilever low-wing monoplane of all-metal construction with fully retractable tailwheel landing gear and the powerplant of two P 3302 turbojets buried in the wing roots. The air ministry ordered Messerschmitt to build a mock-up, and after this had been inspected in January

ABOVE *This three-quarter forward view of an Me 262A-1 reveals the installation of the two Junkers Jumo 004B turbojet in underwing nacelles, and the port-side pair of rectangular openings in the lower fuselage through which the empty 30mm cannon cases were jettisoned.*

1940 the company received a March 1940 order for three flying prototypes and one static-test airframe of the design that now became the Me 262. At much the same time, an order was placed for the rival Heinkel He 280 design.

Engine problems

These orders were placed at a time well past that at which the P 3302, now officially designated as the BMW 109-003, should have been available, and it was clear that the development of this engine to flight-cleared status was going to take considerably longer than had been anticipated. BMW had also been forced to increase the diameter of the engine, and this meant that a wing-root installation was no longer feasible. Messerschmitt therefore submitted to the air ministry in May 1940 a

revised design of somewhat larger dimensions with two BMW 109-003 turbojets in slim nacelles mounted centrally at about quarter-span. The air ministry accepted the new design in July 1940, and Messerschmitt began construction of the prototypes during the following month. Although the airframe was now beginning to make good progress, the same could not be said of the intended engine, which had revealed a rating of only 2.55kN (573lb st) dry thrust in bench-running trials. An alternative engine was in prospect, however, for during the summer of 1939 Junkers had received a development contract for an axial-flow turbojet, the Jumo 109-004 engine with a rating of 5.88kN (1323lb st). This engine was conceived as a low-risk type without novel features so that it could be developed to production status as rapidly and surely as possible. The Jumo 109-004 started its bench-running trials in November 1940, and immediately revealed major problems.

Messerschmitt was thus faced with the prospect of completing an advanced aeroplane without any powerplant, and in February 1941 won approval for the completion of the first prototype with two HWK R II-203b liquid-propellant rocket motors, each rated at 7.355kN (1653lb st), so that at least limited flight trials could be undertaken. The R II-203b engine was not yet flight-cleared, however, and a further revision of the Me 262 programme saw the extraordinary decision to fit the first prototype with a Junkers Jumo 210G piston engine in the fuselage nose so that initial trials could at least be started. It was in this form, without the wing-mounted nacelles and with a piston engine located in the nose to drive a two-blade propeller, that the Me 262 V1 (first of five initial prototypes) made its maiden flight on 18 April 1941. In November 1941 Messerschmitt finally received its first flight-cleared BMW 109-003 turbojets, although these units were each rated at only 4.51kN (1014lb st), and the company decided to retain the piston engine for initial trials after the turbojets had been installed. This precaution was proved sensible during the course of the revised

prototype's first flight in March 1942, when both turbojets flamed in quick succession soon after take-off. BMW now had to redesign the engine as the BMW 109-003A that made its first flight only in October 1943, and then under a Junkers Ju 88A test-bed aeroplane.

Junkers power

Junkers had managed to solve the problems with its Jumo 109-004 turbojet, and work immediately started on the conversion of the Me 262 V3 to take a pair of these engines, which were each rated at 8.24kN (1852lb st). The Jumo 109-004A-0 pre-production engines delivered to Messerschmitt were larger and heavier than the BMW

BELOW *This is an Me 262A-1a fighter of Jagdverbande 44, the Luftwaffe's most successful exponent of the Me 262, which was formed in January 1945 under the command of Adolf Galland with 10 holders of the Knight's Cross among its nominal strength of 50 pilots.*

BELOW *Take-off and landing were the Me 262A's most vulnerable moments. Acceleration with the landing gear and flaps down was sluggish as it took time for the engines to 'spool up'. As a result Allied fighters often lurked near Me 262 airfields to pick off machines in the landing pattern.*

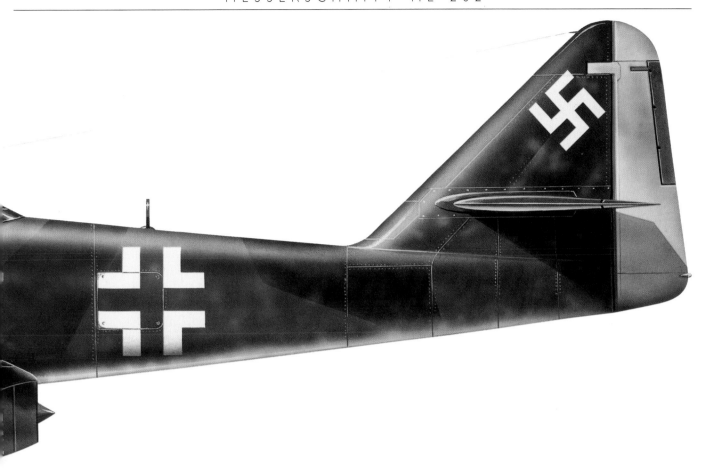

SPECIFICATIONS: Messerschmitt Me 262A-1a

GENERAL
Type: interceptor fighter
Accommodation: pilot in an enclosed cockpit
Equipment: standard communication and navigation equipment, plus a Revi 16/B reflector sight or, in later aircraft, an Askania EZ 42 gyro gun sight
Weights: empty 4420kg (9742lb); normal take-off 6396kg (14,101lb); maximum take-off 7130kg (15,720lb)

MOTIVE POWER
Powerplant: two Junkers Jumo 004B-1/2/3

Orkan turbojet engines each rated at 8.825kN (1984lb st)
Fuel: internal fuel 2570 litres (565.3Imp gal; 678.9US gal); external fuel none

PERFORMANCE
Maximum speed: 870km/h (540mph) at 6000m (19,685ft) declining to 827km/h (514mph) at sea level; cruising speed not available
Initial climb rate: 1200m (3937ft) per minute; climb to 6000m (19,685ft) in 6 minutes 48 seconds
Typical range: 1050km (652 miles)

DIMENSIONS
Wing span: 12.51m (41ft 0.5in)
Wing area: 21.70sq m (233.58sq ft)
Length: 10.60m (34ft 9.3in)
Height: 3.83m (12ft 6.8in)

ARMAMENT
Fixed armament: four 30mm MK108 fixed forward-firing cannon, with 100 and 80 rounds per gun for the upper and lower pairs respectively, in the nose
Disposable armament: none

109-003 units they replaced, and this demanded the use of longer nacelles and, in order to maintain directional stability, an enlargement of the vertical tail surface's area. Trials of the Me 262 V3 started in July 1942, but were initially stymied by the refusal of the Me 262 V3's tail to lift from the runway. It was soon established that the problem lay with the tailwheel landing gear, which meant that the wing blanketed the horizontal tail surface during the take-off run and prevented the elevator from becoming

effective. It was suggested that as a temporary expedient the brakes might be touched at the appropriate moment, the resulting momentary deceleration serving to lift the tail, and this trick worked well enough for the Me 262 V3 to achieve its turbojet-powered maiden flight on 18 July.

The programme was now delayed when the Me 262 V3, which was the sole aeroplane with a turbojet powerplant, was badly damaged. A limited amount of flying was continued with the piston-engined Me 262 V1 as the Me

ABOVE *Seen in American hands after its capture in 1945, this is an example of the Me 262B-2a/U1 night-fighter. The type was used in small numbers for the defence of Berlin, and was fitted on the nose with the antennae for the FuG 218 Neptun V interception radar.*

262 V2 was completed with a powerplant of two Jumo 109-004A turbojets for a first flight in October 1942. Throughout this period there had been considerable high-level scepticism about the Me 262 programme, but the good handling and very useful performance of the Me 262 V3 ensured that another three prototypes and 20 pre-production aircraft were ordered, the latter with a

powerplant of two Jumo 109-004B turbojets that offered the same power as the Jumo 109-004A but at considerable reduced weight.

Luftwaffe evaluation

In April 1942, Generalleutnant Adolf Galland, the inspector of fighters, assessed the Me 262 and decided that the type could have enormous operational potential if only its endurance could be increased significantly. There was adequate volume for an enlargement of the fuel tankage, but this raised the spectre of greater weight (demanding greater power or resulting in degraded performance) and also

spurred the Luftwaffe to demand, despite the protests of Dipl.-Ing. Willy Messerschmitt, the replacement of the current type of tailwheel landing gear by tricycle landing gear for improved performance and safety at take-off. The Luftwaffe felt that the Me 262 with these changes would represent a wholly new aerial capability for virtually unchallengeable air superiority, and demanded large-scale production even if this meant the cancellation of existing production programmes, including that for the Bf 109 fighter but not that of the Focke-Wulf Fw 190 fighter. There followed a period of protracted infighting in the higher echelons of the German air ministry and the Nazi party

machine as the scale and timing of the Me 262 programme became the subject of argument in which considerations of personal standing were more important than Germany's military needs.

As these arguments proceeded, Messerschmitt moved ahead with the development of the Me 262 toward production status with a pressurised cockpit, an ejection seat and, as pioneered in the Me 262 V5 prototype, fixed tricycle landing gear. The Me 262 V6 introduced retractable tricycle landing gear, ports in the upper part of the nose for the proposed armament of four 30mm cannon, and lower-drag nacelles for the two Jumo 109-004B turbojets each

rated at 8.825kN (1984lb st) but 90kg (198lb) lighter than the less powerful Jumo 109-004A turbojets fitted in the early aircraft.

ABOVE *Looking somewhat odd as a result of its tailwheel landing gear, the Me 262 V2 was the second exclusively turbojet-powered Me 262 prototype and the third prototype to fly.*

Me 262 fighter-bombers

In November the Me 262 V7 introduced cabin pressurisation that doubled the apparent altitude, and also a blown canopy. Toward the end of the same month the Me 262 V4 and Me 262 V6 were demonstrated to Adolf Hitler and Reichsmarschall Hermann Göring. The German dictator was particularly impressed with the new type but demanded that the Me 262 should be finalised as a fighter-bomber that would be able to use its speed advantage to take the war to the Allies with offensive action. This meant a revision of the Me 262's armament arrangement, but Hitler's approval of the type ended the previous squabbles and ensured that the Me 262 programme received the highest possible priority. Between December 1943 and February 1944 the remaining pre-production aircraft were completed to the Me 262A-0 basic fighter standard but could not be flown for shortage of the Jumo 109-004B engine, whose development and production programme had fallen well behind schedule and which was also needed for another high-priority programme—the Arado Ar 234 Blitz bomber.

In April 1944 16 of these pre-production aircraft were finally completed and delivered to the Luftwaffe, which now formed Erprobungskommando 262 to introduce the Me 262 to service and develop appropriate operating techniques and tactics. It was at this point that Hitler discovered the fact that none of the aircraft had been completed with bomb-carrying capability (inevitable as these were pre-production aircraft started before his demand for this ability) and, flying into a passionate rage, demanded that such capability be provided forthwith. In fact the ability to carry bombs was already under investigation by Messerschmitt, which evaluated both conventional and unconventional methods of meeting this requirement. The conventional method comprised a side-by-side pair of hardpoints under the fuselage, forward of the main wheel wells, for the carriage of one 1000kg (2205lb) bomb, or two 500 or 250kg (1102 or 551lb) bombs. The unconventional method was the towed bomb, which comprised a single 1000 or 500kg (2205 or 1102lb) weapon fitted with a wooden wing and towed by a rigid 6.1m (20ft) tube attached below the Me 262's tail by a swivel joint permitting horizontal and vertical movement: the tube was hollow and contained the wires to detonate the explosive bolts connecting the bomb to the tube and its wing.

Further delays

Although it has been claimed that the development of a bomb-carrying capability delayed the Me 262 programme by between four and six months, the real cause of the delay was slow progress in Jumo 109-004B production. The design of the engine was finally 'frozen' in June 1944, and resulted in a rapid acceleration of engine production so that the Luftwaffe could take delivery of its first 28 aircraft during that month, followed by 59 in the next month although deliveries fell to 20 in August because of further engine production problems.

The model first delivered to the Luftwaffe was the Me 262A-1a that received the nickname 'Schwalbe' ('swallow') and was basically similar to the Me 262A-0 pre-production fighter apart from its use of the Jumo 109-004B-1 production-standard engine that was later supplanted by the improved Jumo 109-004B-2 and Jumo 109-004B-3 engines. Service trials and initial operational use confirmed that the Me 262A-1a was much faster throughout all parts of the flight envelope than its piston-engined contemporaries, could turn as tightly but held its turning speed better, possessed poorer acceleration and deceleration, had much

superior diving capabilities so long as the limiting Mach number was not exceeded, and had good handling characteristics marred only slightly by modest directional instability that did not materially affect the type's steadiness as a gun platform.

The first operational sorties were flown by Erprobungskommando 262 with Me 262A-0 aircraft late in June 1944, and resulted in the destruction of three Allied high-altitude photo-reconnaissance aircraft before a de

BELOW *The thirst of its engines combined with the weight and drag of its radar limited the endurance of the Me 262B-1a/U1 on internal fuel, so the type was operated with a pair of 300-litre (66Imp gal; 79.26US gal) drop tanks on the paired pylons under the forward fuselage.*

Havilland Mosquito managed to evade an Me 262A in July 1944 and return with direct evidence of the new fighter's operational advent. It was only two days after this that the Gloster Meteor F.Mk I was cleared for operational use as the Allies' first turbojet-powered fighter.

The only other Me 262A variants were the Me 262A-1a/U1, Me 262A-1a/U3 and Me 262A-1b. Only three examples of the first were completed with the nose-mounted armament revised to two 30mm MK103 cannon with 72 rounds per gun, two 30mm MK108 cannon with 66 rounds per gun and two 20mm MG151/20 cannon with 146 rounds per gun. The Me 262A-1a/U3 was a reconnaissance fighter conversion of the standard interceptor with the cannon armament reduced to two 30mm MK108 weapons so that volume would be freed in the nose for two Rb 50/30 cameras or alternatively for single examples of the Rb 20/30 and Rb 75/30 cameras. The Me 262A-1b, of which only small numbers were completed, was fitted with two flush-fitting wooden racks under the wing for the carriage of 24 R4M air-to-air rockets, another pioneering weapon. A different armament installation tested but not approved for production was a single 50mm BK 5 fixed forward-firing gun considered for use as a long-range bomber destroying weapon.

The 'Sturmvogel'

The Me 262A-2 was the fighter-bomber development of the Me 262A fighter, and received the nickname 'Sturmvogel' (storm bird). Delivered from a time early in July 1944, the Me 262A-2a initial model differed from the Me 262A-1a only in having two hardpoints for the carriage of one 500kg (1102lb) or two 250kg (551lb) bombs. Two of the aircraft were evaluated in Me 262A-2a/U1 form with the nose-mounted armament reduced to two 30mm MK108 cannon to allow the installation of the Tief- und Sturzfluganlage (low- and dive-bombing flight device) for improved bombing accuracy, but soon after this Hitler's order that all Me 262 aircraft be completed with bombing capability was revoked and manufacturing priority returned to the interceptor version. One interesting development that proceeded no further than the prototype stage was the Me 262A-2a/U2 with the cannon-carrying metal nose replaced by a plywood nose carrying a prone bombardier position with a bomb-aiming transparency and a gyro-stabilised Lofte 7H bomb sight.

The Me 262A-3 model was introduced to overcome the problems encountered in ground-attack work by the Me 262A-1. These problems included the low muzzle velocity of the MK108 cannon, the relatively small ammunition capacity

of these weapons, and the paucity of protection against ground fire. The Me 262A-3a addressed only the last of these factors, being fitted with additional armour protecting the fuel tanks as well as the floor and sides of the cockpit.

The Me 262A-5 was a reconnaissance fighter version of the standard interceptor with the cannon armament reduced to two 30mm MK108 weapons so that volume would be freed in the nose for two Rb 50/30 cameras or alternatively for single examples of the Rb 20/30 and Rb 75/30 cameras.

The Me 262B was developed as the dual-control conversion trainer counterpart of the Me 262A series with the cockpit lengthened to the rear for the instructor's position. The first version was the Me 262B-1a delivered from November 1944 with the internal fuel capacity sacrificed to the instructor's position. This was partly offset by provision for two drop tanks carried on the underfuselage hardpoints. Deliveries amounted to only 15 aircraft, for operational demands had now overtaken the trainer requirement. Thus the Me 262B-1a was replaced in production by the Me 262B-1a/U1 night-fighter with the rear cockpit occupied by the operator of the FuG 218 Neptun V radar, whose four-pole Hirschgeweih antenna array was installed on the nose, and the FuG 350 ZC Naxos equipment designed to home on the emissions of the H2S radar used by British bombers.

The Me 262B-1a/U1 was considered only an interim type pending the development of the Me 262B-2a as the definitive night-fighter model. This was designed with a fuselage lengthened by the insertion of additional sections fore and aft of the cockpit to increase length by 1.20m (3ft 11.25in) and provide additional volume for fuel tankage that was now increased in capacity to 2900 litres (637.9Imp gal; 766.1US gal) from the figure of 1730 litres (380.6Imp gal; 457US gal) in the Me 262B-1. The Me 262B-2a/U1 retained provision for the two drop tanks under the forward fuselage, and added capability to tow a 1500 litre (330Imp gal; 396.25US gal) flying drop tank from the attachment under the rear fuselage. Like the flying bomb that had originally been intended for this hardpoint, the flying drop tank was supported for take-off on a small two-wheel dolly that fell away after lift-off. The drag of the Hirschgeweih antenna array reduced speed by 60km/h (37mph), so it was decided to replace the FuG 218 radar with the FuG 240 Berlin centimetric air interception radar with a dish antenna inside the nose, but none of these aircraft had been delivered before Germany's surrender.

Another variant that was overtaken by events and thus failed to achieve production status was the Me 262C series with performance boosted by the installation of an HWK 109-509 (Walter R II-211/3) rocket in the extreme tail.

ARADO AR 196

In 1936 the German air ministry issued a requirement for a catapult-launched floatplane to replace the Heinkel He 50 then operating as the primary reconnaissance aircraft for the German navy. The attached specification called for a two-seat aeroplane with one-or two-float alighting gear and a single engine in the power range between 597 and 671 kW (800 and 900 hp).

The winning contender was the Arado Ar 196, a monoplane of basically all-metal construction. Of the five prototypes two were Ar 196As with twin-float alighting gear and the other three were Ar 196Bs with one central float and two small stabilising floats. All five aircraft were powered by the BMW 132Dc engine rated at 656kW (880hp), and for a fuller evaluation there followed 10 and five examples respectively of the Ar 196A-0 and Ar 196B-0 pre-production aircraft with the 708kW (950hp) BMW 132K engine and the armament limited to one 7.92mm MG15 rearward-firing machine-gun. At the conclusion of the evaluation the Ar 196A was preferred for full service.

Production of the Ar 196 totalled 546 aircraft. Some of these were completed in 1942-43 by the SNCA company at St Nazaire, and by Fokker in the Netherlands. The very first deliveries of the Ar 196A-1, with two 7.92mm machine guns and strengthening for catapult launches, were made in the autumn of 1939, and these 20 aircraft were followed by the Ar 196B-2 with two 20mm cannon in the wing and one 7.92mm MG17 in the fuselage. Subsequent variants were the Ar 196A-3 with additional strengthening as well as improved radio equipment and a more efficient propeller, and the Ar 196A-4 (a shipborne counterpart of the A-3). The final model was the Ar 196A-5 with further revised radio equipment and an additional 7.92mm MG81z rearward-firing machine gun. Production of the A-5 totalled 91.

The Ar 196 was used on most of the German navy's major surface warships, and was also used increasingly for the coastal patrol and anti-shipping roles in virtually every theatre in which the Germans fought.

SPECIFICATIONS: Arado Ar 196A-3

GENERAL
Type: coastal reconnaissance and light attack floatplane
Accommodation: pilot and observer/gunner in tandem in an enclosed cockpit
Equipment: standard communication and navigation equipment, plus optical gun sights and provision for a reconnaissance camera
Weights: empty 2572kg (5670lb); normal take-off 3303kg (7282lb); maximum take-off 3730kg (8223lb)

MOTIVE POWER
Powerplant: one BMW 132K radial piston engine rated at 716kW (960hp) for take-off and 723kW (970hp) at 670m (1480ft)

Fuel: internal fuel 600 litres (132Imp gal; 158.5US gal); external fuel none

PERFORMANCE
Maximum speed: 320km/h (199mph) at 900m (2955ft) declining to 312km/h (194mph) at 4000m (13,125ft)
Cruising speed: 268km/h (166.5mph) at 800m (2955ft)
Initial climb rate: 415m (1362ft) per minute
Service ceiling: 7000m (22,960ft)
Maximum range: 1070km (665 miles); typical range 800km (497 miles)

DIMENSIONS
Wing span: 12.44m (40ft 9.77in)
Wing area: 28.30sq m (304.63sq ft)
Length: 10.96m (35ft 11.5in)

Height: 4.45m (14ft 7.25 in)

ARMAMENT
Fixed armament: two 20mm MG FF fixed forward-firing cannon with 60 rounds per gun in the leading edges of the wing, one 7.92mm MG17 fixed forward-firing machine gun with 500 rounds in the starboard side of the forward fuselage with synchronisation equipment to fire through the propeller disc, and one 7.92mm MG15 trainable rearward-firing machine gun with 535 rounds in the cockpit rear
Disposable armament: up to 100kg (220lb) of disposable stores carried on two hardpoints (both under the wing with each unit rated at 50kg [110lb]), and generally comprising two 50kg (110lb) SC-50 bombs

BLOHM UND VOSS BV 138

The Bv 138A-1 was powered by three Jumo 205C-4 engines and possessed a fixed armament of one 20mm trainable cannon in the bow turret and two 7.92mm MG15 trainable machine guns in open positions to the rear of the centreline engine. There followed 14 examples of the Bv 138B-1 with three Jumo 205D engines, heavier defensive armament and, in the Bv 138B-1/U1 subvariant, an option for a heavier bomb load.

The aircraft was designed under the supervision of Dr.-Ing. Richard Vogt at Hamburger Flugzeugbau, which was later absorbed into Blohm und Voss. Delays to the intended engines meant that the design had to be recast for a powerplant of three lower-rated Junkers Jumo 205C Diesel engines. The Ha 138 V1 made its maiden flight on 15 July 1937, but trials revealed that the 'boat' was hydrodynamically and aerodynamically unstable.

Modification of the tail did not provide an adequate cure, and a major redesign followed to create the Bv 138A. This had a much improved hull and altered tail surfaces on larger booms. The Bv 138A-1 was the initial production model; 25 were delivered for operational use in the Norwegian campaign of 1940.

The main production model, of which about 227 were completed, was the Bv 138C-1 with additional structural strengthening, improved defensive armament including two cannon-armed turrets and, in the Bv 138C-1/U1, provision for an enhanced bomb load. The only other variant was the Bv 138MS minesweeping model, of which a small number was created with all armament capability removed and a Dural degaussing loop added.

SPECIFICATIONS: Blohm und Voss Bv 138C-1

GENERAL
Type: maritime reconnaissance flying boat
Accommodation: pilot and co-pilot side-by-side on the enclosed flightdeck, and navigator/radio operator and two gunners carried in the hull
Equipment: standard communication and navigation equipment, plus optical sights and provision for a reconnaissance camera
Weights: empty 11,770kg (25,948lb); normal take-off 14,500kg (31,967lb); maximum take-off 17,650kg (38,912lb)

MOTIVE POWER
Powerplant: three Junkers Jumo 205D vertically opposed Diesel engines each rated at 656kW (880hp) for take-off or 746kW (1000hp) for take-off with water/methanol injection, 559kW (750hp) for 30 minutes, and 484.5kW (650hp) for continuous running; provision was also made for two Walter 109-501 RATO units each rated at 9.81kN (2205lb st) for 42.5 seconds or two

Walter 109-502 RATO units each rated at 14.71kN (3307lb) for 30 seconds
Fuel: internal fuel 2280 litres (501.5Imp gal; 602.3US gal) plus provision for 2940 litres (646.7Imp gal; 776.7US gal) of auxiliary fuel in wing spar tanks; external fuel none

PERFORMANCE
Maximum speed: 285km/h (177mph) at sea level
Cruising speed: maximum 265km/h (165mph) at 1000m (3280ft) and economical 235km/h (146mph) at optimum altitude
Climb: to 3000m (9845ft) in 22 minutes 48 seconds
Service ceiling: 5000m (16,405ft)
Maximum range: 4300km (2672 miles) with auxiliary fuel; typical range 1220km (758 miles) with standard fuel; endurance 18 hours 0 minutes with auxiliary fuel and 6 hours 30 minutes with standard fuel

DIMENSIONS
Wing span: 26.94m (88ft 4.63in)
Wing area: 112.00sq m (1204.60sq ft)
Length: 19.85m (65ft 1.5in)
Height: 5.90m (19ft 4.28in)

ARMAMENT
Fixed armament: one 20mm MG151/20 trainable forward-firing cannon in the power-operated bow turret, one 20mm MG151/20 trainable rearward-firing cannon in the power-operated turret in the rear hull position, one 13mm MG131 trainable rearward-firing machine gun in the open position behind the central engine nacelle, and one 7.92mm MG15 trainable machine gun in a starboard hull hatch position
Disposable armament: up to 300kg (661lb) of disposable stores carried on one hardpoint (under the starboard wing rated at 300kg [661lb]), and generally comprising two 150kg (331lb) depth charges or three 50kg (110lb) SC-50 bombs

DORNIER DO 24

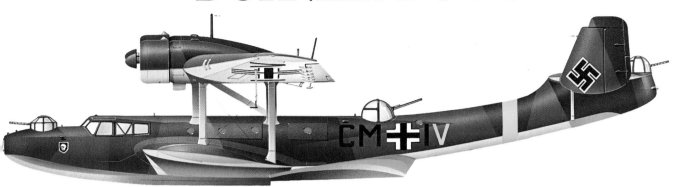

The Dornier Do 24 originated from a requirement issued in 1935 by the Dutch navy for a flying boat to replace its Dornier Wal 'boats'. The Do 24 was an all-metal monoplane with a hull of typical Dornier design and a strut-braced parasol wing that carried the powerplant of three engines. The first two prototypes were completed for evaluation for possible German use, and were each powered by Junkers Jumo 205C Diesel engines. The third prototype, which was actually the first to make its maiden flight on 3 July 1937, and the fourth prototypes were each powered by Wright R-1820-F52 Cyclone radial engines in order to meet the Netherlands' desire to use the same type of engine as fitted on its Martin Model 139 bombers.

The prototypes for the Netherlands completed their evaluation successfully, and another 10 such 'boats' were completed by the Dornier subsidiary in Switzerland with the designation Do 24K-1. Licensed production of 48 Do 24K-2 aircraft, with 746kW (1000hp) R-1820-G102 engines, was started by Aviolanda in the Netherlands with de Schelde building the wings. Only 25 had been delivered before the

German occupation of the Netherlands in May 1940. Three completed 'boats' and a number of partly built airframes were transferred to Germany for evaluation in the air/sea rescue role. As a result the Dutch line was re-established under the control of Weser Flugzeugbau for the production of 170 aircraft in the form of 11 Do 24N-1 'boats' to the Do 24K-2 standard for delivery from August 1941, and 159 examples of the Do 24T with the revised powerplant of three 746kW (1000hp) BMW-Bramo 323R-2 Fafnir radial engines . These 'boats' comprised 110 Do 24T-1 and 49 Do 24T-2 machines, the latter with minor equipment changes, for the use mainly of the 1., 2. and 3./Seenotgruppe based at Biscarosse and Berre in France.

Another 48 Do 24T-1 aircraft were built at the Sartrouville factory of the SNCA du Nord between 1942 and August 1944, and 40 more were delivered to the French navy after the liberation. Twelve more Do 24T-3 aircraft were supplied to Spain under the designation HR.5, deliveries starting in June 1944, to provide search and rescue cover in the Mediterranean for aircrew of both sides.

SPECIFICATIONS: Dornier Do 24T-1

GENERAL
Type: air/sea rescue and transport flying boat
Accommodation: pilot and co-pilot side-by-side in the enclosed cockpit, and navigator, radio operator/gunner and two gunners carried in the hull
Equipment: standard communication and navigation equipment, plus optical gun sights
Weights: empty 10,600kg (23,369lb); normal take-off 16,200kg (35,715lb); maximum take-off 18,400kg (40,565lb)

MOTIVE POWER
Powerplant: three BMW-Bramo 323R-2 Fafnir radial piston engines each rated at 746kW (1000hp) for take-off and 701kW

(940hp) at 4000m (13,125ft)
Fuel: internal fuel 5320 litres (1170.25Imp gal; 1405.4US gal); external fuel none

PERFORMANCE
Maximum speed: 332km/h (206mph) at 2600m (8530ft) declining to 290km/h (180mph) at sea level
Cruising speed: maximum 295km/h (183mph) at 2600m (8530ft) and economical 220km/h (137mph) at optimum altitude
Climb: to 4000m (13,125ft) in 13 minutes 12 seconds
Service ceiling: 8050m (26,405ft)
Maximum range: 4700km (2920.5 miles); typical range 2900km (1802 miles)

DIMENSIONS
Wing span: 27.00m (88ft 6.9in)
Wing area: 108.00sq m (1162.54sq ft)
Length: 22.05m (72ft 4in)
Height: 5.75m (18ft 10.4in)

ARMAMENT
Fixed armament: one 20mm Hispano-Suiza HS-404 trainable cannon with 225 rounds in the dorsal turret, one 7.92mm MG15 trainable forward-firing machine gun with 1200 rounds in the bow turret, and one 7.92mm MG15 trainable rearward-firing machine gun with 1200 rounds in the tail turret
Disposable armament: none

DORNIER DO 215

At the 1937 Zürich international flying meeting considerable interest was shown in Germany's Do 17Z bomber, particularly from Yugoslavia who were considering its capabilities as a potential successor to the earlier Do17K. In an effort to capitalise on this export potential, Dornier redesignated a Do 17Z-0 as the Do 215 V1 for demonstration to potential customers. A production derivative of the Do 215 V3 prototype with 802kW (1075hp) Daimler-Benz DB 601A engines was offered as the Do 215A-1, and in the autumn of 1939 Sweden contracted for 18 aircraft. Before these could be delivered, however, the German government forbade any exports of the bomber.

The aircraft already under construction were completed for the Luftwaffe under the designations Do 215B-0 and B-1 respectively with a four-man crew, bomb load of 1000kg (2205lb), and reconnaissance cameras. The Do 215B-2 was a projected bomber variant which was abandoned at an early stage, while the Do 215B-3 designation was applied to two

aircraft delivered to the USSR early in 1940. The Do 215B-4 was a reconnaissance bomber variant similar to the B-1 but with a different camera fit. Production of the Do 215B-1 and Do 215B-4 totalled 92 aircraft, and these served from a time early in 1940 first with the 3.Aufklärungstaffel of the Luftwaffe high command, later equipping the other two squadrons of the high command reconnaissance wing as well as a small number of other reconnaissance units largely for service over the western USSR.

In 1940 a single night-fighter/intruder prototype was completed under the designation Do 215B-5, with the 'solid' nose of the Do 17Z-10 and an armament consisting of two 20mm MG FF cannon and four 7.92mm MG17 machine guns. There followed four other conversions, and these aircraft were delivered to the 4.Staffel of NG 2 in the spring of 1941 for intruder operations over the British Isles. The Do 215 had disappeared from operational service with the Luftwaffe by 1942, and surviving examples were mostly relegated to various test roles.

SPECIFICATIONS: Dornier Do 215B-1

GENERAL
Type: medium reconnaissance bomber
Accommodation: pilot, navigator/bombardier/gunner, radio operator/gunner and gunner in an enclosed forward-fuselage crew compartment
Equipment: standard communication and navigation equipment, plus an optical bomb sight and optical gun sights
Weights: empty 5775kg (12,731lb); maximum take-off 8800kg (19,400lb)

MOTIVE POWER
Powerplant: two Daimler-Benz DB 601Aa inverted-Vee piston engines each rated at 820kW (1100hp) for take-off
Fuel: internal fuel 1550 litres (341Imp gal; 409.5US gal) plus provision for 895 litres (196.9Imp gal; 236.4US gal) of auxiliary fuel

in a fuselage tank; external fuel none

PERFORMANCE
Maximum speed: 470km/h (292mph) at 5000m (16,405ft) declining to 385km/h (239mph) at sea level
Cruising speed: maximum 410km/h (255mph) at 4000m (13,125ft)
Initial climb rate: 365m (1197ft) per minute; climb to 1000m (3280ft) in 2 minutes 18 seconds
Service ceiling: 9000m (29,530ft)
Maximum range: 2445km (1519 miles) with auxiliary fuel; typical radius 380km (236 miles) with maximum bomb load

DIMENSIONS
Wing span: 18.00m (59ft 0.66in)
Wing area: 55.00sq m (592.03sq ft)
Length: 15.80m (51ft 10.04in)

Height: 4.55m (14ft 11.1in)

ARMAMENT
Fixed armament: two 7.92mm MG15 fixed or trainable forward-firing machine guns in the windscreen, one or two 7.92mm MG15 trainable forward firing machine guns in the nose position, two 7.92mm MG15 trainable lateral-firing machine guns in the side windows, one 7.92mm MG15 trainable rearward-firing machine gun in the dorsal position, and one 7.92mm MG15 trainable rearward-firing machine gun in the ventral position
Disposable armament: up to 1000kg (2205lb) of disposable stores carried in a lower-fuselage weapons bay rated at 1000kg (2205lb), and generally comprising four 250kg (551lb) SC-250 bombs or 10 50kg (110lb) SC-50 bombs

DORNIER DO 335 PFEIL

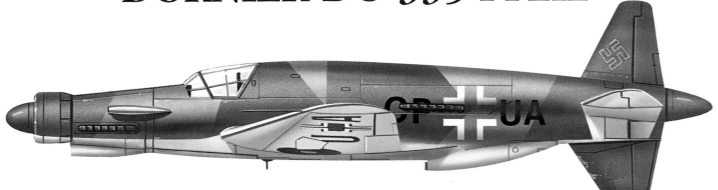

The Dornier Do 335 Pfeil resulted from an attempt to create a single-seat fighter possessing very high outright flight performance through the use of a twin-engined powerplant. The design centred around Prof.-Dr. Dornier's 1937 patent for the installation of the engine on the centre of gravity and driving a rear-mounted propeller. This concept paved the way for the Do 335 Pfeil (arrow). Soon after it had embarked on the detail design of the Do 335, Dornier was informed by the German air ministry that the original bomb-carrying intruder requirement had been abandoned and that the Do 335 was to be finalised as a multi-role fighter with options for development in heavy fighter, fighter-bomber, high-speed light bomber and reconnaissance variants in the baseline single-seat configuration, and in all-weather interceptor and night-fighter variants in a two-seat configuration.

The Do 335 V1 was the first of 14 prototypes and made its maiden flight in October 1943 with two Daimler-Benz DB 603A-2 engines. Test pilots reported excellent flight handling characteristics.

In the late autumn of 1944 production began of the Do 335A-1 Pfeil with two DB 603E-1 engines and underwing hardpoints for the carriage of two bombs or drop tanks. Numerous variants were planned, but by this time the Do 335 programme was suffering seriously from the effects of Germany's increasingly dire situation in the war. There were serious delays in the delivery of engines, propellers, radio equipment, and a number of subcontracted components and assemblies. Even so, the company persevered with production and also with development of improved models.

When advancing US forces overran Dornier's Oberpfaffenhofen facility, Dornier had completed only 11 Do 335A-1 fighters-bombers and two Do 335A-12 conversion trainers, but in final assembly were nine more Do 335A-1, four Do 335A-4 and two Do 335A-12 machines while work on another 70 aircraft was in its earlier stages.

SPECIFICATIONS: Dornier Do 335A-1 Pfeil

GENERAL
Type: fighter-bomber
Accommodation: pilot on a Dornier ejection seat in an enclosed cockpit
Equipment: standard communication and navigation equipment, plus a Revi C 12/D reflector gun/bomb sight
Weights: empty 7260kg (16,005lb); normal take-off 9600kg (21,164lb)

MOTIVE POWER
Powerplant: two Daimler-Benz DB 603E-1 inverted-Vee piston engines each rated at 1342kW (1800hp) for take-off and 1417kW (1900hp) at 1800m (5905ft)
Fuel: internal fuel 1850 litres (407Imp gal; 488.7US gal); external fuel up to 750 litres (165Imp gal; 198.1US gal) in two drop tanks

PERFORMANCE
Maximum speed: 765km/h (475mph) at 6500m (21,325ft)
Cruising speed: maximum 685km/h (426mph) at 7200m (23,620ft) and economical 450km/h (280mph) at 6000m (19,685ft)
Initial climb rate: 660m (2165ft) per minute; climb to 8000m (26,250ft) in 14 minutes 30 seconds
Service ceiling: 11,400m (37,400ft)
Maximum range: 2060km (1280 miles); typical range 1395km (867 miles) with standard fuel at economical cruising speed

DIMENSIONS
Wing span: 13.80m (45ft 3.31in)
Wing area: 38.50sq m (414.42sq ft)
Length: 13.85m (45ft 5.28in)
Height: 5.00m (16ft 4.85in)

ARMAMENT
Fixed armament: one 30mm MK103 fixed forward-firing cannon with 70 rounds in a moteur-canon installation, and two 15mm MG151/15 fixed forward-firing cannon with 200 rounds per gun in the upper part of the forward fuselage with synchronisation equipment to fire through the propeller disc
Disposable weapons: up to 1000kg (2205lb) of disposable stores carried in a lower-fuselage weapons bay rated at 500kg (1102lb) and on two hardpoints, both under the wing with each unit rated at 250kg (551lb), and generally comprising one 500kg (1102lb) SD/PC-500 bomb or two 250kg (551lb) SC-250 bombs carried internally, and two 250kg (551lb) SC-250 bombs carried externally

FIESELER FI 156 STORCH

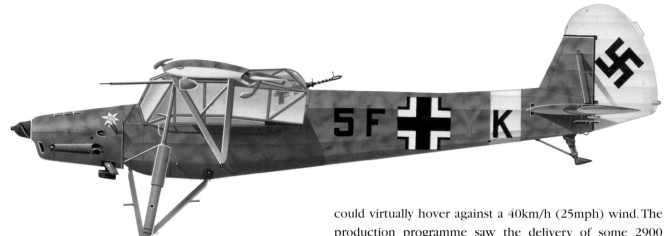

The Fieseler Fi 156 Storch made its maiden flight in the spring of 1936 in response to a German air ministry requirement for a light aeroplane for service in the army co-operation, liaison and casevac roles. The Fi 156 high-lift wing incorporated a fixed slat over the full span of the leading edges and a combination of outboard slotted ailerons and inboard camber-changing flaps along the full span of the trailing edge. The other salient features of the design were a braced high-wing monoplane configuration, a conventional braced tail unit, fixed tailskid landing gear with long-stroke main units, a cabin with extensive glazing for the best possible fields of vision, and an Argus As 10 piston engine.

In a light breeze the Fi 156 could take-off in only 60m (195ft) and land in only one-third of that distance, and could virtually hover against a 40km/h (25mph) wind. The production programme saw the delivery of some 2900 aircraft that operated nearly everywhere that the German forces were engaged right up to the end of World War II. Some remarkable feats of flying were carried out in the Stork, such as the rescue of Mussolini from incarceration in a hotel in the Apennine mountains during September 1943.

During the war the Fi 156 was built for the Luftwaffe by Morane-Saulnier in France and by Mraz in Czechoslovakia. There were numerous wartime developments. The Fi 156C was an improved Fi 156A-1 with raised glazing at the rear of the cabin to allow installation of a 7.92mm trainable machine gun, and was produced in many subvariants. The Fi 156D was the dedicated casevac model with improved facility for one litter and an enlarged loading/unloading hatch, and was produced as the Fi 156D-1 with the As 10P engine. Finally, the Fi 156E had tracked main landing gear units, but was produced to the extent of only 10 Fi 156E-0 pre-production machines.

SPECIFICATIONS: Fieseler Fi 156C-2 Storch

GENERAL

Type: army co-operation, battlefield reconnaissance, liaison and casevac aeroplane

Accommodation: pilot and observer/gunner, or litter, or two passengers in tandem in an enclosed cockpit

Equipment: standard communication and navigation equipment, plus provision for a reconnaissance camera

Weights: empty 940kg (2072lb); normal take-off 1260kg (2778lb); maximum take-off 1320kg (2910lb)

MOTIVE POWER

Powerplant: one Argus As 10C-3 inverted-Vee piston engine rated at 179kW (240hp) for take-off and 149kW (200hp) for continuous running

Fuel: internal fuel 148 litres (32.6Imp gal; 39.1US gal) plus provision for 205 litres (45.1Imp gal; 54.2US gal) of auxiliary fuel in a fuselage tank; external fuel none

PERFORMANCE

Maximum speed: 175km/h (109mph) at sea level

Cruising speed: maximum 145km/h (90mph) at optimum altitude and economical 95km/h (59mph) at optimum altitude

Climb: to 1000 m (3280ft) in 3 minutes 24 seconds

Service ceiling: 5200m (17,060ft)

Maximum range: 1015km (631 miles); typical range 385km (239 miles)

DIMENSIONS

Wing span: 14.25m (46ft 9in)

Wing area: 26.00sq m (279.87sq ft)

Length: 9.90m (32ft 5.75in) with the tail down

Height: 3.05m (10ft 0in) with the tail down

ARMAMENT

Fixed armament: one 7.92mm MG15 trainable rearward-firing machine gun in the cockpit rear

Disposable armament: none

FOCKE-WULF TA 152

Designed to exploit the capabilities inherent in the airframe and engine combination of the Fw 190D for still better high-altitude performance, the Focke-Wulf Ta 152 was initially planned as a simple development of the Fw 190D with hydraulic rather than electrical operation of the flaps and landing gear unit. Following five prototype conversions from Fw 190C standard with the Jumo 213E engine, there appeared four true Ta 152 prototypes with the Jumo 213E engine and a longer wingspan, followed in October 1944 by the first of 20 Ta 152H-0 pre-production aircraft with a pressurised cockpit and provision for one drop tank under the fuselage. The Ta 152H-0's service trials were undertaken by the special Erprobungskommando 152 before the approximately 190 examples of the Ta 152H-1 production model entered service in November 1944 with Jagdgeschwader 301, a unit whose role was the protection of bases used by the Messerschmitt Me 262 turbojet-powered fighter which, as a result of its powerplant's

indifferent acceleration rate, was particularly vulnerable during take-off and landing. That said, the majority of Ta 152s were destroyed by ground-attack Allied aircraft while still awaiting Luftwaffe acceptance. Other Ta 152Hs served alongside Fw 190Ds in the close support role. The Ta 152H-10 was a reconnaissance version of the Ta 152H-1, which was supposed to enter production in May 1945. However, this model failed to see fruition. Another reconnaissance version of the aircraft was the Ta 152E-2, the intended armament for which was an engine-mounted 30mm Mk 103 or Mk 108, and a 20mm MG 151 cannon in each wing root. Planned production was scheduled to begin in March 1945, with 630 examples being delivered by the end of the year. However, production plans for the Ta 152E-2 were scrapped in February 1945. In general, the early Ta 152C series were superb flying machines, but the long-span H series sacrificed guns for speed and height. Only a small number of Ta 152s had been delivered by the time the war ended in May 1945 – 67 excluding development aircraft .

SPECIFICATIONS: Focke-Wulf Ta 152H-1

GENERAL
Type: interceptor fighter
Accommodation: pilot in an enclosed cockpit
Equipment: standard communication and navigation equipment, plus a Revi 16/D reflector gun sight
Weights: empty 4031kg (8887lb); normal take-off 4750kg (10,472lb); maximum take-off 5217kg (11,051lb)

MOTIVE POWER
Powerplant: one Junkers Jumo 213EB inverted-Vee piston engine rated at 1402kW (1880hp) for take-off and 1670kW (2240hp) at high altitude with MW 50 methanol/water injection

Fuel: internal fuel 524 litres (115.25Imp gal; 138.4US gal) plus provision for 115 litres (25.3Imp gal; 30.4US gal) of auxiliary fuel in an optional rear-fuselage tank; external fuel none

PERFORMANCE
Maximum speed: 760km/h (472mph) at 12,500m (41,010ft) with MW 50 and GM 1 power-boost systems, or 745km/h (463mph) at 9500m (31,170ft) with MW 50 power-boost system
Cruising speed: maximum 600km/h (373mph)
Initial climb rate: 1050m (3445ft) per minute
Service ceiling: 14,800m (48,555ft)
Maximum range: 1520km (944 miles);

typical range 1200km (746 miles)

DIMENSIONS
Wing span: 14.50m (47ft 6.86in)
Wing area: 23.50sq m (252.95sq ft)
Length: 10.71m (35ft 1.66in)
Height: 3.38m (11ft 1in)

ARMAMENT
Fixed armament: one 30mm MK108 fixed forward-firing cannon in a Motorkanone installation, and two 20mm MG151/20E fixed forward-firing cannon with 250 rounds per gun in the leading edges of the wing roots with synchronisation equipment to fire through the propeller disc
Disposable armament: none

GOTHA GO 244

Designed by Dipl.-Ing Albert Kalkert, the Gotha Go 242 assault glider received official approval as it provided almost three times the troop-carrying capacity of the DFS 230 then in use as the German airborne arm's standard assault glider. The type was based on a central payload nacelle carried by a high-set wing that supported the twin booms and tail unit. The central nacelle was fabricated of steel tube under a covering of fabric and carried jettisonable landing gear and two retractable skids, and the wings were of wooden construction skinned with plywood and fabric. The Go 242A-1 could embark up to 23 troops; alternative loads were freight or a light vehicle.

Flown in 1941, the two prototypes were followed into service during 1942 by the first of 1526 production gliders in the Go 242A (two subvariants), Go 242B (five subvariants) and Go 242C (one subvariant) series, the last with a planing bottom and underwing stabilising floats for a projected attack on the Royal Navy at Scapa Flow.

With the fall of France in June 1940 and large parts of the western USSR from June 1941, Germany acquired large stocks of 533kW (715hp) Gnome-Rhône 14M and 559kW (750hp) Shvetsov M-25A radial engines. The decision was then made to create a powered version of the Go 242 to provide greater operational versatility even though with either of these engines the type was somewhat underpowered. A number of prototype conversions, some of them with the BMW 132 radial engine, was followed by the Go 244B service version, of which 43 were built and another 133 created as Go 242B conversions. Entering service in May 1942, the type was available in five subvariants based on those of the Go 242B, namely the Go 244B-1 with fixed landing gear, the Go 244B-2 with revised landing gear including a larger semi-retractable nose wheel, the Go 244B-3 and G-244B-4 paratroop-carrying versions of the Go 244B-1 and Go 244B-2 freighters, and the Go 244B-5 trainer with dual controls.

SPECIFICATIONS: Gotha Go 244B-2

GENERAL
Type: medium transport aeroplane
Accommodation: pilot and co-pilot side-by-side in the enclosed cockpit, and up to 23 troops or freight carried in the hold
Equipment: standard communication and navigation equipment, plus optical gun sights
Weights: empty 5225kg (11,517lb); maximum take-off 7800kg (17,196lb)

MOTIVE POWER
Powerplant: two Gnome-Rhône 14M-4/5 radial piston engines each rated at 522kW (700hp) for take-off and 492kW (660hp) at 4000m (13,125ft)
Fuel: internal fuel n/a; external fuel none

PERFORMANCE
Maximum speed: 290km/h (180mph) at 4000m (13,125ft)
Cruising speed: maximum 270km/h (168mph) at 3900m (12,795ft) and economical 250km/h (155mph) at optimum altitude
Climb: to 5000m (16,405ft) in 18 minutes 30 seconds
Service ceiling: 7650m (25,100ft); typical range 740km (460 miles)

DIMENSIONS
Wing span: 24.50m (80ft 4.5in)
Wing area: 64.40sq m (693.22sq ft)
Length: 15.80m (51ft 10.08in)

Height: 4.60m (15ft 1in); wheel track 3.40m (11ft 2in)

ARMAMENT
Fixed armament: one 7.92mm MG15 trainable forward-firing machine gun with 125 rounds in the cockpit roof position, one 7.92mm MG15 trainable rearward-firing machine gun with 125 rounds in the tail of the central nacelle, one 7.92mm MG15 trainable lateral-firing machine gun with 125 rounds in each side of the central nacelle, and provision for the embarked troops to fire up to four 7.92mm MG34 machine guns from the hold windows
Disposable armament: none

HEINKEL HE 162 SALAMANDER

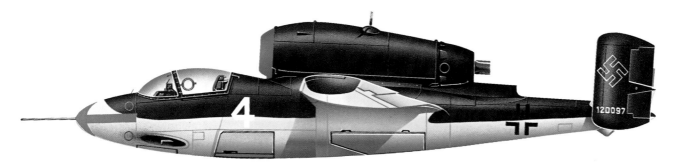

The Heinkel He 162 was in every respect a prodigious effort by the wartime German aero industry. A mere 69 days separated the beginning of the programme from the maiden flight of the He 162 V1 first prototype. The type resulted from a specification issued by the German air ministry in September 1944 calling for high-performance fighter that would be capable of decimating the American bomber fleets that were roaming the skies over Germany with little hindrance, which could be built largely of non-strategic materials by a semi-skilled work force, and which would be available for mass production at the very beginning of January 1945.

Heinkel evolved the He 162 design and built a mock-up in a only 15 days, and just five days later the type was ordered in large numbers. The He 162 was an attractive aeroplane of very clean lines with a mixed light alloy and wood structure, a high-set wing and tricycle landing gear. As Heinkel's facility in Vienna was designing the Salamander and building the prototype and development aircraft, plans were being laid for production of an incredible 4,000 aircraft per month at the Heinkel-Nord facility at Rostock (1,000 machines), the Junkers facility at Dessau (1,000 machines) and Mittelwerke (2,000 machines).

The He 162 V1 prototype made its maiden flight on 6 December 1944 and was later lost after the leading edge of the starboard wing tore off, taking with it the starboard ailerons and wing tip. Development continued with the He 162 V2 and He 162 V3, however, the second and third prototypes that introduced anhedralled wing tips, a weight over the nosewheel unit to move the centre of gravity forward, a larger tail unit, and revisions to the wing roots. A total of 10 true prototypes was completed for the development of the basic aeroplane, and this entered production as the He 162A.

Production started early in 1945, and only some 115 aircraft were completed to two basically similar standards as the He 162A-1 Salamander with a powerplant of one BMW 109-003A-1/2 turbojet and an armament of two 30mm MK108 cannon with 50 rounds per gun, and the He 162A-2 Salamander with a powerplant of one BMW 109-003E-1/2 turbojet and an armament of two 20mm MG151/20 cannon with 120 rounds per gun. The first unit equipped with the type was formed only four days before Germany's surrender in May 1945, and the type saw no real combat. Large numbers of additional aircraft were under construction at the end of the war, and plans had been laid for many developments.

SPECIFICATIONS: Heinkel He 162A-2 Salamander

GENERAL
Type: interceptor fighter
Accommodation: pilot in an enclosed cockpit
Equipment: standard communication and navigation equipment, plus a Revi reflector gun sight
Weights: empty 1663kg (3666lb); normal take-off 2485kg (5478lb); maximum take-off 2605kg (5744lb)

MOTIVE POWER
Powerplant: one BMW 109-003E-1/2 Sturm turbojet engine rated at 7.85kN

(1764lb st) dry
Fuel: internal fuel 950 litres (209Imp gal; 251US gal); external fuel none

PERFORMANCE
Maximum speed: 905km/h (562mph) at 6000m (19,685ft) declining to 790km/h (491mph) at sea level
Cruising speed: not available
Initial climb rate: 594m (1950ft) per minute
Service ceiling: 12,000m (39,370ft);
Maximum range: 975km (606 miles)

DIMENSIONS
Wing span: 7.20m (23ft 7.5in)
Wing area: 11.20sq m (120.56sq ft)
Length: 9.05m (29ft 8.3in)
Height: 2.60m (8ft 6.33in)

ARMAMENT
Fixed armament: two 20mm MG151/20 fixed forward-firing cannon with 120 rounds per gun in the lower sides of the forward fuselage
Disposable armament: none

HENSCHEL HS 123

The Henschel Hs 123 was designed to a 1933 requirement for an interim dive-bomber pending the availability of the Junkers Ju 87. The Henschel Hs 123 V1 made its maiden flight in the spring of 1935 as an unequal-span biplane of metal construction with fabric covering over the wings and moving tail surfaces. Among its features were open accommodation, tailwheel landing gear with wide-track main units that were well faired and carried spatted wheels, and a BMW 132A-3 radial engine, rated at 485kW (650hp), installed under a long-chord cowling. The second prototype introduced a smaller-diameter cowling, with raised blisters over the valve gear, and this was adopted for all later aircraft of the series.

Two of the three initial prototypes were lost as a result of wing failures in the course of diving trials, so a fourth prototype was built with a strengthened wing structure. The success of this machine paved the way for the Hs 123A-1 production model that entered service with the 1.Staffel of Stukageschwader 162 in the autumn of 1936. Production totalled 604 aircraft with the more powerful BMW 132Dc engine, but the type's first-line career as a dive-bomber was comparatively short-lived as it was supplanted by the Ju 87A in 1937 and was then reallocated to the close-support task, for which it was better suited. At the beginning of World War II 40 Hs 123A-1 warplanes equipped the Luftwaffe's sole dedicated close-support unit, II (S)/Lehrgeschwader 2. So successful were the surviving Hs 123A-1 aircraft in the Germans' offensive campaigns between September 1939 and December 1942 that there were demands for production to be resumed. The Hs 123A-1 remained in first-line service to mid-1944, when lack of spares forced its retirement.

In 1938 two more prototypes had been completed with the BMW 132K engine rated at 716kW (960hp) and revised armament as development aircraft for a proposed improved Hs 123B version, but no production followed.

SPECIFICATIONS: Henschel Hs 123A-1

GENERAL
Type: dive-bomber and close-support warplane
Accommodation: pilot in an open cockpit
Equipment: standard communication and navigation equipment, plus an optical gun sight
Weights: empty 1420kg (3131lb); normal take-off 2175kg (4795lb); maximum take-off 2350kg (5181lb)

MOTIVE POWER
Powerplant: one BMW 132A-3 radial piston engine rated at 544kW (730hp) for take-off and 470kW (630hp) at sea level for continuous running
Fuel: internal fuel 270 litres (59.4Imp gal; 71.33US gal); external fuel Disposable armament: up to 130 litres (28.6Imp gal; 34.33US gal) in one drop tank generally

carried on the centreline hardpoint as an alternative to the SC-250 bomb

PERFORMANCE
Maximum speed: 290km/h (180mph) at 2000m (6560ft) declining to 288km/h (179mph) at sea level
Cruising speed: not available
Climb: to 2000m (6560ft) in 4 minutes 24 seconds
Service ceiling: 4100m (13,450ft); typical range 750km (466 miles) with a 100kg (220lb) bomb load or 480km (298 miles) with a 200kg (441lb) bomb load

DIMENSIONS
Wing span: 10.50m (34ft 5.39in)
Wing area: 24.85sq m (267.48sq ft)
Length: 8.66m (28ft 4.94in) with the tail up
Height: 3.76m (12ft 4in) with the tail down

ARMAMENT
Fixed armament: two 7.92mm MG17 fixed forward-firing machine guns with 500 rounds per gun in the upper part of the forward fuselage with synchronisation equipment to fire through the propeller disc
Disposable armament: up to 450kg (992lb) of disposable stores carried on five hardpoints (one under the fuselage rated at 250kg [551lb], and four under the lower wing with each unit of the inboard pair rated at 200kg [441lb] and each unit of the outboard pair at 50kg [110lb]), and generally comprising one 250kg (551lb) SC-250 bomb and four 50kg (110lb) SC-50 bombs, or more often two containers each carrying 92 2kg (4.4lb) SD-2 anti-personnel fragmentation bombs, or two pods each containing one 20mm Oerlikon FF cannon, or four 50kg (110lb) SC-50 bombs

HENSCHEL HS 126

erived from an earlier design, the Hs 122 with a parasol monoplane wing, the Henschel Hs 126 two-seat reconnaissance aircraft was intended to satisfy a German air ministry requirement of the mid-1930s for an army co-operation and short-range tactical reconnaissance aeroplane. By comparison with the Hs 122 (planned as successor to the Heinkel He 45 and He 46), of which three prototypes and a number of pre-production aircraft had been completed, the Hs 126 was a somewhat more sophisticated design and differed from its predecessor in details such as a new wing, cantilever main landing gear units and a canopy over the pilot's cockpit, although the observer/gunner still had an open cockpit.

An Hs 122A airframe was converted as the Hs 126V1 initial prototype with the Junkers Jumo 210 inverted-Vee engine rated at 455kW (610hp), and this made the new type's maiden flight in the autumn of 1936. There followed two development prototypes, the Hs 126 V2 and V3, with a redesigned rudder, a more extensively braced tailplane and, most significantly, the uprated powerplant of one BMW-Bramo 323A-1 Fafnir radial engine rated at 619kW (830hp).

The third prototype formed the basis for the Hs 126A-0 pre-production model, of which 10 were delivered in 1937 for service trials, and the Hs 126A-1 initial production variant with the BMW 132Dc engine, rated at 656kW (880hp), entered service in 1938 initially with Aufklärungsgruppe 35.

By the outbreak of World War II the re-equipment of the Luftwaffe's short-range reconnaissance units was well under way, and the Hs 126A-1 was complemented from the summer of 1939 by the Hs 126B-1 that had improved radio equipment as well as the revised powerplant of one BMW-Bramo 323 Fafnir radial engine for better take-off and flight performance. The surviving aircraft of the Hs 126 series, of which about 800 had been delivered, were withdrawn from first-line service during 1942 with the advent of larger numbers of the altogether superior Focke-Wulf Fw 189.

SPECIFICATIONS: Henschel Hs 126B-1

GENERAL
Type: tactical reconnaissance and army co-operation aeroplane
Accommodation: pilot and observer/gunner in tandem in enclosed and semi-enclosed cockpits
Equipment: standard communication and navigation equipment, plus optical gun sights and provision for a reconnaissance camera
Weights: empty 2032kg (4480lb); maximum take-off 3270kg (7209lb)

MOTIVE POWER
Powerplant: one BMW-Bramo 323A-1 or Q-1 Fafnir radial piston engine rated at 634kW (850hp) for take-off and 619kW (830hp) at 4000m (13,125ft)
Fuel: internal fuel 540 litres (118.8Imp gal; 142.65US gal); external fuel none

PERFORMANCE
Maximum speed: 355km/h (221mph) at 4000m (13,125ft) declining to 310km/h (193mph) at sea level
Cruising speed: maximum 335km/h (208mph) at 4200m (13,780ft) and economical 270km/h (168mph) at optimum altitude
Climb: to 4000m (13,125ft) in 7 minutes 12 seconds
Service ceiling: 8230m (27,000ft)
Maximum range: 720km (447 miles); endurance 2 hours 15 minutes

DIMENSIONS
Wing span: 14.50m (47ft 6.86in)
Wing area: 31.60sq m (340.14sq ft)
Length: 10.85m (35ft 7in)
Height: 3.75m (12ft 3.5in)

ARMAMENT
Fixed armament: one 7.92mm MG17 fixed forward-firing machine gun with 500 rounds in the starboard upper part of the forward fuselage with synchronisation equipment to fire to the propeller disc, and one 7.92mm MG15 trainable rearward-firing machine gun with 975 rounds in the rear cockpit
Disposable armament: up to 150kg (331lb) of disposable stores carried in a lower-fuselage weapons bay rated at 100kg (220lb) and on one hardpoint (on the port side of the fuselage rated at 110lb [50kg]), and generally comprising one 50kg (110lb) SC-50 bombs and 10 10kg (22lb) SC-10 bombs

JUNKERS JU 52/3M

The Ju 52/3m's operational versatility was enhanced by its ability to operate on skis or floats as alternatives to the standard wheels. This was a factor that attracted the German military, whose still secret Luftwaffe evaluated the type in the early 1930s and then ordered its initial two variants as the Ju 52/3m ge interim bomber with three 492kW (660hp) BMW 132A-1 radial engines and then the improved Ju 52/3m g3e bomber/transport with 541kW (725hp) BMW 132A-3 engines, a defensive armament of two 7.92mm MG15 trainable machine guns and up to 500kg (1102lb) of bombs as alternative to passengers or freight. The aircraft first saw action in the Spanish Civil War, initially ferrying some 10,000 Nationalist troops from Morocco to Spain. The last 'interim' model was the Ju 52/3m g4e with a tailwheel rather than a skid and provision for a heavier bomb load. Deliveries of these first three models were more than 500 aircraft.

More than 4000 further machines were completed up to mid-1944 for service as the Luftwaffe's single most important transport in World War II. German production was supplemented by French factories.

The Ju 52/3m operated in the paratroop transport and glider-towing roles as well as standard transport tasks in the hands of the Luftwaffe. Among the most important variants delivered for service in World War II were the Ju 52/3m g5e with three 619kW (830hp) BMW 132T engines, Ju 52/3m g6e development of the Ju 52/3m g5e with simplified radio, and the Ju 52/3m g7e development of the Ju 52/3m g6e with an autopilot and large loading hatch. There was also the Ju 52/3m g9e with strengthened landing gear and glider-towing equipment as standard, Ju 52/3m g10e with provision for float alighting gear, Ju 52/3m g12e with BMW 132L engines, and Ju 52/3m g14e final production version similar to the Ju 52/3m g9e but improved armour protection for pilot and heavier defensive armament.

SPECIFICATIONS: Junkers Ju 52/3m g7e

GENERAL
Type: medium transport aeroplane
Accommodation: pilot and co-pilot side-by-side in the enclosed cockpit, radio operator/gunner in the fuselage, and up to 18 troops, or 12 litters or freight carried in the cabin
Equipment: standard communication and navigation equipment, plus optical gun sights
Weights: empty 6500kg (14,336lb); normal take-off 10,500kg (23,148lb); maximum take-off 11,030kg (24,317lb)

MOTIVE POWER
Powerplant: three BMW 132T-2 radial piston engines each rated at 544kW (730hp) for take-off and 410kW (550hp)

for cruising flight
Fuel: internal fuel 2480 litres (545.5Imp gal; 655.1US gal); external fuel none

PERFORMANCE
Maximum speed: 286km/h (178mph) at 1400m (4590ft) declining to 272km/h (169mph) at sea level
Cruising speed: maximum 257km/h (160mph) at optimum altitude and economical 216km/h (134mph) at optimum altitude
Climb: to 3000m (9845ft) in 17 minutes 30 seconds
Service ceiling: 5900m (19,360ft)
Maximum range: 1305km (811 miles) with overload fuel; typical range 1100km (683.5 miles) with standard fuel

DIMENSIONS
Wing span: 29.25m (95ft 11.5in)
Wing area: 110.50sq m (1189.41sq ft)
Length: 18.90m (62ft 0in)
Height: 5.55m (18ft 2.5in)

ARMAMENT
Fixed armament: one 13mm MG131 or 7.92mm MG15 trainable rearward-firing machine gun with 1050 rounds in the rear dorsal position, provision for one 7.92mm MG15 trainable rearward-firing machine gun in the forward dorsal position, and provision for one 7.92mm MG15 trainable lateral-firing machine gun in each of the two beam positions
Disposable armament: none

JUNKERS JU 86

Designed as a 10-passenger airliner or four-seat bomber, the Junkers Ju 86 was schemed round the powerplant of two Junkers Jumo 205 Diesel engines. The Ju 86a prototype made its maiden flight in 1934. Performance was deemed to be disappointing, but the type still entered production in airliner and bomber forms in late 1935. The first 20 Ju 86A-1 production aircraft were delivered in early 1936.

The Ju 86B and Ju 86C were civil models, so the next military variant was the Ju 86D-1, of which about 140 were completed to an improved Ju 86A-1 standard with a longer tail cone and 447kW (600hp) Jumo 205C engines. The type served during the Spanish Civil War, but proved wholly inferior to the Heinkel He 111. Export orders included the Ju 86K-1 for South Africa and Sweden with Pratt & Whitney Hornet radial engines; the Ju 86K-2 for Hungary; the Ju 86K-4, K-5 and K-13 for Sweden with Bristol Pegasus engines; and the Ju 86K-6 for Brazil, Chile and Portugal.

The unhappiness of the Luftwaffe with the Ju 86D led to the development of the Ju 86E-1 with more reliable 604kW (810hp) BMW 132F radial engines and the Ju 88E-2 with 645kW (865hp) BMW 132N engines. Improvements during production of the first 50 aircraft resulted in the redesignation of the last 40 Ju 86E bombers as Ju 86G-1 aircraft with glazed noses for delivery in 1938.

In 1939 three Ju 86D airframes were converted as Ju 86P prototypes for the high-altitude reconnaissance bomber role with Jumo 207A engines, increased span and a pressurised cabin. Successful trials led to two initial versions, the Ju 86P-1 bomber and Ju 86P-2 reconnaissance bomber, the latter with a ceiling of about 12,800m (41,995ft). Greater altitude capability was needed, however, so a wing spanning 32.00m (104ft 11in) was developed for Ju 86R-1 reconnaissance and Ju 86R-2 bomber aircraft. Only a few of these aircraft entered service. The planned Ju 86R-3 and Ju 186 four-engined high-altitude bomber were both cancelled.

SPECIFICATIONS: Junkers Ju 86D-1

GENERAL
Type: medium bomber
Accommodation: pilot in an enclosed cockpit, and navigator/bombardier/gunner, radio operator/gunner and gunner carried in the fuselage
Equipment: standard communication and navigation equipment, plus a Lofte C/6C optical bomb sight and optical gun sights
Weights: empty 5800kg (12,786lb); normal take-off 8060kg (17,770lb); maximum take-off 8200kg (18,078lb)

MOTIVE POWER
Powerplant: two Junkers Jumo 205C-4 vertically opposed Diesel engines each rated at 447kW (600hp) for take-off and 380kW (510hp) for cruising flight
Fuel: internal fuel 920 litres (202.4Imp gal; 243US gal) plus provision for

Disposable armament: up to 500 litres (110Imp gal; 132.1US gal) of auxiliary fuel in two wing tanks; external fuel none

PERFORMANCE
Maximum speed: 325km/h (202mph) at 3000m (9845ft) declining to 300km/h (186mph) at sea level
Cruising speed: 275km/h (171mph) at 1000m (3280ft)
Initial climb rate: not available
Service ceiling: 5900m (19,360ft)
Maximum range: 1500km (932 miles) with auxiliary fuel; typical range 1140km (708 miles) with maximum bomb load

DIMENSIONS
Wing span: 22.50m (73ft 9.83in)
Wing area: 82.00sq m (882.64sq ft)
Length: 17.56m (57ft 7.8345in)

Height: 5.06m (16ft 7.21in)

ARMAMENT
Fixed armament: one 7.92mm MG15 trainable forward-firing machine gun in the nose position, one 7.92mm MG15 trainable rearward-firing machine gun in the dorsal position, and one 7.92mm MG15 trainable rearward-firing machine gun in the retractable ventral 'dustbin' turret
Disposable armament: up to 1000kg (2205lb) of disposable stores carried in a lower-fuselage weapons bay rated at 1000kg (2205lb), and generally comprising four 250kg (551lb) SC-250 bombs, or eight 100kg (220lb) SC-100 bombs, or 16 50kg (110lb) SC-50 bombs, or four containers each carrying 16 10kg (22lb) or 144 1kg (2.2lb) bomblets

JUNKERS JU 188

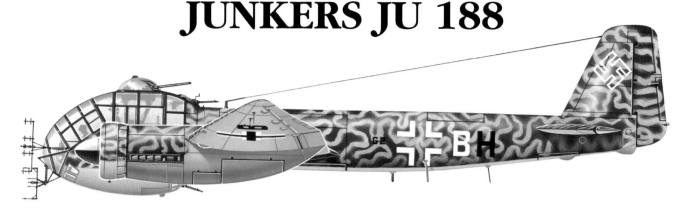

Although by the outbreak of World War II Junkers was well advanced with the design of the Junkers Ju 288 as successor to the Ju 88, a succession of development delays meant that by 1942 it had become clear that the type's operational debut was still some time off, and therefore that an interim successor to the Ju 88 was needed. The origin of this interim type was found in the Ju 88B that had flown during 1940 as a development of the Ju 88 with a considerably enlarged forward fuselage and a wing of increased span. The Ju 88B did not enter full production, a mere 10 pre-production Ju 88B-0 aircraft being completed, but it led to the development of the enhanced Ju 88E-0 that was then used as the basis for the Ju 188 interim bomber and reconnaissance aircraft.

The Ju 188 V1 and V2 prototypes first flew early in 1942 and 1943 respectively, and their successful trials led to the development of a production model that was purposefully designed for the use (without airframe modification) of either the BMW 801 radial engine or the Junkers Jumo 213 inverted-Vee engine (the latter with an annular radiator). The first production model was the Ju 188E-1 with BMW 801ML engines each rated at 1193kW (1600hp), and this entered service in February 1943. The first Junkers-powered model was the Ju 188A-2 with two Jumo 213A-1 engines each rated at 1670kW (2240hp) with water-methanol injection.

Production of the Ju 188 totalled more than 1100 aircraft, more than half of this figure being reconnaissance aircraft. Variants included the Ju 188A-2 bomber and Ju 188A-3 torpedo-bomber, the Ju 188D-1 and Ju 188D-2 reconnaissance aircraft, the Ju 188E-1 bomber and Ju 188e-2 torpedo-bomber, the Ju 188F-2 reconnaissance aircraft with BMW 801D engines, the Ju 188S-1 high-altitude intruder and the Ju 188T-1 high-altitude reconnaissance models, both of the last without defensive armament.

SPECIFICATIONS: Junkers Ju 188E-1

GENERAL
Type: medium bomber
Accommodation: pilot, navigator/bombardier/gunner, radio operator/gunner and gunner in the enclosed crew compartment
Equipment: standard communication and navigation equipment, plus an optical bomb sight and optical gun sights
Weights: empty 9410kg (20,745lb); maximum take-off 14,570kg (32,121lb)

MOTIVE POWER
Powerplant: two BMW 801D-2 radial piston engines each rated at 1250kW (1677hp) for take-off and 1059kW (1420hp) at 6000m (19,685ft)
Fuel: internal fuel 3650 litres (802.8Imp gal; 964.25US gal); external fuel none

PERFORMANCE
Maximum speed: 544km/h (338mph) at 8000m (26,245ft) with GM 1 power boost declining to 425km/h (264mph) at sea level
Cruising speed: 375km/h (233mph) at 5000m (16,405ft)
Climb: to 6000m (19,685ft) in 17 minutes 24 seconds
Service ceiling: 10,100m (33,135ft)
Maximum range: 3120km (1939 miles) with maximum fuel; typical range 2480km (1541 miles) with a 1500kg (3307lb) weapons load

DIMENSIONS
Wing span: 22.00m (72ft 2in)
Wing area: 56.00sq m (602.78sq ft)
Length: 15.06m (49ft 4.9in)
Height: 4.46m (14ft 7.6in) with the tail down

ARMAMENT
Fixed armament: one 20mm MG151/20 trainable forward-firing cannon with 200 rounds in the nose position, one 13mm MG131 trainable machine gun with 750 rounds in the power-operated EDL 131 dorsal turret, one 13mm MG131 trainable rearward-firing machine gun with 750 rounds in the cockpit rear, and one 7.92mm MG81z trainable rearward-firing two-barrel machine gun with 1000 rounds in the rear of the undernose gondola
Disposable armament: up to 3000kg (6614lb) of disposable stores carried in a lower-fuselage weapons bay rated at 1400kg (3086lb) and on four hardpoints (all under the wing with each unit of the inboard pair rated at 1000kg [2205lb] and each unit of the outboard pair at 500kg [1102lb]), and generally comprising 20 70kg (154lb) SD-70 or two 240kg (551lb) SC-250 bombs carried internally, and two 1000kg (2205lb) SC/SD-1000 bombs, or four 500kg (1102lb) SC/SD-500 bombs, or four 250kg (551lb) SC-250 bombs carried externally

MESSERSCHMITT ME 323 GIGANT

The Messerschmitt Me 321 Gigant (giant) was originally schemed as a heavy glider for the invasion of the UK, an operation that was then cancelled but nonetheless left a requirement for a glider of this type for use in the German invasion of the USSR. Messerschmitt received a contract for 100 aircraft, which first flew on 25 February 1941 as the Me 321 V1 prototype. A jettisonable take-off dolly was used for flight testing, the aircraft then landing on sprung skids, and up to eight rockets, could be installed to assist the take-off behind a tug such as the Junkers Ju 90.

The Me 321A-1 entered service late in 1941, and 100 gliders of this initial type with a crew of one were followed by 100 examples of the Me 321B-1 with a crew of three and two defensive machine guns. A spate of take-off accidents clearly indicated the need for a more powerful tug, resulting in the use of three Messerschmitt Bf 110 twin-engined fighters. It became clear that what was really needed was a

powered version, and this was developed as the Me 323 with multi-wheel landing gear, structural strengthening and, in the V1 and V2 prototype conversions from Me 321B standard, the powerplant of four or six Gnome-Rhône radial engines. The four-engined Me 323C was not produced, and the initial production variant was the Me 323D-1 with the ability to carry a payload of 9750kg (21,495lb) over a range of 1000km (621 miles). Deliveries began in August 1942, and in November of the same year the Me 323D began full service with flights across the Mediterranean in support of the Afrika Korps, soon suffering very heavy losses despite its relatively potent defensive armament. The three Me 323E subvariants introduced a stronger structure, greater fuel capacity and heavier defensive armament including, in the Me 323E-3/WT escort model, 11 20mm trainable cannon and four 13mm trainable machine guns. The Me 323 ended its operational career in mid-1944, by which time it was serving only on the Eastern Front.

SPECIFICATIONS: Messerschmitt Me 323E-2 Gigant

GENERAL

Type: heavy transport aeroplane
Accommodation: pilot and co-pilot side-by-side and flight engineer and radio operator on an enclosed flightdeck, load master and up to six gunners, and up to 120 troops, or 60 litters plus attendants, or freight carried in the hold
Equipment: standard communication and navigation equipment, plus optical gun sights
Weights: empty 29,600kg (65,256lb); maximum take-off 45,000kg (99,206lb)

MOTIVE POWER

Powerplant: six Gnome-Rhône 14N-48/49 radial piston engines each rated at 850hp (1140hp) for take-off and 772kW (1035hp)

at 4800m (15,750ft)
Fuel: internal fuel 10,740 litres (2362.5Imp gal; 2837.2US gal); external fuel none

PERFORMANCE

Maximum speed: 253km/h (157mph) at sea level declining to 220km/h (137mph) at 3000m (9845ft)
Cruising speed: economical 225km/h (140mph) at sea level
Initial climb rate: 264m (866ft) per minute
Service ceiling: 4500m (14,760ft)
Typical range: 1300km (808 miles)

DIMENSIONS

Wing span: 55.00m (180ft 5.35in)

Wing area: 300.00sq m (3229.17sq ft)
Length: 28.50m (93ft 6in)
Height: 9.60m (31ft 6in)

ARMAMENT

Fixed armament: one 20mm MG151/20 trainable cannon in each of two power-operated EDL 151 wing turrets, one 13mm MG131 trainable forward-firing machine gun in each of the two nose door positions, one 13mm MG131 trainable rearward-firing machine gun in the rear of the flightdeck, and one 13mm MG131 trainable lateral-firing machine gun in each of the two forward and two beam positions
Disposable armament: none

MESSERSCHMITT ME 410 HORNISSE

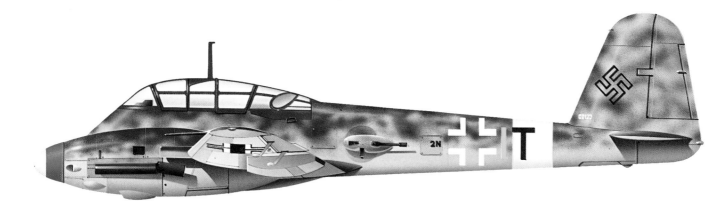

The Messerschmitt Me 410 Hornisse (hornet) was in essence an attempt to rectify the problems of the Me 210 twin-engined heavy fighter, and emerged as an excellent example of this type of warplane. Prefaced by the Me 210 V17 prototype conversion from Me 210A-0 standard and then by 22 Me 410 prototypes, the Me 410A initial production model entered service in January 1943 with the powerplant of two Daimler-Benz DB 603A inverted-Vee engines each rated at 1305kW (1750hp). Included in the total of 1138 production aircraft delivered by Messerschmitt and Dornier up to September 1944 were the Me 410A-1 high-speed bomber with provision for 1000kg (2205lb) of bombs, the Me 410A-1/U1

reconnaissance model, the Me 410A-1/U2 heavy fighter, the Me 410A-2 heavy fighter with dive-bombing capability, and the Me 410A-3 long-range reconnaissance model.

The Me 410B switched to DB 603G engines each rated at 1417kW (1900hp). The main subvariants of the Me 410B were the Me 410B-1 high-speed bomber with Me 410B-1/U2 and U4 subvariants equivalent to those of the Me 410A-1, the Me 410B-2 heavy fighter with U2 and U4 subvariants, the Me 410B-3 long-range reconnaissance model, the Me 410B-5 torpedo-fighter, the Me 410B-6 heavy and night fighter with heavier fixed forward-firing armament and provision for radar, and the Me 410B-7 and Me 410B-8 day and night reconnaissance models.

SPECIFICATIONS: Messerschmitt Me 410A-1/U2

GENERAL
Type: heavy fighter and fighter-bomber
Accommodation: pilot and radio operator/gunner in tandem in an enclosed cockpit
Equipment: standard communication and navigation equipment, plus a Revi C/12D reflector gun sight and a remote sighting system for the lateral barbettes
Weights: empty 7518kg (16,574lb); normal take-off 9651kg (21,276lb)

MOTIVE POWER
Powerplant: two Daimler-Benz DB 603A inverted-Vee piston engines each rated at 1305kW (1750hp) for take-off and 1212kW (1625hp) at 5700m (18,700ft)

Fuel: internal fuel 2420 litres (532.3Imp gal; 639.3US gal); external fuel none

PERFORMANCE
Maximum speed: 624km/h (388mph) at 6700m (21,980ft) declining to 507km/h (315mph) at sea level
Cruising speed: maximum 587km/h (365mph)
Climb: to 6700m (21,980ft) in 10 minutes 42 seconds
Service ceiling: 10,000m (32,810ft)
Maximum range: 1670km (1050 miles)

DIMENSIONS
Wing span: 16.35m (53ft 7.7in)
Wing area: 26.20sq m (389.69sq ft)

Length: 12.48m (40ft 11.3in)
Height: 4.28m (14ft 0.5in)

ARMAMENT
Fixed armament: two 20mm MG151/20 fixed forward-firing cannon with 350 rounds per gun in the nose, two 20mm MG151/20 fixed forward-firing cannon with 250 rounds per gun in a ventral tray, two 7.92mm MG17 fixed forward-firing machine guns with 1000 rounds per gun in the nose, and one 13mm MG131 trainable lateral/rearward-firing machine gun with 500 rounds in each of the two remotely controlled power-operated FDSL barbettes on the sides of the fuselage
Disposable armament: none

German Fighter Aces during World War II

Highest-scoring ace:	*Major Erich Hartmann*	352 victories
Highest-scoring night-fighter ace:	*Major Heinz Schnaufer*	121 victories
First ace to score 100 victories:	*Major Werner Moelders*	15 July 1941
First ace to score 150 victories:	*Major Gordon Gollob*	29 August 1942
First ace to score 200 victories:	*Hauptmann Hermann Graf*	2 October 1942
First ace to score 250 victories:	*Major Walter Nowotny*	14 October 1943
First ace to score 300 victories:	*Hauptmann Erich Hartmann*	14 August 1944
First and only ace to score 350 victories:	*Major Erich Hartmann*	8 May 1945
Most victories gained in one day:	*Major Emil Lang*	18 victories
Most victories in one sortie:	*Major Erich Rudorffer*	(6 November 1943) 13 victories
Most victories gained against the Western Allies:	*Hauptmann Hans-Joachim Marseille*	158 victories
Most victories gained on the Eastern Front:	*Major Erich Hartmann*	352 victories
Best victory average per sortie (day fighters):	*Leutnant Guenther Scheel*	70 sorties/71 victories
Highest-scoring day ace against multi-engined aircraft:	*Leutnant Herbert Rollwage*	101 victories
Highest-scoring night ace against multi-engined aircraft:	*Major Heinz Schnaufer*	121 victories
Highest-scoring jet ace:	*Oberleutnant Kurt Weller*	20+ victories

LUFTWAFFE ACES WITH 100 OR MORE VICTORIES IN THE AIR

	Name	Rank	Victories
1	*Hartmann, Erich*[4]	Major	352 (including one four- and 90 two-engined aircraft)
2	*Barkhorn, Gerhard*[3]	Major	301
3	*Rall, Guenther*[3]	Major	275
4	*Kittel, Otto*[3]	Oberleutnant	267
5	*Nowotny, Walter*[4]	Major	258
6	*Batz, Wilhelm*[3]	Major	237
7	*Rudorffer, Erich*[3]	Major	222
8	*Baer, Heinrich*[3]	Oberstleutnant	220
9	*Graf, Hermann*[4]	Oberst	212
10	*Ehrler, Heinrich*[2]	Major	209 (possibly 220)
11	*Weissenberger, Theodor*[2]	Major	208 (8 in Me 262 jet fighter)
12=	*Philipp, Hans*[3]	Oberstleutnant	206
12=	*Schuck, Walter*[2]	Oberleutnant	206
14	*Hafner, Anton*[2]	Oberleutnant	204
15	*Lipfert, Helmut*[2]	Hauptmann	203
16	*Krupinski, Walter*[2]	Major	197
17	*Hackl, Anton*[3]	Major	192
18=	*Brendel, Joachim*[2]	Hauptmann	189
18=	*Stotz, Max*[2]	Hauptmann	189
20	*Kirschner, Joachim*[2]	Hauptmann	188
21	*Brandle, Werner-Kurt*[2]	Major	180
22	*Josten, Guenther*[2]	Leutnant	178
23	*Steinhoff, Johannes*[3]	Oberstleutnant	176
24=	*Reinert, Ernst-Wilhelm*[3]	Oberleutnant	174
24=	*Schack, Guenther*[2]	Hauptmann	174
26=	*Schmidt, Heinz*[2]	Hauptmann	173
26=	*Lang, Emil*[1]	Hauptmann	173
28	*Adameit, Horst*[2]	Major	166
29	*Wilcke, Wolf-Dietrich*[3]	Oberstleutnant	162
30	*Marseille, Hans-Joachim*[4]	Hauptmann	158 (including 17 in one day)
31=	*Sturm, Heinrich*[1]	Hauptmann	157
31=	*Thyben, Gerhard*[2]	Oberleutnant	157
33=	*Duettmann, Peter*[1]	Leutnant	152
33=	*Beisswenger, Hans*[2]	Oberleutnant	152
35	*Gollob, Gordon*[4]	Oberst	150
36	*Tegtmeier, Fritz*[2]	Oberleutnant	146
37	*Wolf, Albin*[2]	Oberleutnant	144 (possibly 176)
38	*Tanzer, Kurt*[1]	Oberleutnant	143
39	*Mueller, Friedrich-Karl*[2]	Major	140
40=	*Gratz, Karl*[1]	Oberleutnant	138
40=	*Setz, Heinrich*[2]	Major	138
40=	*Truenkel, Rudolf*[1]	Hauptmann	138
43	*Schall, Franz*[2]	Hauptmann	137

43= *Wolfrum, Walter*[1]	Oberleutnant	137
45= *Dickfeld, Adolf*[2]	Oberstleutnant	136
45= *von Fassong, Horst-Guenther*[1]	Hauptmann	136
45= *Foennekold, Otto*[1]	Oberleutnant	136
45= *Weber, Karl-Heinz*[2]	Major	136
49 *Muencheberg, Joachim*[3]	Major	135
50 *Waldmann, Hans*[2]	Oberleutnant	134
51= *Grislawski, Alfred*[2]	Hauptmann	133
51= *Wiese, Johannes*[2]	Major	133
53= *Borchers, Adolf*[1]	Major	132
53= *Clausen, Erwin*[2]	Major	132
55 *Lemke, Wilhelm*[2]	Hauptmann	131
56= *Ihlefeld, Herbert*[3]	Oberstleutnant	130
56= *Sterr, Heinrich*[2]	Oberleutnant	130 (including 7 in Spain)
58 *Eisenach, Franz*[1]	Major	129
59= *Dahl, Walther*[2]	Oberst	128
59= *Doerr, Franz*[1]	Hauptmann	128
61 *Obleser, Friedrich*[1]	Oberleutnant	127
62= *Rademacher, Rudolf*[1]	Leutnant	126
62= *Zwernemann, Josef*[2]	Oberleutnant	126
64= *Hoffmann, Gerhard*[1]	Oberleutnant	125
64= *Hrabak, Dietrich*[2]	Oberstleutnant	125
64= *Oesau, Walter*[3]	Oberstleutnant	125 (including 8 in Spain)
67 *Ettel, Wolf-Udo*[2]	Oberleutnant	124
68 *Tonne, Wolfgang*[2]	Hauptmann	122
69= *Marquardt, Heinz*[1]	Oberfeldwebel	121
69= *Schnaufer, Heinz-Wolfgang*[4]	Major	121 (all at night)
69= *Weiss, Robert*[2]	Hauptmann	121
72 *Leie, Erich*[1]	Major	118
73= *Beerenbrock, Hans*[2]	Leutnant	117
73= *Birkner, Hans-Joachim*[1]	Leutnant	117
73= *Norz, Jakob*[1]	Leutnant	117
73= *Wernicke, Heinz*[1]	Leutnant	117
77 *Lambert, August*[1]	Oberleutnant	116 (including 17 in one day)
78 *Moelders, Werner*[4]	Oberst	115 (including 14 in Spain)
79= *Crinius, Wilhelm*[2]	Leutnant	114
79= *Schroer, Werner*[3]	Major	114
81= *Dammers, Hans*[1]	Leutnant	113
81= *Korts, Berthold*[1]	Leutnant	113
83 *Buehligen, Kurt*[3]	Oberstleutnant	112
84= *Lent, Helmut*[4]	Oberstleutnant	110 (including 102 at night)
84= *Ubben, Kurt*[2]	Major	110
84= *Woidich, Franz*[1]	Leutnant	110
87 *Seiler, Reinhard*[2]	Major	109 (including 9 in Spain)
88= *Bitsch, Emil*[1]	Hauptmann	108
88= *Hahn, Hans (Assi)*[2]	Major	108
88= *Luetzow, Guenther*[3]	Oberstleutnant	108
88= *Vechtel, Bernard*[1]	Leutnant	108
92= *Bauer, Viktor*[2]	Hauptmann	106
92= *Lucas, Werner*[1]	Hauptmann	106
94= *Galland, Adolf*[4]	Generalleutnant	104
94= *Sachsenberg, Heinz*[1]	Leutnant	104
96 *Grasser, Hartmann*[2]	Major	103
97= *Freytag, Siegfried*[2]	Major	102
97= *Geisshardt, Friedrich*[2]	Hauptmann	102
97= *Mayer, Egon*[3]	Oberstleutnant	102
97= *Ostermann, Max-Hellmuth*[3]	Oberleutnant	102
97= *Rollwage, Herbert*[2]	Oberleutnant	102 (including 44 four-engined aircraft)
97= *Wurmheller, Josef*[3]	Major	102
103= *Miethig, Rudolf*[1]	Oberleutnant	101
103= *Mueller, Rudolf*[1]	Oberfeldwebel	101
103= *Priller, Josef (Pips)*[3]	Oberst	101
103= *Wernitz, Ulrich*[1]	Leutnant	101
107 *Daehne, Paul-Heinrich*[1]	Oberleutnant	100

LUFTWAFFE ACES WITH 50 OR MORE NIGHT VICTORIES

	Name	Rank	Victories
1	*Schnaufer, Heinz-Wolfgang* [4]	Major	121
2	*Lent, Helmut* [4]	Oberst	102 (plus 8 by day)
3	*zu Sayn-Wittgenstein, Prinz Heinrich* [3]	Major	83
4	*Streib, Werner* [3]	Oberst	66
5	*Meurer, Manfred* [2]	Hauptmann	65
6=	*Radusch, Guenther* [2]	Oberst	64
6=	*Roekker, Heinz* [2]	Hauptmann	64
6=	*Schoenert, Rudolf* [2]	Major	64
9	*Zorner, Paul* [2]	Major	59
10	*Raht, Gerhard* [2]	Hauptmann	58
11=	*Becker, Martin* [1]	Hauptmann	57
11=	*Herget, Wilhelm* [2]	Major	57 (plus 14 by day)
13=	*Francsi, Gustav* [1]	Oberleutnant	56
13=	*Kraft, Josef* [2]	Hauptmann	56
13=	*Struening, Heinz* [2]	Hauptmann	56
16	*Frank, Hans-Dieter* [2]	Hauptmann	55
17	*Vinke, Heinz* [2]	Oberfeldwebel	54
18=	*Geiger, August* [2]	Hauptmann	53
18=	*Luetje, Herbert* [2]	Oberstleutnant	53
20=	*Drewes, Martin* [2]	Major	52
20=	*Hoffmann, Werner* [1]	Major	52
22	*zu Lippe-Weissenfeld, Prinz Egmont* [2]	Major	51
23=	*Welter, Kurt* [2]	Oberleutnant	50
23=	*Greiner, Hermann* [2]	Hauptmann	50

[1] *Knight's Cross of the Iron Cross*
[2] *Knight's Cross of the Iron Cross with Oak Leaves*
[3] *Knight's Cross of the Iron Cross with Oak Leaves and Swords*
[4] *Knight's Cross of the Iron Cross with Oak Leaves, Swords and Diamonds*

GERMAN JET ACES OF WORLD WAR II

	Name	Rank	Victories
1	*Welter, Kurt*	Oberleutnant	20
2	*Baer, Heinz*	Oberstleutnant	16
3	*Schall, Franz*	Hauptmann	14
4=	*Buchner, Hermann*	Oberfeldwebel	12
4=	*Eder, Georg-Peter*	Major	12
4=	*Rudorffer, Erich*	Major	12
7	*Schnörrer, Karl*	Leutnant	11
8=	*Büllner, Erich*	Oberfeldwebel	8
8=	*Lennartz, Helmut*	Feldwebel	8
8=	*Rademacher, Rudolf*	Leutnant	8
8=	*Schuck, Walter*	Oberleutnant	8
8=	*Wegmann, Günther*	Oberleutnant	8
8=	*Weibs, Hans-Dieter*	Leutnant	8
8=	*Weissenberger, Theodor*	Major	8
15=	*Ambs, Alfred*	Leutnant	7
15=	*Arnold, Heinz*	Oberfeldwebel	7
15=	*Becker, Karl-Heinz*	Feldwebel	7
15=	*Galland, Adolf*	Generalleutnant	7
15=	*Köster, Franz*	Unteroffizier	7
20=	*Müller, Fritz*	Leutnant	6
20=	*Steinhoff, Johannes*	Oberst	6
22=	*Baudach, Helmut*	Oberfeldwebel	5
22=	*Ehrler, Heinrich*	Major	5
22=	*Grünberg, Hans*	Oberleutnant	5
22=	*Helm, (name not known)*	Gefreiter	5
22=	*Neumann, Klaus*	Leutnant	5
22=	*Schreiber, Alfred*	Leutnant	5
22=	*Späte, Wolfgang*	Major	5

Luftwaffe Order of Battle (1 September 1939)

LEHRDIVISION (OPERATIONAL TRAINING AND DEVELOPMENT DIVISION)

Strategic reconnaissance units

7.(F)/LG 2	Jüterbog-Damm	Dornier Do 17 (12)
8.(F)/LG 2	Jüterbog-Damm	Dornier Do 17 (12)

Tactical reconnaissance units

9.(H)/LG 2	Jüterbog-Damm	Henschel Hs 126 (11)

Fighter units

Stab/LG 2	Jüterbog-Damm	Messerschmitt Bf 109 (3)
I (J)/LG 2	Garz	Messerschmitt Bf 109 (36)
11.(N)/LG 2	Garz	Messerschmitt Bf 109 (10)

Heavy fighter unit

I (Z)/LG 1	Barth	Messerschmitt Bf 110 (32)

Bomber units

Stab (K)/LG 1	Greifswald	Heinkel He 111 (10)
II (K)/LG 1	Neubrandenburg & Schwerin	Heinkel He 111 (41)
III (K)/LG 1	Greifswald	Heinkel He 111 (10)
10.(See)/LG 2	Travemünde	Heinkel He 111 (9)

Dive-bomber unit

IV (St)/LG 1	Barth	Junkers Ju 87 (39)
		Dornier Do 17 (3)

LUFTFLOTTE I (1ST AIR FLEET) in north-east Germany

Strategic reconnaissance units

3.(F)/10	Neuhausen	Dornier Do 17 (12)
2.(F)/11	Grossenhain	Dornier Do 17 (12)
3.(F)/11	Grossenhain	Dornier Do 17 (10)
4.(F)/11	Grossenhain	Dornier Do 17 (11)
1.(F)/120	Neuhausen	Dornier Do 17 (13)
1.(F)/121	Prenzlau	Dornier Do 17 (11)
2.(F)/121	Prenzlau	Dornier Do 17 (10)
3.(F)/121	Prenzlau	Dornier Do 17 (12)
4.(F)/121	Prenzlau	Dornier Do 17 (11)

Tactical reconnaissance units

1.(H)/10	Neuhausen	Henschel Hs 126 (11)
2.(H)/10	Neuhausen	Henschel Hs 126 (12)
1.(H)/11	Grossenhain	Henschel Hs 126 (9)
		Heinkel He 46 (3)
1.(H)/21	Stargard	Henschel Hs 126 (12)
2.(H)/21	Stargard	Henschel Hs 126 (12)
3.(H)/21	Stargard	Henschel Hs 126 (11)
4.(H)/21	Stargard	Heinkel He 45 (9)
1.(H)/41	Reichenberg	Henschel Hs 126 (12)
2.(H)/41	Reichenberg	Henschel Hs 126 (11)
3.(H)/41	Reichenberg	Henschel Hs 128 (9)
		Heinkel He 46 (2)

Fighter units

I/JG 1	Seerappen	Messerschmitt Bf 109 (54)
I./JG 21	Jesau	Messerschmitt Bf 109 (29)
I./JG 2	Döberitz	Messerschmitt Bf 109 (42)
10.(N)/JG 2	Fürstenwalde	Messerschmitt Bf 109 (9)
1. & 2./JG 20	Fürstenwalde	Messerschmitt Bf 109 (21)

Stab/JG 9	Bernburg	Messerschmitt Bf 109 (3)
I/JG 3	Zerbst	Messerschmitt Bf 109 (48)

Heavy fighter units

I/ZG 1	Jüterbog-Damm	Messerschmitt Bf 110 (32)
II/ZG 1 (JGr 101)	Fürstenwalde	Messerschmitt Bf 109 (36)
I/ZG 2 (JGr 102)	Bernburg	Messerschmitt Bf 109 (44)

Bomber units

Stab/KG 1	Neubrandenburg	Heinkel He 111 (7)
I/KG 152 (II/KG 1)	Neubrandenburg	Heinkel He 111 (37)
I/KG 1	Kolberg	Heinkel He 111 (38)
Stab/KG 2	Cottbus	Dornier Do 17 (11)
I/KG 2	Liegnitz	Dornier Do 17 (37)
II/KG 2	Liegnitz	Dornier Do 17 (32)
Stab/KG 3	Elbing	Dornier Do 17 (9)
II/KG 3	Heiligenbeil	Dornier Do 17 (36)
III/KG 9	Heiligenbeil	Dornier Do 17 (38)
I /KG 25	Rechlin	Junkers Ju 88 (18)
Stab/KG 4	Erfurt	Heinkel He 111 (6)
I/KG 4	Gotha	Heinkel He 111 (31)
II/KG 4	Erfurt	Heinkel He 111 (32)
III/KG 4	Nordhausen	Heinkel He 111 (33)

Dive-bomber units

I/StG 1	Insterburg	Junkers Ju 87 (35)
		Dornier Do 17 (3)
I/StG 2	Cottbus	Junkers Ju 87 (38)
II/StG 2	Stolp-Reitz	Junkers Ju 87 (38)
III/StG 2	Langensalza	Junkers Ju 87 (40)

Ground-attack unit

II (Schl)/LG 2	Tutow	Henschel Hs 123 (40)

LUFTFLOTTE 2 (2ND AIR FLEET) in north-west Germany

Strategic reconnaissance units

1.(F)/22	Kassel-Rothwesten	Dornier Do 17 (11)
2.(F)/22	Kassel-Rothwesten	Dornier Do 17 (12)
9.(F)/22	Kassel-Rothwesten	Dornier Do 17 (12)
1.(F)/122	Goslar	Dornier Do 17 (6)
3.(F)/122	Goslar	Dornier Do 17 (12)

Tactical reconnaissance units

1.(H)/12	Münster-Loddenheide	Henschel Hs 126 (12)
2.(H)/12	Münster-Loddenheide	Henschel Hs 126 (12)
3.(H)/12	Münster-Loddenheide	Henschel Hs 126 (9)
		Heinkel He 46 (1)
4.(H)/12	Münster-Loddenheide	Heinkel He 46 (9)
		Heinkel He 45 (3)
4.(H)/22	Kassel-Rothwesten	Henschel Hs 126 (12)

Fighter units

I/JG 26	Köln-Ostheim	Messerschmitt Bf 109 (48)
II/JG 26	Düsseldorf	Messerschmitt Bf 109 (48)
10.(N)/JG 26	Düsseldorf	Messerschmitt Bf 109 (9)

Heavy fighter units

I/ZG 26	Dortmund	Messerschmitt Bf 109 (52)
II/ZG 26	Werl	Messerschmitt Bf 109 (48)
III/ZG 26 (JGr 126)	Lippstadt	Messerschmitt Bf 109 (49)

Bomber units

Stab/KG 26	Lüneburg	Heinkel He 111 (8)
I/KG 26	Lübeck-Blankensee	Heinkel He 111 (32)
II/KG 26	Lüneburg	Heinkel He 111 (35)
Stab/KG 27	Hannover-Langenhagen	Heinkel He 111 (6)
I/KG 27	Hannover-Langenhagen	Heinkel He 111 (34)
II/KG 27	Wunstorf	Heinkel He 111 (26)
III/KG 27	Delmenhorst	Heinkel He 111 (28)
II/KG 28	Gütersloh	Heinkel He 111 (35)

LUFTFLOTTE III (3RD AIR FLEET)
in south-west Germany

Strategic reconnaissance units

1.(F)/123	Würzburg	Dornier Do 17 (12)
2.(F)/123	Würzburg	Dornier Do 17 (12)
3.(F)/123	Würzburg	Dornier Do 17 (13)

Tactical reconnaissance units

1.(H)/13	Göppingen	Henschel Hs 126 (12)
2.(H)/13	Göppingen	Henschel Hs 126 (11)
3.(H)/13	Göppingen	Henschel Hs 126 (12)
4.(H)/13	Göppingen	Henschel Hs 126 (9)
		Heinkel He 46 (3)
5.(H)/13	Göppingen	Henschel Hs 126 (9)
		Heinkel He 45 (3)
1.(H)/23	Eschwege	Henschel Hs 126 (12)
2.(H)/23	Eschwege	Heinkel He 46 (12)
4.(H)/23	Eschwege	Heinkel He 46 (9)
		Heinkel He 45 (3)

Fighter units

I/JG 51	Bad Aibling	Messerschmitt Bf 109 (47)
I/JG 52	Böblingen	Messerschmitt Bf 109 (39)
I/JG 53	Wiesbaden-Erbenheim	Messerschmitt Bf 109 (51)
II/JG 53	Mannheim-Sandhofen	Messerschmitt Bf 109 (43)
1. and 2./JG 70	Nürnberg	Messerschmitt Bf 109 (24)
1./JG 71	Friedrichshafen	Messerschmitt Bf 109 (15)
2./JG 71	Friedrichshafen	Messerschmitt Bf l09 (24)
10.(N)/JG 72	Mannheim-Sandhofen	Arado Ar 68 (16)
11.(N)/JG 72	Stuttgart-Echterdingen	Arado Ar 68 (12)

Heavy fighter unit

I/ZG 52 (JGr 152) Illesheim		Messerschmitt Bf 109 (44)

Bomber units

Stab/KG 51	Landsberg	Heinkel He 111 (6)
		Dornier Do 17 (9)
I/KG 51	Landsberg	Heinkel He 111 (36)
III/KG 53	Memmingen	Heinkel He 111 (36)
Stab/KG 53	Ansbach	Heinkel He 111 (6)
I/KG 53	Ansbach	Heinkel He 111 (32)
II/KG 53	Schwäbisch-Hall	Heinkel He 111 (32)
III/KG 53	Giebelstadt	Heinkel He 111 (35)
Stab/KG 54	Fritzlar	Heinkel He 111 (9)
I/KG 54	Fritzlar	Heinkel He 111 (36)
Stab/KG 55	Giessen	Heinkel He 111 (9)
I/KG 55	Langendiebach	Heinkel He 111 (39)
II/KG 55	Giessen	Heinkel He 111 (31)

Dive-bomber units

III/StG 51	Wertheim	Junkers Ju 87 (46)
		Dornier Do 17 (3)

LUFTFLOTTE IV (4TH AIR FLEET)
in south-east Germany, Austria and Czechoslovakia

Strategic reconnaissance units

4.(F)/14	Köttingbrunn	Dornier Do 17 (11)
3.(F)/31	Brieg	Dornier Do 17 (12)
l.(F)/124	Wiener-Neustadt	Dornier Do 17 (11)

Tactical reconnaissance units

1.(H)/14	Köttingbrunn	Henschel Hs 126 (9)
		Heinkel He 46 (3)
2.(H)/14	Köttingbrunn	Henschel Hs 126 (12)
3.(H)/14	Köttingbrunn	Henschel Hs 126 (9)
		Heinkel He 46 (3)
1.(H)/31	Brieg	Henschel Hs 126 (9)
2.(H)/31	Brieg	Heinkel He 46 (8)
4.(H)/31	Brieg	Heinkel He 46 (9)
		Heinkel He 45 (3)

Fighter units

I/JG 76	Wien-Aspern	Messerschmitt Bf 109 (49)
I/JG 77	Breslau	Messerschmitt Bf 109 (50)
II/JG 77	Pilsen	Messerschmitt Bf 109 (50)

Heavy fighter units

I/ZG 76	Olmütz	Messerschmitt Bf 110 (31)
II/ZG 76 (JGr 176) Gablingen		Messerschmitt Bf 109 (40)

Bomber units

Stab/KG 76	Wiener-Neustadt	Dornier Do 17 (9)
I/KG 76	Wiener-Neustadt	Dornier Do 17 (36)
III/KG 76	Wels	Dornier Do 17 (39)
Stab/KG 77	Prag-Kbely	Dornier Do 17 (9)
I/KG 77	Prag-Kbely	Dornier Do 17 (37)
II/KG 77	Brünn	Dornier Do 17 (39)
III/KG 77	Olmütz	Dornier Do 17 (34)

Dive-bomber units

Stab/StG 77	Breslau-Schöngarten	Junkers Ju 87 (3)
I/StG 77	Brieg	Junkers Ju 87 (40)
II/StG 77	Breslau-Schöngarten	Junkers Ju 87 (42)
I/StG 76	Graz	Junkers Ju 87 (39)
		Dornier Do 17 (3)

Transport units

Stab/KGzbV 1	Fürstenwalde & Burg	
I/KGzbV 1	Burg	
II/KGzbV 1	Stendal	
III/KGzbV 1	Berlin-Tempelhof	
IV/KGzbV 1	Braunschweig	
Stab/KGzbV 2	Neuruppin	
I/KGzbV 2	Tutow	Junkers Ju 52/3m (496)
II/KGzbV 2	Fassberg	
III/KGzbV 2	Lechfeld	
I/KGzbV 172	Berlin-Tempelhof	
II/KGzbV 172	Berlin-Tempelhof	
I/KGzbV 172	Berlin-Tempelhof	
II/KGzbV 172	Berlin-Tempelhof	
10./KGzbV 172	Berlin-Tempelhof	
KGzbV 9	Berlin-Tempelhof	Junkers Ju 52/3m (56)
		Focke-Wulf Fw 200 (2)
		Junkers Ju 90 (2)
		Junkers G 38b (1)

Coastal units: North Sea

Stab/KüFlGr 106 Norderney
1.(M)/KüFlGr 106 Norderney
2.(F)/KüFlGr 106 Borkum
3.(Mz)/KüFlGr 106 Borkum
1.(M)/KüFlGr 306 Norderney
Stab/KüFlGr 406 List/Sylt
1.(M)/KüFlGr 406 List/Sylt
2.(F)/KüFlGr 406 List/Sylt
3.(Mz)/KüFlGr 406 List/Sylt

Dornier Do 18 (36)
Heinkel He 59 (31)
Heinkel He 60 (54)
Heinkel He 115 (8)

Shipborne unit: North Sea

1./BFlGr 196   Wilhelmshaven   Arado Ar 106 (6)

Coastal units: Baltic

Stab/KüFlGr 506 Dievenow
1.(M)/KüFlGr 506 Dievenow
2.(F)/KüFlGr 506 Dievenow
3.(Mz)/KüFlGr 506 Dievenow
Stab/KüFlGr 706 Kamp bei Kolberg
1.(M)/KüFlGr 506 Kamp bei Kolberg
3.(Mz)/KüFlGr 506 Kamp bei Kolberg
2.(F)/KüFlGr 606 Kamp bei Kolberg

Dornier Do 18 (27)
Heinkel He 60 (27)
Heinkel He 111 (21)

Shipborne units: Baltic

5./BFlGr 196	Kiel-Holtenau	Arado Ar 196 (8)
4.(St)/TrGr 186	Kiel-Holtenau	Junkers Ju 87 (12)
5.(J)/TrGr 186	Kiel-Holtenau	Messerschmitt Bf 109 (12)
6.(J)/TrGr 186	Kiel-Holtenau	Messerschmitt Bf 109 (12)

Luftwaffe Order of Battle in the West for Adler Tag (13 August 1940) in the Battle of Britain

LUFTFLOTTE II (2ND AIR FLEET) in the Low Countries and north-eastern France, headquartered at Brussels in Belgium

I.Fliegerkorps (1st Flying Corps) headquartered in Beauvais

Strategic reconnaissance units

5.(F)/122	Dutch airfields	Heinkel He 111
		Junkers Ju 88
4.(F)/123	Belgian airfields	Heinkel He 111
		Junkers Ju 88

Bomber units

Stab/KG 1	Rosières-en-Santerre	Heinkel He 111H
I/KG 1	Montdidier	Heinkel He 111H
II/KG 1	Montdidier	Heinkel He 111H
III/KG 1	Rosiéres-en-Santerre	Junkers Ju 88A-1
Stab/KG 76	Cormeilles-en-Vexin	Dornier Do 17Z
I/KG 76	Beauvais-Tille	Dornier Do 17Z
II/KG 76	Creil	Junkers Ju 88A
III/KG 76	Cormeilles-en-Vexin	Dornier Do 17Z

II.Fliegerkorps (2nd Flying Corps) headquartered at Ghent

Bomber units

Stab/KG 2	Arras	Dornier Do 17Z
I/KG 2	Cambrai-Epinoy	Dornier Do 17Z
II/KG 2	Arras	Dornier Do 17Z
III/KG 2	Cambrai-Niergnies	Dornier Do 17Z
Stab/KG 3	Le Culot	Dornier Do 17Z
I/KG 3	Le Culot	Dornier Do 17Z
II/KG 3	Antwerp-Duerne	Dornier Do 17Z
III/KG 3	St Trond	Dornier Do 17Z
Stab/KG 53	Lille-Nord	Heinkel He 111H
I/KG 53	Lille-Nord	Heinkel He 111H
II/KG 53	Lille-Nord	Heinkel He 111H
III/KG 53	Lille-Nord	Heinkel He 111H
II/LG 2	St Omer	Dornier Do 17

Dive-bomber units

II/StG 1	Pas-de-Calais	Junkers Ju 87B
IV (St)/LG 1	Tramecourt	Junkers Ju 87B

Long-range fighter unit

ErprGr 210	Calais-Marck	Messerschmitt Bf 109E
		Messerschmitt Bf 110C

IX.Fliegerdivision (9th Flying Division) headquartered at Soesterberg

Strategic reconnaissance unit

3.(F)/122	various	Junkers Ju 88A
		Heinkel He 111

Bomber units

Stab/KG 4	Soesterberg	Heinkel He 111H
I/KG 4	Soesterberg	Heinkel He 111H
II/KG 4	Eindhoven	Heinkel He 111H
III/KG 4	Amsterdam-Schiphol	Junkers Ju 88A

Maritime reconnaissance and air/sea rescue unit

KuFlGr 106	various	Heinkel He 115
		Dornier Do 18

Anti-ship units

KGr 100	Vannes-Meucon	Heinkel He 111H
Stab/KG 40	Brest-Guipavas	Focke-Wulf Fw 200C
I/KG 40	Brest-Guipavas	Focke-Wulf Fw 200C
KGr 126	not available	Heinkel He 111

Jagdfliegerführer 2 (Jafü 2, or fighter leader 2) headquartered at Wissant

Fighter units

Stab/JG 3	Samer	Messerschmitt Bf 109E
I/JG 3	Colombert	Messerschmitt Bf 109E
II/JG 3	Samer	Messerschmitt Bf 109E
III/JG 3	Desvres	Messerschmitt Bf 109E
Stab/JG 26	Audembert	Messerschmitt Bf 109E
I/JG 26	Audembert	Messerschmitt Bf 109E
II/JG 26	Marquise	Messerschmitt Bf 109E
III/JG 26	Caffiers	Messerschmitt Bf 109E
Stab/JG 51	Wissant	Messerschmitt Bf 109E
I/JG 51	Wissant	Messerschmitt Bf 109E
II/JG 51	Wissant	Messerschmitt Bf 109E
III/JG 51	St Omer	Messerschmitt Bf 109E
Stab/JG 52	Coquelles	Messerschmitt Bf 109E
I/JG 52	Coquelles	Messerschmitt Bf 109E
II/JG 52	Peuplinghe	Messerschmitt Bf 109E
Stab/JG 54	Campagne	Messerschmitt Bf 109E
I/JG 54	Guines	Messerschmitt Bf 109E
II/JG 54	Hermalinghen	Messerschmitt Bf 109E
III/JG 54	Guines	Messerschmitt Bf 109E
I(J)/LG 2	Calais-Marck	Messerschmitt Bf 109E

Heavy fighter units

Stab/ZG 26	Lille	Messerschmitt Bf 110C
I/ZG 26	Yvrench	Messerschmitt Bf 110C
II/ZG 26	Crécy-en-Ponthieu	Messerschmitt Bf 110C
III/ZG 26	Barley	Messerschmitt Bf 110C
Stab/ZG 76	Laval	Messerschmitt Bf 110C
II/ZG 76	Abbeville-Drucat	Messerschmitt Bf 110C
III/ZG 76	Laval	Messerschmitt Bf 110C

LUFTFLOTTE III (3RD AIR FLEET) in north-western France, headquartered at Chantilly in France

IV.Fliegerkorps (4th Flying Corps) headquartered in Dinard

Reconnaissance unit

3.(H)/31	various	Messerschmitt Bf 110
		Henschel Hs 126

Bomber units

Stab/LG 1	Orléans-Bricy	Junkers Ju 88A
I/LG 1	Orléans-Bricy	Junkers Ju 88A
II/LG 1	Orléans-Bricy	Junkers Ju 88A
III/LG 1	Chateaudun	Junkers Ju 88A

Stab/KG 27	Tours	Heinkel He 111H
I/KG 27	Tours	Heinkel He 111H
II/KG 27	Dinard	Heinkel He 111H
III/KG 27	Rennes-St Jacques	Heinkel He 111H
Stab/StG 3	various	Heinkel He 111
		Dornier Do 17
KGr 806	Nantes	Junkers Ju 88A

V.Fliegerkorps (5th Flying Corps) headquartered at Villacoublay

Bomber units

Stab/KG 51	Orly	Junkers Ju 88A
I/KG 51	Melun	Junkers Ju 88A
II/KG 51	Orly	Junkers Ju 88A
III/KG 51	Etampes	Junkers Ju 88A
Stab/KG 54	Evreux-en-Fauville	Junkers Ju 88A
I/KG 54	Evreux-en-Fauville	Junkers Ju 88A
II/KG 54	St André-de-l'Eure	Junkers Ju 88A
Stab/KG 55	Villacoublay	Heinkel He 111H
I/KG 55	Dreux	Heinkel He 111H
II/KG 55	Chartres	Heinkel He 111H
III/KG 55	Villacoublay	Heinkel He 111H

VIII.Fliegerkorps (8th Flying Corps) headquartered at Deauville

Strategic reconnaissance units

II/LG 2	Böblingen	Dornier Do 17
2.(H)/11	Le Bourget	Dornier Do 17
2.(F)/123	various	Junkers Ju 88

Dive-bomber units

Stab/StG 1	Angers	Dornier Do 17Z
I/StG 1	Angers	Junkers Ju 87B
III/StG 1	Angers	Junkers Ju 87B
Stab/StG 2	St Malo	Junkers Ju 87B
I/StG 2	St Malo	Junkers Ju 87B
II/StG 2	Lannion	Junkers Ju 87B
Stab/StG 77	Caen-Carpiquet	Junkers Ju 87B
I/StG 77	Caen-Carpiquet	Junkers Ju 87B
II/StG 77	Caen-Carpiquet	Junkers Ju 87B
III/StG 77	Caen-Carpiquet	Junkers Ju 87B

Heavy fighter unit

V (Zerst)/LG 1	Caen-Carpiquet	Messerschmitt Bf 110C

Jagdfliegerführer 3 (Jafü 3, or fighter leader 3) headquartered at Cherbourg

Fighter units

Stab/JG 2	Evreux-Fauville	Messerschmitt Bf 109E
I/JG 2	Beaumont-le-Roger	Messerschmitt Bf 109E
II/JG 2	Beaumont-le-Roger	Messerschmitt Bf 109E
III/JG 2	Le Havre-Octeville	Messerschmitt Bf 109E
Stab/JG 27	Querqueville	Messerschmitt Bf 109E
I/JG 27	Plumetôt	Messerschmitt Bf 109E
II/JG 27	Crépon	Messerschmitt Bf 109E
III/JG 27	Carquebut	Messerschmitt Bf 109E
Stab/JG 53	Cherbourg	Messerschmitt Bf 109E
I/JG 53	Rennes	Messerschmitt Bf 109E
II/JG 53	Dinan	Messerschmitt Bf 109E
III/JG 53	Sempy	Messerschmitt Bf 109E

Heavy fighter units

Stab/ZG 2	Toussous	Messerschmitt Bf 110C
I/ZG 2	Amiens-Glisy	Messerschmitt Bf 110C
II/ZG 2	Guyancourt	Messerschmitt Bf 110C

LUFTFLOTTE V (5TH AIR FLEET) in Norway, headquartered in Stavanger-Sola

X.Fliegerkorps (10th Flying Corps)

Strategic reconnaissance units

1.(F)/120	Stavanger-Sola	Heinkel He 111
		Junkers Ju 88
1.(F)/121	Stavanger-Sola	Heinkel He 111
		Junkers Ju 88
AufklGrObdL	Stavanger-Sola	Dornier Do 215

Coastal reconnaissance and air/sea rescue unit

KuFlGr 506	Stavanger & Trondheim	Heinkel He 115C

Fighter unit

II/JG 77	Stavanger & Vaernes	Messerschmitt Bf 109E

Heavy fighter unit

I/ZG 76	Stavanger-Sola	Messerschmitt Bf 110D

Bomber units

Stab/KG 26	Stavanger-Sola	Heinkel He 111H
I/KG 26	Stavanger-Sola	Heinkel He 111H
III/KG 26	Stavanger-Sola	Heinkel He 111H
Stab/KG 30	Aalborg	Junkers Ju 88A
I/KG 30	Aalborg	Junkers Ju 88A
III/KG 30	Aalborg	Junkers Ju 88A

Luftwaffe Order of Battle of the Western Front (26 June 1944)

LUFTFLOTTE III (3RD AIR FLEET) headquartered in Paris

Strategic reconnaissance units

Stab/FAGr 123	Toussus	Focke-Wulf Fw 190
		Junkers Ju 188
4.(F)/123	St André	Messerschmitt Bf 109 (9)
5.(F)/123	Monchy-Breton	Messerschmitt Bf 109 (8)
1.(F)/121	Toussus	Messerschmitt Me 410 (7)

II.Fliegerkorps (2nd Flying Corps) headquartered in Chartres Fliegerführer West (Schlacht), or flying leader West (Ground-Attack)

Tactical reconnaissance units

Stab/NAGr 13	Chartres	Messerschmitt Bf 109	
		Focke-Wulf Fw 190	
1./NAGr 13	Chartres	Messerschmitt Bf 109	}11
		Focke-Wulf Fw 190	
1./NAGr 13	Laval	Messerschmitt Bf 109	}10
		Focke-Wulf Fw 190	

Ground-attack units

III/SG 4	Clermont-Ferrand	Focke-Wulf Fw 190	}52
III/SG 4 (det)	Avord	Focke-Wulf Fw 190	

IX.Fliegerkorps (9th Flying Corps) headquartered at Beauvais-Tille

Strategic reconnaissance units

3.(F)/122	Soesterberg	Junkers Ju 188 (7)	
		Junkers Ju 88	}6
6.(F)/123	Cormeilles	Junkers Ju 188	

Bomber units

Stab/KG 2	Gilze Rijen	Junkers Ju 188 (4)
I/KG 2	Gilze Rijen	Junkers Ju 188 (10)
II/KG 2	Gilze Rijen	Junkers Ju 188
III/KG 2	Hesepe	Dornier Do 217 (6)
5./KG 76	Gilze Rijen	Junkers Ju 88
III/KG III	Hesepe	Heinkel He 111
Stab/KG 6	Melun-Villaroche	Junkers Ju 188
I/KG 6	Melun-Villaroche	Junkers Ju 188 (16)
II/KG 6	Melun-Villaroche	Junkers Ju 188
III/KG 6	Melun-Villaroche	Junkers Ju 188 (7)
Stab/KG 30	Zwischenahn	Junkers Ju 88
I/KG 30	Leck	Junkers Ju 88 (20)
4. and 6./KG 51	Soesterberg	Messerschmitt Me 410 (14)
5./KG 51	Gilze Rijen	Messerschmitt Me 410
Stab/KG 54	Eindhoven	Junkers Ju 88 (2)
I/KG 54	Eindhoven	Junkers Ju 88 (14)
III/KG 51	Eindhoven	Junkers Ju 88 (13)
I/KG 66	Montdidier	Junkers Ju 88
		Junkers Ju 188 }6
EinsSt. IV/KG 101	St Dizier	Junkers Ju 88 (6)
Stab/LG 1	Melsbroek	Junkers Ju 88 (1)
I/LG 1	Le Culot	Junkers Ju 88 (13)
II/LG 1	Melsbroek	Junkers Ju 88 (13)

Fighter-bomber unit

I/SKG 10	Tours	Focke-Wulf Fw 190 (19)

X.Fliegerkorps (10th Flying Corps) headquartered at Angers

Strategic and maritime reconnaissance units

Stab/FAGr 5	Mont de Marsan	Junkers Ju 290	
1.(F)/5	Mont de Marsan	Junkers Ju 290	}15
2.(F)/5	Mont de Marsan	Junkers Ju 290	
4.(F)/5	Nantes	Junkers Ju 290 (4)	
3.(F)/123	Corme Ecluse	Junkers Ju 88 (7)	
1.(F)/SAGr 129	Biscarosse	Blohm und Voss Bv 222 (4)	

Maritime bomber units

Stab/KG 40	Bordeaux-Mérignac	Focke-Wulf Fw 200	
1. and 2./KG 40	Toulouse-Blagnac	Heinkel He 177 (12)	
II/KG 40	Bordeaux-Mérignac	Heinkel He 177 (12)	
7./KG 40	St Jean d'Angely	Focke-Wulf Fw 200	}23
8. and 9./KG 40	Cognac	Focke-Wulf Fw 200	

2.Fliegerdivision (2nd Flying Division) headquartered at Montfrin

Strategic, tactical and maritime reconnaissance units

1.(F)/33	St Martin	Junkers Ju 88	}11
		Messerschmitt Me 410	
2./NAGr 13	Cuers	Messerschmitt Bf 109	}10
		Focke-Wulf Fw 190	
2./SAGr 128	Berre	Arado Ar 196 (4)	

Bomber units

Stab/KG 26	Montpellier	Junkers Ju 88
II/KG 26 (LT)	Valance	Junkers Ju 88 (27)
III/KG 26 (LT)	Montpellier	Junkers Ju 88 (22)
III/KG 26 (LT) det	Valance	Junkers Ju 88
Stab/KG 77	Salons de Provence	Junkers Ju 88 (1)
I/KG 77 (LT)	Orange-Caritat	Junkers Ju 88 (18)
III/KG 77 (LT)	Orange-Caritat	Junkers Ju 88 (16)
6./KG 77	Istres	Junkers Ju 88 (8)
4./KG 77	Istres	Junkers Ju 88 (7)
Stab/KG 100	Toulouse-Francazals	Dornier Do 217 (1)
		Heinkel He 177 (1)
III/KG 100	Toulouse-Francazals	Dornier Do 217 (26)

II.Jagdkorps (2nd Fighter Corps) headquartered at Chantilly

4.Jagddivision (4th Fighter Division) headquartered at Metz with Jafü 4 (Jagdführer 4, or fighter leader 4) at St Pol-Brias

Fighter units

Stab/JG 1	St Quentin-Clastres	Focke-Wulf Fw 190 (3)
I/JG 3	St Quentin-Clastres	Messerschmitt Bf 109 (14)
I/JG 5	Mons en Chaussée	Messerschmitt Bf 109 (14)
II/JG 11	Mons en Chaussée	Messerschmitt Bf 109 (19)
I/JG 301	Epinoy	Messerschmitt Bf 109 (13)
Stab/JG 27	Champfleury	Messerschmitt Bf 109 (6)
I/JG 27	Vertus	Messerschmitt Bf 109 (39)
III/JG 27	Connantre	Messerschmitt Bf 109 (32)
IV/JG 27	Champfleury	Messerschmitt Bf 109 (31)

Night-fighter units

Stab/NJG 4	Chenay	Messerschmitt Bf 110 (2)
I/NJG 4	Florennes	Junkers Ju 88 (34)
III/NJG 4	Juvincourt	Junkers Ju 88 (18)
Stab/NJG 5	Hagenau	Messerschmitt Bf 110
I/NJG 5	St Dizier	Messerschmitt Bf 110 (15)
III/NJG 5	Athies sur Laon	Messerschmitt Bf 110

5.Jagddivision (5th Fighter Division) headquartered at Jouy-en-Josas with Jafü 5 (Jagdführer 5, or fighter leader 5) at Bernay

Fighter units

Stab/JG 2	Creil	Focke-Wulf Fw 190 (2)
I/JG 2	Creil	Focke-Wulf Fw 190 (16)
II/JG 2	Creil	Messerschmitt Bf 109 (46)
III/JG 2	Creil	Focke-Wulf Fw 190 (18)
Stab/JG 3	Evreux	Messerschmitt Bf 109 }3
		Focke-Wulf Fw 190
II/JG 3	Guyancourt	re-equipping
III/JG 3	Mareilly	Messerschmitt Bf 109 (23)
II/JG 5	Evreux	Messerschmitt Bf 109 (51)
Stab/JG 11	Le Mans	Focke-Wulf Fw 190
1./JG 11	Le Mans	Focke-Wulf Fw 190 (19)
10./JG 11	Le Mans	Focke-Wulf Fw 190
I/JG 1	Alençon	Focke-Wulf Fw 190 (17)
II/JG 1	Alençon	Focke-Wulf Fw 190
Stab/JG 26	Guyancourt	Focke-Wulf Fw 190 (3)
I/JG 26	Guyancourt	Focke-Wulf Fw 190 (27)
II/JG 26	Guyancourt	Focke-Wulf Fw 190 (12)

Night-fighter units

Stab/NJG 2	Coulommiers	Junkers Ju 88 (4)
I/NJG 2	Chateaudun	Junkers Ju 88 (10)
II/NJG 2	Coulommiers	Junkers Ju 88 (24)
II/NJG 4	Coulommiers	Junkers Ju 88 (19)

Jafü Brest (Jagdführer Brest, or fighter leader Brest) at Brest

Fighter units

II/JG 53	Vannes	Messerschmitt Bf 109 (32)

Jafü Südfrankreich (Jagdführer Südfrankreich, or fighter leader southern France) at Aix

Fighter units

1. and 3./JGr 200	Orange-Caritat	Focke-Wulf Fw 190 }34
2./JGr 200	Avignon	Focke-Wulf Fw 190

Jagdabschnittführer Bordeaux (fighter sector leader Bordeaux) at Bordeaux

Heavy fighter units

Stab/ZG 1	Bordeaux-Mérignac	Junkers Ju 88 (1)
1. and 3./ZG 1	Corme Ecluse	Junkers Ju 88 (4)
2./ZG 1	Châteauroux	Junkers Ju 88 (10)
III/JG 1	Cazaux	Junkers Ju 88 (7)

Luftwaffe Order of Battle on the Eastern Front (26 June 1944)

LUFTFLOTTE V (5TH AIR FLEET) in the far northern sector, headquartered at Oslo in Norway with the subordinate commander of the German air forces in Finland at Rovaniemi in Finland

Fliegerführer 3 (FlFü 3, or fighter leader 3) at Kirkenes

Strategic reconnaissance units

1.(F)/124	Kirkenes	Junkers Ju 88	} 20
		Messerschmitt Bf 109	
1.(F)/32	Kemijärvi	Focke-Wulf Fw 189	} 15
		Messerschmitt Bf 109	

Maritime reconnaissance unit

3.(F)/SAGr 130	Kirkenes	Blohm und Voss Bv 138 (8)y 1~8

Ground-attack unit

I/SG 5	Kirkenes	Focke-Wulf Fw 190	} 51
		Junkers Ju 87	

Jafü Norwegen (fighter leader Norway) at Petsamo

Fighter unit

III/JG 5	Petsamo	Messerschmitt Bf 109 (24)

Heavy fighter unit

13./ZG 5	Kirkenes	Messerschmitt Bf 110 (16)

LUFTFLOTTE I (1ST AIR FLEET) in the northern Baltic sector, headquartered at Malpils in Latvia

Strategic reconnaissance units

Stab/FAGr 1	Riga-Spilve	not known
3. (F)/22	Riga-Spilve	Junkers Ju 188 (7)
5. (F)/122	Mitau	Junkers Ju 88 (8)
NSt 3	Riga-Spilve	Dornier Do 217 (15)

Maritime reconnaissance unit

1./SAGr 127	Reval-Uleministe	Arado Ar 196	} 12
		Henschel He 126	
		Junkers Ju 60	

Bomber unit

14./KG 55	Jakobstadt	Heinkel He 111 (9)

3.Fliegerdivision (3rd Flying Division) headquartered at Petseri

Tactical reconnaissance units

Stab/NAGr 5	Petseri	Messerschmitt Bf 109	} 4
		Focke-Wulf Fw 189	
1./NAGr 5	Idriza	Messerschmitt Bf 109	} 13
		Focke-Wulf Fw 189	
1./NAGr 31	Wesenberg	Focke-Wulf Fw 189	} 11
		Henschel Hs 126	

Ground-attack units

II/SG 3	Jakobstadt	Junkers Ju 87	} 35
		Focke-Wulf Fw 190	

Night ground-attack units

Stab/NSGr 1	Idriza	Gotha Go 145	} 28
		Junkers W 34	
3./NSGr 1	Idriza	Gotha Go 145	
		Junkers W 34	
1. and 2./NSGr 1	Kovno	re-equipping	
Stab/NSGr 3	Vecumi	Gotha Go 145	} 49
		Arado Ar 66	
1. and 2./NSGr 3	Vecumi	Gotha Go 145	} 49
		Arado Ar 66	
1./NSGr 12	Vecumi	not available (18)	
Stab/NSGr 11	Rahkla	Arado Ar 66	} 31
		Heinkel He 50	
		Fokker C.V	
1. and 2./NSGr 11	Rahkla	Arado Ar 66	
		Heinkel He 50	
		Fokker C.V	
2./NSGr 12	Libau	forming	

Jagdabschnittsführer Ostland (fighter sector leader Baltic States) headquartered at Riga-Spilve in Latvia

Fighter units

Stab/JG 54	Dorpat	Focke-Wulf Fw 190 (12)
1./JG 54	Turku	Focke-Wulf Fw 190
2. and 3./JG 54	Reval-Laksberg	Focke-Wulf Fw 190 (22)

Gefechtsverband Kulmey (Battle-unit Kulmey) headquartered at Immola in Finland

Tactical reconnaissance unit

1./NAGr 5	Immola	Messerschmitt Bf 109

Fighter unit

II/JG 54	Immola	Focke-Wulf Fw 190

Ground-attack units

Stab/SG 3	Immola	Junkers Ju 87
1./SG 3	Immola	Focke-Wulf Fw 190
2. and 3./SG 3	Immola	Junkers Ju 87

LUFTFLOTTE VI (3RD AIR FLEET) in the central sector, headquartered at Priluki

Strategic reconnaissance units

Stab/FAGr 2	Baranovichi	not available	
4.(F)/11	Baranovichi	Junkers Ju 188 (1)	
		Heinkel He 111 (1)	
4.(F)/14	Baranovichi	Junkers Ju 188	} 15
		Dornier Do 217	
NSt 4	Bobruysk	Junkers Ju 88	} 7
		Junkers Ju 188	

Bomber units

14./KG 3	Puchivichi	Junkers Ju 88 (13)
Stab/KG 1	Prohwehren	Junkers Ju 88 (1)
II/KG 1	Prohwehren	Junkers Ju 88 (43)

IV.Fliegerkorps (4th Flying Corps) headquartered at Brest-Litovsk

Strategic reconnaissance unit

1.(F)/100	Pinsk	Junkers Ju 88 (14)

Tactical reconnaissance units

Stab/NAGr 4	Biala-Podlaska	Messerschmitt Bf 109
		Focke-Wulf Fw 189
		Henschel Hs 126
3./NAGr 4	Kobryn	Messerschmitt Bf 109
		Focke-Wulf Fw 189
		Henschel Hs 126
12./NAGr 3	Brest-Litovsk	Messerschmitt Bf 109 ⎫
		Focke-Wulf Fw 189 ⎬ 8
		Henschel Hs 126 ⎭

Bomber units

Stab/KG 4	Bialystok	Heinkel He 111
		Junkers Ju 88
II/KG 4	Baranovichi	Heinkel He 111 (34)
III/KG 4	Baranovichi	Heinkel He 111 (40)
Stab/KG 27	Krosno	Heinkel He 111 (1)
I/KG 27	Krosno	Heinkel He 111 (41)
II/KG 27	Mielec	Heinkel He 111 (35)
Stab/KG 53	Radom	Heinkel He 111 (1)
I/KG 53	Radom	Heinkel He 111 (36)
II/KG 53	Piastov	Heinkel He 111 (37)
III/KG 53	Radom	Heinkel He 111 (36)
Stab/KG 55	Deblin-Irena	Heinkel He 111 (1)
I/KG 55	Deblin-Ulez	Heinkel He 111 (35)
II/KG 55	Deblin-Irena	Heinkel He 111 (35)
III/KG 55	Groyek	Heinkel He 111 (36)

1.Fliegerdivision (1st Flying Division) headquartered at Bobruysk

Tactical reconnaissance units

Stab/NAGr 15	Uretsye	Focke-Wulf Fw 189
1./NAGr 4	Bobruysk	Focke-Wulf Fw 189 (12)
11./NAGr 11	Uretsye	Focke-Wulf Fw 189 (9)
11./NAGr 12	Uretsye	Focke-Wulf Fw 189 (7)

Ground-attack units

Stab/SG 1	Pastovichi	Focke-Wulf Fw 190 (5)
III/SG 1	Pastovichi	Focke-Wulf Fw 190 (38)

4.Fliegerdivision (4th Flying Division) headquartered at Orcha

Tactical reconnaissance units

Stab/NAGr 10	Toloschin	Messerschmitt Bf 109
		Focke-Wulf Fw 189
		Henschel Hs 126
2./NAGr 4	Orcha	Messerschmitt Bf 109 ⎫
		Focke-Wulf Fw 189 ⎬ 13
		Henschel Hs 126 ⎭
13./NAGr 14	Toloschin	Messerschmitt Bf 109 ⎫
		Focke-Wulf Fw 189 ⎬ 7
		Henschel Hs 126 ⎭

Ground-attack units

I/SG 1	Toloschin	Junkers Ju 87 (44)
II/SG 1	Vilna	Focke-Wulf Fw 190 ⎫
		Junkers Ju 87 ⎬ 73
10.(Pz)/SG 1	Boyari	Junkers Ju 87 (20)
10.(Pz)/SG 3	Toloschin	Junkers Ju 87
Stab/SG 10	Dokudovo	Junkers Ju 87
III/SG 10	Dokudovo	Focke-Wulf Fw 190 (39)

Fliegerführer 1 (FlFü 1, or flying leader 1) headquartered at Minsk

Tactical reconnaissance units

12./NAGr 12	Mogilev	Messerschmitt Bf 109 (12)
2./NAGr 5	Budeslav	not available
1./NAGr 31	Budeslav	Focke-Wulf Fw 189 (6)

Night ground-attack units

Stab/NSGr 2	Lida	Junkers Ju 87 (1)
		Arado Ar 66 (1)
1./NSGr 2	Bobruysk	Junkers Ju 87 (14)
3./NSGr 2	Lida	Junkers Ju 87 (21)
4./NSGr 2	Mogilev	Junkers Ju 87 ⎫
		Arado Ar 66 ⎬ 17
1.OstFlSt (Russ.)	Lida	Gotha Go 145 ⎫
		Arado Ar 66 ⎬ 9
		Polikarpov U-2 ⎭
1. and 2./NSGr 1	Kovno	re-equipping
Stab 1./EinsGrFl SchDiv	Borisov	not available ⎫
		⎬ 42
1./EinsGrFl SchDiv	Dubinskaya	not available ⎭

Jagdabschnittsführer 6 (fighter sector leader 6) headquartered in Priluki

Fighter units

Stab/JG 51	Orcha	Messerschmitt Bf 109
		Focke-Wulf Fw 190
Stab/StJG 51	Orcha	Messerschmitt Bf 109
		Focke-Wulf Fw 190
I/JG 51	Orcha	Messerschmitt Bf 109 (35)
III/JG 51	Bobruysk	Messerschmitt Bf 109 (31)
IV/JG 51	Mogilev	Messerschmitt Bf 109
III/JG 11	Dokudovo	Messerschmitt Bf 109

Night-fighter units

Stab I./NJG 100	Baranovichi	not available ⎫
1./NJG 100 (dets)	Baranovichi & Biala-Podlaska	Focke-Wulf Fw 189
		Dornier Do 217 ⎬ 51
		Junkers Ju 88
3./NJG 100	Radom & Rokudovo	Focke-Wulf Fw 189
		Dornier Do 217
		Junkers Ju 88
4./NJG 100	Puckovichi	Junkers Ju 88 ⎭

LUFTFLOTTE IV (4TH AIR FLEET) in the southern sector, headquartered in Morczyn in Poland

Strategic reconnaissance units

2.(F)/11	Jasionka	Junkers Ju 88 (9)
2.(F)/21	Focsani	Junkers Ju 88 (8)
2.(F)/100	Lublin	Junkers Ju 88 (7)

I.Fliegerkorps (1st Flying Corps) headquartered at Focsani in Romania

Strategic reconnaissance units

3.(F)/121	Zilistea	Junkers Ju 88 (8)
NSt 1	Focsani	Dornier Do 217
		Heinkel He 111 } 14

Tactical reconnaissance units

Stab/NAGr 1	Kishinev	Messerschmitt Bf 109
		Focke-Wulf Fw 189 } 3
2./NAGr 16	Kishinev	Messerschmitt Bf 109
		Focke-Wulf Fw 189 } 10
Stab/NAGr 14	Comrat	Messerschmitt Bf 109 (3)
1./NAGr 14	Comrat	Messerschmitt Bf 109 (12)
2./NAGr 14	Bacau	Messerschmitt Bf 109 (15)

Maritime reconnaissance units

Stab/FAGr 125 (See)	Constanza	not available
1.(F)/125 (See)	Varna	Blohm und Voss Bv 138
		Arado Ar 196 } 9
9. (F)/125 (See)	Mamaia	Blohm und Voss By 138
		Arado Ar 196 } 8
Rum. ASt 22/1	Ciocarlia	not available (8)
Rum. 101 ASt	Mamaia	not available (12)
Bulg. See ASt	Varna	not available (12)

Fighter units

Stab/JG 52	Manzar	Messerschmitt Bf 109 (1)
I/JG 52	Leipzig	Messerschmitt Bf 109 (23)
II/JG 52	Manzar	Messerschmitt Bf 109 (11)
III/JG 52	Roman	Messerschmitt Bf 109 (19)
15.(Kroat)/JG 52	Zilistea	re-equipping

Ground-attack units

Stab/SG 2	Husi	Junkers Ju 87 (1)
I/SG 2	Husi	Junkers Ju 87 (29)
II/SG 2	Zilistea	Focke-Wulf Fw 190 (27)
III/SG 2	Husi	Junkers Ju 87 (43)
10.(Pz)/SG 2	Husi	Junkers Ju 87 (16)
II/SG 10	Culm	Focke-Wulf Fw 190 (28)
10.(Pz)/SG 9	Trotus	Henschel Hs 129 (15)
14.(Pz)/SG 9	Trotus	Henschel Hs 129 (15)

Night ground-attack units

Stab/NSGr 5	Manzar	Gotha Go 145
		Arado Ar 66
1./NSGr 5	Roman	Gotha Go 145
		Arado Ar 66 } 21
2. and 3./NSGr 5	Kishinev	Gotha Go 145
		Arado Ar 66 } 40

Bomber unit

I/KG 4	Focsani	Heinkel He 111 (43)

VIII.Fliegerkorps (8th Flying Corps) headquartered at Lublin in Poland

Strategic reconnaissance units

2.(F)/11	Jasionka	Junkers Ju 88 (8)
2.(F)/100	Lublin	Junkers Ju 188 (7)

Tactical reconnaissance units

Stab/NAGr 2	Strunybaby	Messerschmitt Bf 109 (5)
1./NAGr 2	Stry	Messerschmitt Bf 109 (11)
2./NAGr 2	Strunybaby	Messerschmitt Bf 109 (13)

Ground-attack units

Stab IV (Pz)/SG 9	Lysiatycze	Henschel Hs 129 (6)
12.(Pz)/SG 9	Stry	Henschel Hs 129
13.(Pz)/SG 9	Lysiatycze	Henschel Hs 129 (16)
Stab/SG 77	Jadonka	re-equipping
I/SG 77	Jadonka	re-equipping
II/SG 77	Lemberg	Focke-Wulf Fw 190 (33)
III/SG 77	Cuniov	Junkers Ju 87 (42)
10.(Pz)/SG 17	Starzava	Junkers Ju 87 (19)
Ung. SSt 102/1	Cuniov	not available (11)

Night ground-attack units

Stab/NSGr 4	Hordinia	Gotha Go 145 (4)
1./NSGr 4	Hordinia	Gotha Go 145 (28)

Bomber unit

14./KG 27	Krosno	Heinkel He 111 (15)

Fliegerführer 102 Ungarn (FlFü 102 Ungarn, or flying leader 102 Hungary) headquartered at Labunia

Tactical reconnaissance units

Ung. NASt 102/1	Labunia	not available (8)
7./NAGr 32	Labunia	Messerschmitt Bf 109
		Focke-Wulf Fw 189

Fighter unit

Ung. JSt 102/1	Zamocz	not available (8)

Bomber unit

Ung. KSt 102/1	Klemensova	not available (5)

Fast bomber unit

Ung. SKSt	not available	not available (12)

Rum. I.Fliegerkorps (1st Romanian Flying Corps) headquartered at Tecuci in Romania

Strategic reconnaissance units

Rum. 2.(F) ASt	Ivesti	not available (5)
Rum. 102 ASt	Vilkov	not available (11)

Fighter units

Rum. II/JG 3	Bacau	IAR 80 (18)
Stab Rum. IV JGr	Janca	not available
Rum. 45.JSt	Janca	not available
Rum. 46.Jst	Janca	not available
Rum. 49.JSt	Janca	re-equipping
Rum. IX JGr	Tecuci	Messerschmitt Bf 109 (23)

Dive-bomber units

Rum. III StGr	Carlamanesti	Junkers Ju 87 (24)
Rum. VI StGr	Husi	Junkers Ju 87 (23)
Rum. VIII StGr	Matca	Junkers Ju 87 (39)

Bomber units

Rum. II KGr	Tandarei	not available (10)
Rum. IV KGr	Janca	not available (15)
Rum. V KGr	Ivesti	not available (16)
Rum. KSt 1./3	Ciocarlia	not available (9)

DEUTSCHE LUFTWAFFE IN ROMANIEN (GERMAN AIR FORCE IN ROMANIA) headquartered in Bucharest

Jagdabschnittsfuhrer Rumanien (fighter sector leader Romania) headquartered in Bucharest

Fighter units

I./JG 53	Targsorul-Nou	Messerschmitt Bf 109 (28)
III./JG 53	Mizil	Messerschmitt Bf 109 (28)
Rum. I./JG 2	Rodori	IAR 80
Rum. VI./JG 2	Poperti-Leordeni	IAR 80 (16)
Rum. VII JGr	Boteni	Messerschmitt Bf 109 (12)
Rum. 51.JSt	Tepes-Voda	not available (21)
Rum. 52.JSt	Mamaia	not available (14)
Rum. 58.JSt	Pipera	not available (4)

Night-fighter units

10. and 12/NJG 6	Otopeni	Messerschmitt Bf 110 (25)
11./NJG 6	Zilistea	Messerschmitt Bf 110
2./NJG 100	Otopeni	Junkers Ju 88
		Dornier Do 217
		Focke-Wulf Fw 189
4./JG 301	Mizil	Messerschmitt Bf 109 (6)
6./JG 301	Targsorul-Nou	Messerschmitt Bf 109 (7)
Rum. 1/NJSt	Otopeni	not available (4)

APPENDIX 6
German Air-launched Weapons

BOMBS AND SIMILAR 'DUMB' ORDNANCE

The designation *Brandbombe* was used for incendiary bombs, of which the Germans employed just one type, namely the 2.2-lb (1-kg) BB-1.

The designation *Luftmine* was used for high-capacity bombs with a high ratio of explosive to casing for maximum blast effect, and the two main types were the LMA with a notional weight of 1102lb (500kg) and the LMB with a notional weight of 2205lb (1000kg).

The designation *Panzersprengbombe Cylindrisch* was used for armour-piercing bombs, and the two main types were the PC-1000 with a notional weight of 2205lb (1000kg) and the PC-1800 Satan with a notional weight of 3968lb (1800kg).

The designation *Sprengbombe Cylindrisch* was used for general-purpose bombs, and the main types were the SC-50 with a notional weight of 110lb (50kg), the SC-250 with a notional weight of 551lb (250kg), the SC-500 with a notional weight of 1102lb (500kg), the SC-1000 Hermann with a notional weight of 2205lb (1000kg), the SC-1800 with a notional weight of 3968lb (1800kg), and the SC-2500 with a notional weight of 5511lb (2500kg). The SC-250 had a lethal radius of 27ft (8.25m) and showed its splinters to a radius of 213ft (65m), and among its other data were a filling of 297.5lb (135kg) of high explosive, a length of 6ft 4.3in (1.938m) and a diameter of 1ft 0.9in (0.328m). These proportions were generally typical of the SC series of bombs.

The designation *Sprengbombe Dickwändig* was used for semi-armour-piercing bombs, and the main types were the SD-2 with a notional weight of 4.4lb (2kg), the SD-50 with a notional weight of 110lb (50kg), the SD-250 with a notional weight of 551lb (250kg), the SD-500 with a notional weight of 1102lb (500kg), the SD-1000 Esau with a notional weight of 2205lb (1000kg), and the SD-1400 Fritz with a notional weight of 3086lb (1400kg).

MACHINE-GUNS AND CANNON

The *Rheinmetall-Borsig MG 15* was the standard trainable weapon used in German warplanes at the beginning of World War II, and was a completely orthodox light air-cooled machine gun most notable for the use of a 75-round saddle magazine. Among the weapon's other data were a calibre of 0.312in (7.92mm), weight of 17.85lb (8.1kg), muzzle velocity of 2520ft (765m) per second, rate of fire of 1250 rounds per minute, operation by the short-recoil method, overall length of 3ft 6.875in (1.09m), and effective range of 655yds (600m).

The *Rheinmetall-Borsig MG 17* was the development of the MG 15 for use in fixed installations, and its salient details included a length of 3ft 10.25in (1.82m), height of 6.3in (0.16m), weight of 22.5lb (10.2kg), muzzle velocity of 2477ft (755m) per minute and rate of fire of 1200 rounds per minute. In its initial form the weapon fired its ball and tracer ammunition from a non-disintegrating belt 5ft 6in (1.675m) long and carrying 100 rounds, but the definitive model was supplied with 500 rounds from a disintegrating-link belt weighing 32.5lb (14.75kg). The original type of ball ammunition had the theoretical capability to penetrate 5mm (0.2in) of armour at a range of 110yds (100m), but later an improved SmKv round was introduced with the theoretical capability to penetrate 17mm (0.67in) of armour at 55yds (50m).

The *Rheinmetall-Borsig MG 131* was the standard heavy-calibre machine gun used by the Germans, and was a notably effective machine gun with a calibre of 0.51in (13mm), length of 3ft 10in (1.17m), height of 4.75in (0.12m), weight of 43.5lb (19.75kg), muzzle velocity of 2461ft (750m) per minute, and rate of fire of 930 rounds per minute. The type was supplied with ammunition from 100-round belts of the disintegrating-link type, each belt measuring 7ft 10.5in (2.40m) in length and weighing 17.5lb (7.95kg).

The *Mauser MG 151* was the smallest-calibre cannon used by the Luftwaffe, and was designed in the mid-1930s by Dr Doerge and Dir. von Lossnitzer for production from 1938. The weapon's salient details included a length of 6ft 3.5in (1.92m), height of 7.75in (0.20m), weight of 91.5lb (41.5kg), muzzle velocity of 3133ft (955m) per minute with the standard HE projectile, and rate of fire of 700 rounds per minute. The type's muzzle energy was very considerable for the period, but this had the disadvantage of causing rapid barrel wear and this loss of performance. The 100-round belt of ammunition weighed 37lb (16.8kg), and there was also a specialised anti-tank projectile with a muzzle velocity of 3363ft (1025m) per second.

The *Mauser MG 151/20* was basically the MG 151 enlarged to 20-mm calibre as the Luftwaffe's standard medium-calibre cannon of World War II. The type was designed to fire standard 20-mm ammunition (supplied in 100-round belts weighing 43.75lb/19.85kg) in the air-to-air role, but for the anti-tank role could also fire a special 15-mm round with a muzzle velocity of 2313ft (705m) per second for the theoretical ability to penetrate 43mm (1.7in) of armour at a range of 55yds (50m). The weapon's other details included a length of 5ft 7.25in (1.71m), weight of 93.7lb (42.5kg), muzzle velocity of 2592ft (790m) per second, and rate of fire of between 780 and 80 rounds per minute (cyclic).

The *Oerlikon MG FF* was evolved in Switzerland on the basis of the German Becker cannon developed late in World War I but was then built under licence in Germany. This was the first standard cannon adopted by the Luftwaffe. The weapon's salient details included a length of 4ft 4.7in (1.34m), height of 5.25in (0.13m), weight of

78.75lb (35.7kg), and rate of fire of 540 rounds per minute. Although it was a reliable weapon, the MG FF was hampered by its low rate of fire and ammunition feed from a 45-, 60- or 100-round drum magazine weighing 36.25, 44.75 or 73 lb (16.4, 20.3 or 33.1 kg) respectively. The type was used in a wing-mounted installation in some aircraft, but was most generally used in its MG FF/M form in a moteur-canon installation between the cylinder banks of a Vee-type piston engine and firing through the propeller shaft.

Later German cannon were of the considerably more devastating 30-mm calibre, and included the *Rheinmetall MK 101* with a length of 8ft 7.9in (2.64m), weight of 306.4lb (139kg), rate of fire of 260 rounds per minute, and muzzle velocity of 3018ft (920m) per second; the *Rheinmetall MK 103* with a length of 7ft 7.25in (2.318m), weight of 321.9lb (146kg), rate of fire of 440 rounds per minute, and muzzle velocity of 2822ft (860m) per second; the Rheinmetall MK 108 with a length of 3ft 5.6in (1.057m), weight of 127.9lb (58kg), rate of fire of 660 rounds per minute, and muzzle velocity of 1706ft (520m) per second; and most importantly of all for the longer-term development of aircraft cannon, the *Mauser MG 213/20* that introduced the revolver cannon concept and whose

data included a length of 6ft 4in (1.93m), weight of 165.3lb (75kg), rate of fire of 1300 rounds per minute, and muzzle velocity of 3494ft (1065m) per minute.

Air-to-surface cannon, used mainly in the anti-tank role, included the 37-mm *Rheinmetall BK 3.7*, the 50-mm *Rheinmetall BK 5*, the 75-mm *Rheinmetall BK 7.5* and the 88-mm *Rheinmetall Düka 88*.

TORPEDOES

The Imperial German navy air service had made limited use of the air-launched torpedo in the course of World War I, its standard weapon in this category being an 18-in (457-mm) weapon with a weight of 1598lb (725kg). From the late 1930s right through World War II, the Germans' primary air-launched torpedo was the LT F5b, which was a moderately effective if not inspired weapon. The type was evolved through several variants that retained the diameter of the original but had different lengths and weights, the latter up to a maximum of 1764lb (800kg). The weapon was later redesignated as the LT 1A-1 or, with different water running speeds, LT 1A-2 and LT 1A-3. The LT 1B had electrical adjustment for range variations. The data for the 17.7-mm (445-mm) LT F5b included an overall weight of 1686lb (765kg) and length of 17ft 7in (5.36m).

INDEX